Alice Joanne
Howard

LIFE-READING SERVICE

ELSON-GRAY

# BASIC READERS

## BOOK FIVE

*by*

WILLIAM H. ELSON
*and*
WILLIAM S. GRAY

## SCOTT, FORESMAN AND COMPANY
CHICAGO · ATLANTA · DALLAS · NEW YORK

# ACKNOWLEDGMENTS

For permission to use copyright material, grateful acknowledgment is made to A. L. Burt Company for "With Admiral Byrd in Little America" from *Rear Admiral Byrd and the Polar Expeditions* by Coram Foster; to The Century Company for "Balto, the Best Lead-Dog in Alaska" from "Balto, the Dog That Saved Nome's Children" in *Uncle Sam's Animals* by Frances Margaret Fox, copyright 1927; for "The Feathered Masters of the Air" from "Migration of the Birds," in *St. Nicholas Book of Science* by Floyd L. Darrow, copyright 1928; for "A Hero for a Friend" from "An Adventure on Skis" by Joseph B. Ames in *St. Nicholas* and in *Playing the Game* by Mullen and Lanz; to W. A. Wilde Company for "Lindbergh, Pioneer Air Scout" from "The Man Who Was Ready" in *Little Stories of Well-Known Americans* by Laura Antoinette Large; to Gordon Hillman for "The Air Mail"; to *The Youth's Companion* (now combined with *The American Boy*) for "Knights of the Air" by Jessica Pryse Arthur, for "The Little Flags" by Mary Lee Dalton, for "A Mile at a Time" by Nancy Byrd Turner, and for "A May Day Princess" from "The Princess in the Sedan Chair" by Myrtle Jamison Trachsel; to Clinton Scollard for "I Love All of Out-of-Doors" from "Song in Summer" in *A Boy's Book of Rhyme*, and for "Let the Flag Wave"; to D. Appleton & Company for "Pembe Kubwa, the Big Tusker," from "The Big Tusker" in *Alice in Elephantland* by Mary Hastings Bradley; to *John Martin's Magazine* and the author for "The Little American Woodcutter" from "The Little Woodcutter" by Clarence Hawkes; to Doubleday, Doran & Company, Inc., for "Waste Land: A Wild-Life Preserve" from "Waste Land" in *Children of Swamp and Wood* by Archibald Rutledge, copyright 1927; to Dodd, Mead & Company, Inc., for "The Pine Caterpillar" from *Insect Adventures* by Jean Henri Fabre, copyright 1917; to Robert M. McBride & Company for "The Weather Question" and "Arabian Nights" from *The Gentlest Giant* by Anna Bird Stewart; to the author for "The Lake and the Sky" by Mary Barton; to Henry Holt and Company for "Betsy Finds a Way" from "Betsy Has a Birthday" in *Understood Betsy* by Dorothy Canfield Fisher; to the authors and *Child Life* for "George Washington" from "Washington" by Nancy Byrd Turner, and for "Josie's Home Run" by Ruth Gipson Plowhead; to the author for "Robert E. Lee: From Manliness to Manhood" by Edith A. Heal; to *Safety Education* for "How a Boy Scout Builds a Campfire" from "The Boy and the Camper" by E. V. Jotter; to *Outdoor Life* for verse from "Forest Fire" by John E. Gribble; to A. Flanagan Company for "To Every Child of Every Land" from *The Little Swiss Wood-Carver* by Madeline Brandeis; to Helen Coale Crew for "Grandmother's Trip to Naples"; to Caroline Mabry for "Esteban, Page to a Carnival Queen"; to Coward-McCann, Inc., for "Abdul Aziz, Boy of the Desert" from *Boy of the Desert* by Eunice Tietjens, copyright 1928; to A. C. McClurg & Co. for "John Goes Down to Toy Valley" from *Donkey John of the Toy Valley* by Margaret Warner Morley; to the *Northwestern Christian Advocate* and the author for "The Clock Calls to Work" from "The Clock" in *Kitchen Sonnets* by Helen Coale Crew; to the author and the Milton Bradley Company for "Cyrus Hall McCormick Invents the Reaping Machine" from "How the Reaping Hook Became a Machine" in *American Childhood;* to the author for "The Story of Bread" by Alice Thompson Paine; to The Penn Publishing Company for "Donald's Visit to the Woolen Mills" from *The Story of Wool* by Sara Ware Bassett; to the *Scientific American* for "How Candy Mints Are Made" from "Rebuilding a Broken Business" by Milton Wright; to Harold Ober, Agent, for "Dick's Thanksgiving Snowshoes" from "The Thanksgiving Snowshoes" by Ben Ames Williams.

"Guillaume's Flute" is taken by permission from Crownfield's *The Feast of Noel*, published and copyright by E. P. Dutton & Co., New York.

Acknowledgment is made to Merlin Moore Taylor for "The Mail Must Go Through," courtesy of *Boy's Life*, published by The Boy Scouts of America and D. Appleton & Company.

*Elson-Gray Basic Readers, Book Five*, is a revision of *The Elson Basic Readers, Book Five*.

371.3

# PREFACE

The authors of the "Basic Readers" have attempted to provide an interesting, purposeful, and comprehensive reading course for the middle grades.

The primary aim of any reading course is to lead pupils to become voluntary and eager readers for both pleasure and information. To achieve this purpose the authors have assembled materials from the world-wide field of children's favorite readings. All of the selections included are of recognized worth in providing pleasure, imparting information, cultivating desirable attitudes, and developing appreciation. Such qualities are essential if the activities of the reading period are to result in enriched experience and permanent reading interests.

While selecting and classifying material for these readers the authors carefully surveyed the field of child literature in order to find selections that appeal strongly to children's interests. The stories and poems chosen have also been evaluated and graded in the light of present-day classroom realities. The material is so organized as to make each of the "Basic Readers" at its appropriate grade level the central core or framework of a larger reading plan. Each unit of *Basic Readers, Book Five,* initiates a theme or field of interest which can be followed up and developed through the materials of various readers, library books, reference books, and other sources. Such a plan gives purpose and continuity to all reading materials available in the classroom. This correlation of varied reading-matter is made conveniently effective through the use of a special bibliography in the *Teacher's Guidebook* for *Basic Readers, Book Five.*

A systematic and carefully organized plan of teaching is provided in the "Guidebooks" for use in promoting growth of reading habits and interests from grade to grade. This plan is made concrete and usable through a series of carefully prepared lesson helps for each of the selections in *Basic Readers, Book Five*. This expert guidance helps teachers in making needed preparation for the day's lesson or for larger units of work. Additional exercises in the *Extension-Reading Work-Book* reinforce and extend the training of pupils in correct reading interests and habits. Thus basic reading attitudes and habits are developed through the purposeful use of interesting and significant content.

# CONTENTS

## PART THREE
### STORIES WE ALL SHOULD KNOW

## PART FOUR
### YOUNG AMERICAN CITIZENS

## PART FIVE
## BOYS AND GIRLS OF OTHER LANDS

## PART SIX
## WORKERS AND THEIR WORK

## PART SEVEN
## FAMOUS HEROES OF LONG AGO

8     CONTENTS

## PART EIGHT
## HOLIDAYS AND FESTIVALS

# BOOKS ARE STOREHOUSES

WHEN Admiral Byrd went down to the bottom of the world to explore the regions of the South Pole, he carried with him a library of one thousand books. Think of it! If you read one book every day, it would take you nearly three years to finish that many. Admiral Byrd must indeed have thought that books were valuable to his men. He needed all the room in his ships for food, gasoline, and other supplies; yet he found a place for this large library.

Admiral Byrd knew that during his stay in the Polar regions there would be a long night of many months, when the sun would not shine. The men would have to stay inside, shut in by the darkness and the fierce storms, with very little to do. Books would give them many pleasant hours. Books would help them to forget that they were shut in.

So we can imagine these forty-two brave explorers quietly reading in the light of their lamps, with the terrific storms raging outside, and their building completely buried in snow. Here is one man reading a story of Africa. His mind is far away from the ice and snow; his book has carried him to a hot, sweltering country of wide grassy plains, sandy deserts, and thick jungles. Another man is reading of a land of great, busy cities full of people; he has for a time forgotten that for a thousand miles and more in every direction there is not another person in all the vast region where he and his comrades are.

Have you ever read about the Little Lame Prince and his magic cloak that took him wherever he wanted to go? Books are like magic cloaks; they can take us wherever we want to go. You could not go to the South Pole with Admiral Byrd; but you can read the book that he wrote. You cannot hunt lions in Africa, but you will read in this book of yours how three Boy Scouts hunted them.

Books can do even more than the magic cloak could do. It could only carry the Little Lame Prince to different places. But books can carry us into people's minds and show us what they have thought and learned. There are men and women who have spent years of hard, patient work finding out the wonderful things that are in this world of ours. All that they have learned and thought we can have for our own— wonderful and interesting facts about the stars, the trees and flowers, the animals, the great machines that do our work—all the things that are on the earth, in the earth, and even far down in the depths of the ocean waters.

Finally, books can carry us far, far back, thousands of years, and show us how people lived in those days. We can know the kinds of clothes they wore, the food they ate, the games they played, and even some of the jokes at which they laughed. Isn't it strange! Those people never dreamed of us; we could not possibly go back and live in their day. Yet we can know almost as much about them as we know about the people of our own times.

Now do you see why we say that books are storehouses? In them are stored up for us all the things that men and women have thought and done and learned for thousands of years. In them are kept the stories that people have loved through all time.

You are now going to enter just one little part of the great storehouse of books. Let us see first what this part of the storehouse has for you.

On page 5 you will find a list of stories and poems. These are the "Contents," or the things you will find in this book storehouse. You will see also that this collection of stories and poems is divided into Parts. Each Part tells about the same kind of things. Part Two tells of The Outdoor World—the world of animals, trees and flowers, and birds. Part Five carries you far across the sea to the village of Abdul Aziz, the Arab boy, and the home of John Hofer, high up in the Alps Mountains. Other boys and girls of far-away lands are waiting for you in this Part. What are the names of the other Parts in the book?

As you read these stories, probably you will many times wish that you knew of others like them. At the end of each story you will find the names of other stories you would enjoy reading. Then, if you want to read still more, turn to pages 431 to 434. There you will find a list of books that boys and girls all over our country are reading and enjoying. The librarian in your school or your town will always be glad to help you find interesting stories.

There is one more thing you ought to know about this little book storehouse that you are going to read. If you turn to the very back of your book—to page 435—you will find a list of words called a "Glossary." You can think of "Glossary" as meaning "Little Dictionary." In the stories that you are to read, you will probably find some words that are new to you. Of course, you will not be able to understand the story very well if you do not know what the words mean. Or you may not know how to pronounce a word. Your Glossary is there to help you. It will often save your going to the dictionary. But you may have to look up some word that is not in the Glossary. Then, of course, you will need your dictionary.

Don't forget to use the Glossary and the dictionary to help you understand and pronounce words. And when you look up a word, try to remember what it means. You may need that word some day when you are telling something or trying to understand what someone is saying to you. A person who tries to write or talk with only a few words is like a workman without enough tools.

# PART ONE
## · SKYWAYS AND HIGHWAYS ·

## KNIGHTS OF THE AIR

JESSICA PRYSE ARTHUR

Up from the airports the swift ships are zooming
Over the cities and countrysides fair,
Off toward the mountains, where snow peaks are
    looming,
Upward ye! Forward ye! Knights of the Air!

Over Sahara, where hot sands are sliding,
Over each tropical jungle and lair,
Over the forests, where wild things are hiding,
Onward still! Forward still! Knights of the Air!

Over the green glassy seas you are flashing,
Down toward the south polar regions you bear,
Over far oceans, where icebergs are crashing!
Onward ye! Forward ye! Knights of the Air!

# THE WORLD IS GROWING SMALLER

THE WORLD is growing smaller. Perhaps you don't believe it. Well, it took Christopher Columbus sixty-nine days to cross the Atlantic Ocean, when traveling just as fast as anyone could in those days. But Charles Lindbergh crossed the ocean in less than two days. The Atlantic must have grown smaller!

When President Lincoln was killed, only about seventy years ago, it was seven days before the people in California learned about what had happened, although the news was rushed across our country with the greatest speed. But today you can sit in your home here in America and listen to a man talking in Germany, or England, or Italy. Admiral Byrd, far down at the bottom of the world, told us almost every day what his men were doing.

Yes, it does seem as though our world is growing smaller. It seems also that we are living closer together than people did one hundred years ago. Why? You have probably already guessed the answer. Because men have learned things and invented machines—machines that make it possible for people to move rapidly from place to place and to send messages with lightning speed.

You are going to read about how men travel and send messages. You will learn of Admiral Byrd's Antarctic trip, how brave dogs and men carried medicine over ice and snow to save lives in the far North, how the mail was carried before the railroads came, and how Lindbergh flew from New York to Paris. As you read these stories, think of how progress in transportation and communication makes the world grow smaller.

# WITH ADMIRAL BYRD IN LITTLE AMERICA

### CORAM FOSTER

At the bottom of the world, in the South Polar Regions, Admiral Byrd and his men lived for fourteen months where no man had ever been able to stay more than a month or two. During a part of this time it was impossible for them to leave or for anyone to get to them. Yet they listened to music and messages from all over the world, and almost every day they sent out to the world the story of what they were doing.

### AT THE BOTTOM OF THE WORLD

When the Byrd expedition sailed from New York City to Antarctica, it carried a library of a thousand volumes. This library was for the most part a collection of adventure stories which Admiral Byrd had selected to give pleasure to his men through the long darkness of the antarctic night.

These books were all at hand whenever a man had a few hours off for candy eating and reading. There had been provided for every man on the expedition a hundred pounds of candy—about a quarter of a pound for each day the party remained in Antarctica. This amount of candy was at least four times what the men would have eaten back home, but it was no more than enough for them. The terrific cold of Antarctica compelled every man to keep up in his body more heat than would have been necessary in warmer lands, and candy makes great heat in the body. Admiral Byrd believed in taking the best care of his party; for this reason his men always had candy to eat and books to read during leisure moments.

And certainly there was plenty of leisure after the dark months arrived, following the construction of the village of Little America upon Ross Ice Field. The buildings of this little settlement, arranged in three groups, formed the largest and the most nearly complete community that had ever been built in the Polar regions. They also provided both homes and workshops for Admiral Byrd's men.

Of the chief group, the Administration Building was most important. Besides living quarters for a number of the party, including Admiral Byrd, it contained a radio laboratory with instruments for sending and receiving messages. Directly behind this building were the house for medical supplies and that which contained the food supplies. These two were separated from each other to reduce loss in case of fire. It was, indeed, the danger of fire which made it necessary to separate all of the main buildings from each other.

Chief among the buildings of the second group was the Mess Hall. Here were more living quarters, a radio station, a storehouse, and a photo workshop, all under one roof. A little distance away were the quarters for the dogs, and the sledge-repair and blacksmith shop.

The third group of buildings included the aviation repair shop and storage space for the gasoline supply.

### THE LONG DARKNESS

None of Admiral Byrd's important work in Little America was done between late March and the middle of October, 1929. This does not, of course, mean either that the sun vanished for all that period of time or that work stopped completely. As a matter of fact, the sun was still a daily visitor in April, and it again became a daily visitor in late August. Moreover, even without the light of the sun, some outdoor activity was possible. There were always the twilight hours of noon-time provided by the moon.

No air flights could be made, however, and only the most necessary travel with dog sleds was attempted; for even with the aid of the moon, the light at best was poor. There was another, even more important, reason why little work could be done during these months: this was the time of the winter storms. These, in their full strength, brought winds that no man could stand against, and such snows as are unheard of elsewhere in the world.

When Little America was first set up on the Ross Ice Field, its tiny buildings made black spots against the surrounding whiteness. Long before the winter was over, however, snow had banked and drifted over all except the tallest points. A bit of the roof of the Mess Hall could be seen at times. Some of the tall radio towers managed to stay clear. But the rest of the buildings could be located only by the unevenness of the snow's surface where an airplane hangar, the dogs' quarters, the Mess Hall, the gymnasium, or some other building lay buried.

No small part of those winter months was lived underground by Byrd and his men, or nearly underground. They went by tunnel from the Administration Building to the Mess Hall. By tunnel, too, they could reach others of the most important buildings. Poking their heads out of doors into the gray blackness of the night, Byrd's men were almost sure at times that they heard the singing of birds. Often two of the men would look sharply at each other in wondering surprise as their ears caught sounds which were strangely like the shrill, sharp cries of animals.

At other times there were curious groans and moans. And even in the shelter of their quarters sometimes the men caught a rumbling, rolling murmur which could have been nothing but a trolley car in the distance, except that they knew that there were no such things as trolley cars about. All these magic sounds, and more, were made by the restless shifting of the ice upon which their houses stood; by the pressure of the water beneath the ice; and by the furious winds which tore constantly at the roofs.

These magic sounds would have been even more disturbing than they were if the inside of the Mess Hall and the Administration Building had been as dark as was the icy snow-field without. Happily, the Byrd expedition brought with it a complete outfit of electric equipment to brighten its antarctic home.

With the last of April the sun disappeared, leaving only a faint glint of brightness now and then along the horizon. Inside the huts, however, a flood of light for all purposes was provided by an electric generator, which was run by a gasoline engine. This was the first machine of its kind ever carried into the antarctic regions. It was by electric light that the storekeeper checked his goods. The cook turned an electric switch when he went into his kitchen to prepare a meal.

Not only did the men of Little America have electricity for lighting, but they had it for medical purposes as well. There was enough electricity to run the two powerful sun lamps which Doctor Francis D. Codman, chief physician of the party, had brought along. Each member of the expedition was required to bathe regularly in the light rays of these lamps. This rule was followed throughout the entire time of the long winter night, while the sun was not present to furnish a natural health-giving light.

IN TOUCH WITH THE WORLD

The electrical equipment, too, ran the radio. Other Polar explorers had carried radios, but none ever had provided such equipment as Byrd took. So complete was his preparation in this direction that all through his stay in Little America he lived with his finger tip on an electric bell, by which he could practically ring up the entire world.  Nothing like it had ever been done before. At almost a moment's notice Byrd could call New York, South America, Europe, San Francisco, Australia, and practically any spot upon the world's surface.  Each day he was able, if he wished, to inform the world what was happening in Little America.

By radio Byrd was able to tell the outside world when he started out men with dog teams to lay supplies of food and gasoline southward in order to prepare for his flight to the South Pole itself.  He was able to inform his vast audience when the first supplies had been placed a hundred miles or so from Little America; when the second supplies had been placed a hundred miles beyond the first; when the third supplies had been left, and the fourth.  He was able to let the world know that he was doing this work with four teams of dogs, and that each team carried about a thousand pounds of provisions. These supplies were to be used in case Byrd's plane was forced to land somewhere on the flight to the Pole and back to Little America.

Radio, too, carried amusement and information to Little America as easily as it carried news from Little America to the world.  Sometimes a theater would broadcast its program for Byrd's men.  While gathered around the receiving set in the Administration Building one afternoon, Byrd's party heard the welcome word that a supply of athletic equipment from the University of Pennsylvania was on its way to Little America.

Once, when Admiral Byrd was puzzled about the problem of comfortable sleeping conditions, the radio brought him the advice of other polar explorers. Fitzhugh Green and Captain Bob Bartlett, two famous explorers and adventurers, sent suggestions by radio as to how the party in Antarctica could avoid frozen clothes and other inconveniences while sleeping.

Every holiday which arrived while the expedition was at Antarctica was made cheerful by the radio. The day of the anniversary of Byrd's flight across the Atlantic brought messages of congratulation from all the world. On Easter, music fitting to the day was sent on from New York. On the Fourth of July there were addresses and music. And, finally, it was the radio which told the waiting world that the long darkness at Little America was at an end. This news was flashed out into space on August 25, 1929.

### THE SUN RETURNS TO LITTLE AMERICA

For days the twilight hours which had numbered less than four in the middle of the long southern night had been lengthening, a little at a time. One week, there were five hours of twilight; the next six. Then there were ten, and down along the horizon could be seen for a space each day a promising golden tint. Finally there came a day when the sun itself was actually visible for a minute or so. This was not a true sunrise, however. But only a few days later, the sun itself rose majestic and bright one morning above the horizon. The little village in Antarctica was like another world!

For the stalwart crew and their slim, quiet commander, that must have been a time of great excitement which followed the return of the sun to the vast whiteness that made up the Ross Ice Field. There was, to begin with, the change from the glow of electricity inside the houses and the gray blackness of the out-of-doors to the sparkling beauty which the new sunlight made of the ice and snow.

But there was much more than that. There was, for example, the little thaw which every day of sunlight brought, gradually uncovering roofs to break the snowy stretches of Little America. Now a man could get out of the houses to stretch his legs, for the storms, or at least the most terrible storms, were past, and one dared to walk out in the open. There was work; and work, after the long days of idleness, was highly welcome to Byrd's men.

The dogs were mad with delight at being free from their winter quarters. They yelped and tugged joyfully as they were harnessed again to the sleds. The photographers brought out their cameras, and when nothing better offered, took pictures of the penguins waddling along, upright, like dignified old gentlemen; or of the

killer-whales which began to push their long, slender snouts through the melting ice of the bay; or of a seal spinning in a frenzy with his mouth full of a half-swallowed fish that would neither go in nor out; or of the airplane hangars and their machine shops slowly coming out from under their coverings of snow. Little America had become a whirlpool of activity!

## NOTES AND QUESTIONS

1. Name three ways of travel that Admiral Byrd and his men used from the time they left New York.

2. To see whether you know what Little America was like, write on your paper the words that belong where the letters

are in the lines below. Your answer for the first letter is
(a) *Ross Ice Field.*

Little America was built on the ....(*a*).... in the ....(*b*)....
polar region. In June it is ....(*c*).... in Antarctica, while it
is ....(*d*).... in our country. The buildings were arranged in
....(*e*).... to avoid the danger from ....(*f*)..... After the snows
came, only the high ....(*g*).... of the ....(*h*).... could be seen.
Then the men passed from one building to another through
....(*i*)..... Except for the moonlight, it was dark during the
months of ....(*j*)..... During the long night the men could
do little out of doors because of the ....(*k*).... and ....(*l*).....

3. Which of these animals and birds did the men see?

Eagles, wolves, seals, walruses, whales, horses, penguins.

4. Below are eight words, and eight sentences with letters
in them. Choose the right word for each letter.

|          |           |         |          |
|----------|-----------|---------|----------|
| vanished | community | fitting | frenzy   |
| leisure  | equipment | visible | compelled |

Hunger ....(*a*).... them to eat grass and roots.

During vacation we have plenty of ....(*b*).....

The village of Lakeside is a pleasant little ....(*c*).....

The automobile ....(*d*).... in the darkness.

Father bought all kinds of camping ....(*e*).... for our trip.

The night was so dark that the road was not ....(*f*).....

*America* is a ....(*g*).... song to sing on the Fourth of July.

Elephants threw the horses into a ....(*h*).... of excitement.

*Get the habit of using the Glossary* that begins on page 435
to find the meanings of words. Use your dictionary, too.

Eagle Scout Paul Siple went with Admiral Byrd. You
will like to read "Erecting Little America" and "The Winter Night," both in Paul's book, *A Boy Scout with Byrd.*

# BALTO, THE BEST LEAD-DOG IN ALASKA

## Frances Margaret Fox

Perhaps you think that dogs are used only as pets. Do you know that for hundreds of years dogs have been helpers of man? They have hunted food for him, carried his loads and messages, and guarded his home. In this story you will read how faithful dogs helped brave men in a time of great need.

Balto was a dog of the United States Postal Service in far-off Alaska. In the city of Nome, one black morning, he stepped into the world's Story-Book of Shining Deeds. That picture-book opened wide and took him in forever.

It was mid-winter, and an epidemic of diphtheria had broken out in Nome. They called it the "Black Death" up there, for the disease carried off not only the children but their fathers and mothers. Indeed, whole families were swept away during the time of that dreadful sickness. If the disease could not be stopped in Nome, it was likely to spread over all the territory of which that city was the center—to the east one thousand miles, and north even as far as the Arctic Ocean. In this region there lived eleven thousand people. To care for them there was in Nome but one doctor, who with his little band of nurses belonged to the United States Public Health Service.

Far away in the United States there was a cure for diphtheria, called antitoxin serum. The doctor sent out a frantic appeal for help. A twenty-pound package of

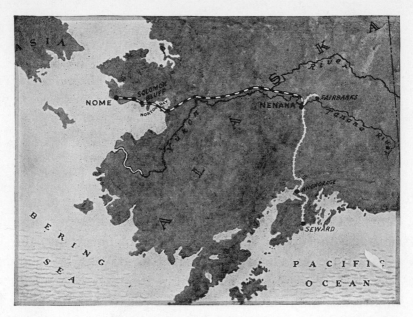

the precious serum for fighting diphtheria would save the
children, the families at Nome, and all the surrounding
territory from the Black Death.

Immediately the serum was rushed toward Alaska.
Without loss of time the railroad carried the package of
serum from Seward to Nenana.   Dog-teams must continue the journey six hundred and sixty-five miles by
trail westward to Nome.   Never before that time had the
journey from Nenana to Nome been made in less than
nine days.   The heroic drivers of the dog-teams risked
their lives by taking cross-cuts, never attempted in such
weather before.   The serum reached Nome in five and
one-half days!

But for the glorious deed of the dog, Balto, in the last sixty miles of the dash for Nome, this remarkable feat could not have been accomplished. However, if it had not been for the work of other heroic dogs and their drivers, big black Balto would not have had his chance to reach Nome with the serum and thus save hundreds of lives.

It was the driver Leonard Seppala who chose to cross the entrance to Norton Bay, instead of following the long shore-line around the bay. Because a hurricane was raging and the ice was breaking up and drifting out to sea, Seppala was warned not to try the short-cut across the bay. He thought of the long bay stretching up into the land, with a shore-line requiring days to travel, while children were dying at Nome—children whose lives might be saved if only the precious serum could reach them in time. The brave man and his twenty dogs crossed the bay in that frightful storm, with Scotty and Togo in the lead. He admitted to the next driver, Charlie Olsen, that he had a bad trip across the bay.

At the village of Bluff, Charlie Olsen found Gunnar Kasson waiting with his dog-team, headed by Balto, the best lead-dog in Alaska. So cold was it then, and the wind was blowing so hard, that the men feared the serum might freeze. They took it into a cabin to warm it. There Gunnar Kasson waited, hoping the wind would go down. Instead, it blew faster, and the cold grew more intense. Two hours passed. The wind blew faster than the men had ever known it to blow before, and the temperature had gone down to twenty-eight below zero. Suddenly Kasson decided that it was useless to wait any longer.

The dogs were hitched and he started, hoping to reach Safety, the station thirty-four miles away, before the trails were too deeply buried under the fast-falling snow. It was then ten o'clock on Sunday night. Kasson was dressed in sealskins from top to toe, but the wind was blowing so hard it went through the fur.

At Safety another driver with a dog-team would be waiting to carry the serum on through the last twenty-one miles. But before Kasson arrived, the driver at Safety sent word to Nome that the wind was blowing eighty miles an hour, with snow coming down in such heavy whirling drifts that no man or dog could keep the trail.

In the meantime, Balto struggled on through the drifts with Gunnar Kasson. Six hundred feet up a hill, he and the other dogs climbed in the storm; and then down the other side in the lashing wind, to a spot where for six miles the traveling was hard in any weather. The driver could not see his dogs, not even the nearest one. He could hardly see his hand before his face. Then he knew that he was lost. He could not even guess where he was.

More than half-way between Bluff and Safety there was a station called Solomon. There a message from Nome was waiting for Balto's driver, warning him to stop. The night was so cold and the storm was so furious that it was believed that man and dogs would surely perish in the blizzard if they attempted to go on.

Long before the sled reached Solomon, Balto was in charge of the journey. He alone knew in what direction to continue traveling. Regardless of darkness, cold, and blinding snow, the dog scented out the trail on the wind-swept ice and traveled on and on past Solomon. The bewildered driver missed the message from Nome; and in the face of the worst wind that he had ever known, Kasson followed blindly the leading of Balto.

Many times the sled tipped over and spilled everything in the soft snow. Again and again the driver straightened the sled and begged Balto to go on through the blackness, where no human being could have found the way.

At last the trail turned, so that the wind was behind the travelers, and helped them instead of hindering. Then, when the dogs reached Safety, the wind went down. The little house at Safety was dark; so instead of awakening the relay driver and wasting time, Kasson and his dog-team dashed by with the serum.

It was twenty-one miles from Safety to Nome, and the trail along the sea was heavy with drifted snow. By this time, though, it was no longer so dark, and the driver could see the trail. At thirty-six minutes past five on that wild dark morning, the half-frozen team, headed by Balto, arrived at Nome with the life-saving serum.

No wonder the driver almost wept, as he knelt in the snow and began pulling the slivers of ice from Balto's torn and bleeding feet. For it was Balto alone who had known the trail that stormy night and had carried the serum safely through to suffering Nome. Perhaps if the noble dog could speak he would merely repeat words he had heard over and over in Alaska from the brave men who serve the United States Government through sunshine and tempest, and who say, "It is all in the day's work for Uncle Sam."

## NOTES AND QUESTIONS

1. What great danger faced the people of Nome? Find the lines that tell just what the trouble was. Be ready to read them, or to tell what they say.

2. Find lines that tell exactly what Balto did that saved the serum. Be ready to read them, or to tell in one sentence how Balto saved the serum.

3. Find the lines that tell how one driver took a cross-cut that saved time. Be ready to read them, or to tell what the driver did.

4. On a wall map show just where the serum was carried in Alaska. Or make an outline map of Alaska and draw a line to show how the serum was carried from the time it reached Alaska. The map on page 27 will help you.

5. Do you know a story of a dog who helped his master? Tell it to the class.

Did you find some hard words in this story—words like *epidemic, disease, feat, bewildered?* Don't forget to use the Glossary that begins on page 435 to find the meanings of words.

If you like this story, you will want to read "Dogs of the United States Army Signal Service in Alaska," Fox (in *Uncle Sam's Animals*); and *Flash, the Lead Dog,* Marsh.

# THE MAIL MUST GO THROUGH

## Merlin Moore Taylor

The same bravery and faithfulness that made Gunnar Kasson, Leonard Seppala, and their dogs carry the serum to Nome were in the hearts of the men and horses of the Pony Express long years ago. In spite of Indians and blizzards and dangerous mountain trails, the Express riders carried the mails two thousand miles from the Missouri River to California. William Saunders was only a boy, but he did a man's work when duty called him to carry the mail.

### THE FIRST PONY EXPRESS RIDER

In a log house at St. Joseph, Missouri, on April 3, 1860, half a dozen men were gathered around a rough pine table. At the head of the table stood William Majors, manager for the firm of Russell, Majors and Waddell. This company operated a line of stagecoaches and wagon trains which carried passengers and freight across the western plains and the Rocky Mountains to California, two thousand miles away.

The railroad from the eastern part of the United States ended at St. Joseph; travelers desiring to reach the gold fields and fertile lands of the Far West faced a weary trail of many weeks over plains and mountains. Every foot of the way was full of danger, mostly from the Indians. It was Russell, Majors and Waddell who made that trail as safe as it could possibly be made, who kept in touch with weather conditions and the temper of the

redskins, and whose men guided the coaches and wagon trains across the wilderness.

On this day Russell, Majors and Waddell were sending out the first riders of the famous Pony Express. Up to that time the mails between the east and west coasts of our country were months on the way. It had become important that the time should be made shorter. Russell, Majors and Waddell had agreed to carry the mails west from St. Joseph.

Hundreds of fleet horses were purchased and distributed in strong corrals placed every ten or fifteen miles along the trail to California, each corral in charge of two or three men. From among the most skillful plainsmen, scouts, and Indian fighters riders had been chosen for these animals. Each man was given a stretch of the road about sixty miles long.

Receiving the mail pouch, containing no more than ten pounds of letters, each rider was expected to gallop away to the next relay station and then turn it over to the next rider. At each corral he passed, the rider leaped from his horse, pouch in hand, sprang upon the back of another horse already saddled and in waiting, and was off as hard as he could go. There was no time for more than "Hello" and "Good-by," or perhaps a brief warning that the Indians were coming; the regular schedule of nine days between St. Joseph and the western coast had to be kept. Night and day, rain or shine, the mails must go through as nearly on time as possible.

The half-dozen men who had gathered with Majors in his office on this day were there to find out which of them should have the honor of carrying the first pouch of mail on the first relay to the West.

Majors set his hat upon the table upside down.

"Boys," he said solemnly, "it is a great thing we are undertaking this day. Our government has entrusted to us the safe carrying and delivery of its mails. I have only this to say to you: Come what may, *the mail must go through*. In my hat I am placing a slip of paper for each of you. Upon one of the slips I have marked a cross in pencil. He who draws the cross shall carry the first pouch. Draw!"

Eagerly they crowded around him and drew.

"I've got it," yelled Johnny Frye joyfully. One after another, his fellows stepped up to shake his hand and wish him luck, in spite of their own disappointment.

"Now for the horse that shall bear you," said Majors. "You shall have your pick from the corral. William!"

Out from the corner where he had been an interested listener, William Saunders, a sturdy boy of sixteen, approached his employer. His blue eyes glowed with excitement. Through his veins the blood was racing madly with the thrill of knowing that he had a part, small as it was, in this great day. He held his head high; he had been employed by Russell, Majors and Waddell to take charge of the horses kept ready for the riders of the Pony Express between St. Joseph and the first relay station on the long trail westward.

"William," Majors ordered, "take Johnny Frye to the corral and let him look over the ponies. You will see that the one he chooses is properly groomed, saddled, and bridled, and is on hand at the railroad station when the train from the East arrives."

Proudly the boy conducted the honored rider out of the log house to the corral. Frye looked over the ponies with a shrewd eye.

"Good horses, those," he voiced his opinion. "Any one of them suits me, but I'd like to have the best."

"Then," said William Saunders quickly, "you will take that bay pony over there in the corner. I've ridden them all, and he's my favorite. I should like to see you pick him. Please, Mr. Frye. I know horses, and there isn't a better pony in the settlement."

Frye nodded solemnly. "The bay it is, lad," he agreed. "I'll rope him, and we'll slick him down between us; see that he is fed and watered, and you shall ride him to the station for me."

Long before the train from the East, drawn by a queer, wood-burning locomotive, was due, every man, woman, and child in the settlement had gathered to see Johnny Frye start off on his first trip. There were several speeches, everybody shook Frye's hand a last time, and they settled down to await the train.

At a spot where the baggage and mail car usually came to a stop, William Saunders stood holding the bay pony. On the ground near by lay Frye's saddle. The rider himself, in a new flannel shirt, buckskin trousers, high boots, and wide-brimmed hat, caressed the pony's nose, making friends with the animal.

Far down the shining twin rails of steel sounded the piercing whistle of the locomotive. Frye seized his saddle, clapped it upon the pony's back, tightened it with quick, skillful motions, saw that the bridle was in place, his rifle in its holster and pistols in his belt, and sprang into the saddle just as the train came in. From the train the mail pouch for California was tossed out. Willing hands caught it in mid-air and handed it to Frye.

"I bid you Godspeed in this your first journey, and now I say 'Go'!" yelled the mayor of St. Joseph, and he brought the broad palm of his hand down smartly upon the bay pony's flank.  As if he had been shot from a gun, the animal sprang away and galloped toward the big ferryboat that waited at the bank of the Missouri River to carry man and pony across.

### WILLIAM'S SERVICE TO THE PONY EXPRESS

For a moment William Saunders stared after them, his blood tingling with the thrill of the occasion.  Then, with two-score other youngsters at his heels, he raced for the top of a big bluff at the edge of the river in order to keep the horse and rider in sight as long as possible after they had reached the sandy stretch on the other side of the river.

From the top of that bluff in the days that followed the boy kept frequent watch with his spyglass.  And it was he who sighted the rider bringing the first pouch of mail from the West; he ran through the streets shouting the news aloud so that when the ferry touched the near bank, the Pony Express rider found himself surrounded by a throng of excited settlers.

To the boy, "The mail must go through" had become a slogan which guided his daily life.  His part, though small, was as important to him as if upon his shoulders alone rested the responsibility for seeing that the mail did go through.  His job was to see that the Express ponies were kept in condition for their difficult work, and he watched and tended them with a care and faith-

fulness that became a sort of joke in the settlement.
"The mail must go through!" William would exclaim
stoutly. "How is it going to do that, tell me, if I don't
see that the ponies are always fit?"

The exact hour of the arrival of the mail from the
West was always doubtful. Any one of a hundred
things might hinder its progress from the coast. But
from the earliest possible moment when it might ar-
rive, William was on the watch for it. Night or day,
it made no difference, he was on hand to greet the rider,
to awaken the clerk if need be, or to poke his head
through the door of Mr. Majors's office and sing out,
"The mail has come through, sir."

Then he took the pony in charge, cooled him down,
blanketed him if the weather was severe, fed and watered him, and examined him for any wound or injury
that needed attention. The riders, depending for their
very lives upon those ponies, repaid him with the stories
of their adventures. They passed on to him what they
knew of the plains and Indians and woodcraft until the
boy became wise in the ways of the plains country.

### CARRYING SUPPLIES TO A RELAY STATION

In time, William went to his employer with the thing
closest to his heart.

"I want to be a Pony Express rider, sir," he said.

Mr. Majors did not laugh, as William had half feared
he would. Instead, he patted the boy on the shoulder.

"You're a bit young yet, lad," he said kindly.

"You gave a job as rider to Willy Cody" (the famous Buffalo Bill), pointed out the boy. "He's only a year older than I am."

"True, but he had been across the plains, had fought Indians, and was more experienced in every way," was the reply. "Still, you've been a good boy, attended to your duties faithfully, helped to make the Pony Express successful. I want to help you along, and merely raising your wages won't do that. I'll tell you what I'll do. I'll put you in charge of one of the wagons that carries supplies to the relay stations. That will give you trail experience, and it'll give you fighting experience, too. The redskins have been active lately, and scarcely a wagon train has come through without a brush with them. Will that do for the present? In a year or so, if you make good, I'll give you a riding job."

With that William was forced to be content. Once he made the long journey by wagon train to California and back again, with hardly a rest between. There were meetings with hostile Indians, both coming and going, and the boy proved a cool, clear-headed fighter. But still he was denied his dearest wish.

"Make one more trip with supplies, and we shall see," he was told; and cheerfully he set about doing it.

Already there was a hint of winter in the air. The stream of pioneers, westbound, had stopped until spring again made the hardships of life in a prairie schooner more bearable for women and children. Only the Pony Express riders now rode out of St. Joseph with their faces turned toward the golden coast of California.

Winter and summer, the mails must go through, and in their lonely posts at remount and relay stations the men who looked after the ponies must be fed. Already those on the far side of the mountains had received their supplies from a wagon train which had gone out several weeks before. Now it was necessary only to supply the posts closer to St. Joseph. A swiftly moving train of twenty wagons, drawn by mules and in charge of experienced fighting men, left the settlement; and with it rode William Saunders. His duty was to check the supplies as they were dealt out, to keep the records for Russell, Majors and Waddell.

Three days out of St. Joseph and a hundred miles to the west, a lone rider overtook the wagons and passed them at a gallop with a wave of the hand by way of greeting. It was the Pony Express rider carrying the mail from the East on the second relay west. Five miles ahead lay a remount corral; ten miles beyond it was the relay station where the pouch would be turned over to the man who would ride the third stretch.

"There's snow a-coming," said Big Jim Bartigan, leader of the wagon train, sniffing the air. "We'll try to make the relay station before night."

When they arrived, the wagons were parked in a circle for the best protection, the mules and saddle animals were put in the corral, sentinels were selected, and the others set about getting supper. Half an hour later one of the sentinels cried out that a horse and rider were coming down the trail. The man slumped heavily forward upon the neck of the beast, clutching at the pommel of his saddle. The animal shuffled slowly along staggering from side to side, and as he came up to the wagons, stumbled, fell, and did not rise again. Wearily the rider dragged himself from beneath the animal, picked up his saddlebags, staggered into the ring of wagons, and sank beside a fire.

"The Indians got me," he said. It was the rider who earlier in the afternoon had passed them. He had spied the Indians first, and had ridden around them without being seen. A few miles out he had met the Express rider from the West. They had exchanged pouches, and he had turned back.

"I figured on getting a fresh horse from you," he said to Bartigan. "Then I ran into the redskins again, and they would have caught me if I'd had any further to go. My pony was done for, and I was wounded. Give me some coffee and a bite to eat. Then give me a horse and—"

His words died away to a murmur; he dropped back.

"The man is in bad shape," said Bartigan, rising from a hasty examination of his wound, "and he'll not be able to ride on. We'll do the best we can by him, and take him with us when we go in the morning."

William Saunders thrust himself forward.

"But the pouch, Mr. Bartigan," he cried. "The mail for the East. That ought to be on the way now."

The big plainsman shrugged his shoulders. "I can't spare any of the riders or any of the scouts to turn back with the pouch."

"The mail must go through," declared the boy.

"We'll take the pouch with us and turn it over if we meet an Express rider," replied Bartigan. "If not, we'll leave it at the next relay station."

He turned his back upon the boy and went about his duties. For a moment William stood thinking, his eyes upon the saddlebags that held the mail pouch, where they lay upon the ground beside the fire. Then he bent over, picked them up, slipped out of the circle of wagons, and made his way to the corral near by. William's horse was tethered near the gate.

"What are you up to, son?" asked the sentinel as the boy led out his pony and began to saddle it.

"Tell Mr. Bartigan someone else will have to check the supplies, for I have gone to take the mail through," was the reply, and William rode off into the darkness.

### THE MAIL GOES THROUGH

A few scattered flakes of snow began to fall as his pony galloped easily along the trail by which they had come that day. William did not want to push the animal. He could get no fresh horse closer than twenty

miles or more; he must save his pony as much as possible at first.

Within the boy's breast there was a fierce pride and joy. He was riding a Pony Express relay, and the mail was going through. The wind was rising now, and the snow was falling faster and faster. Suddenly out of the storm and darkness loomed up the corral of the remount station which earlier in the day had been surprised by the Indians. It was deserted. William turned his pony into the trail again. As if the little animal had gone weary at being denied the rest and food which his day's hard work had earned him, he began to slow down. From a gallop his gait dropped to a trot, then to a fast shuffle, and by and by into a walk, until finally he was merely plodding along.

The cold had begun to chill the boy. He felt sleepiness stealing over him. He stopped the pony, got stiffly down from the saddle, and started the blood to circulate freely again by thrashing his body with his arms. Then, leading the pony, he began to walk. Warmed again, he remounted and kept his heels beating a tattoo against the pony's ribs. When he grew numb again, he dismounted and once more walked.

All at once before his eyes appeared other tracks in the fresh snow. He bent over to examine them, puzzled that the wind had not filled them up almost as soon as made. Then the truth burst upon him. They were his own tracks and those of his pony. Leading the way, he had been walking in a short circle!

Panic clutched at him as he climbed back into the saddle. Unless the pony's sense of direction came to their rescue, they were lost. He loosened the reins, and the pony whirled around and plodded off in another direction. Two hours later the patient animal began to show signs of renewed life; his head came up, his ears went forward, and he began to whinny. From somewhere ahead came an answering whinny, a fence loomed up out of the darkness and, following it around, they came to the cabin of the remount station.

Fifteen minutes later, warmed by the hot coffee he had found ready and with a fresh horse under him,

William was off for the relay station a dozen miles away. Before his eyes rose visions of hot food, a roaring fire in a big stove, and a warm bunk when he should have turned over the mail to the rider of the final relay into St. Joseph, fifty-odd miles away.

"Bless me," yelled the man at the relay station. "It's William Saunders. Where did you drop from, boy? Thought you were headed west with the supply train."

Briefly, William explained, as he took off his coat and gloves, and warmed himself at the fire.

"Where's the other rider?" the boy demanded. "He ought to be starting now with the pouch."

The man's face grew grave.

"He got in about an hour ago, all worn out from facing the storm," he said. "He's in a bunk in the other room dead to the world."

"Wake him," ordered William. "The mail must go through."

But the Express rider could not be aroused. He made a brave effort to get up, fell back, and was sound asleep again instantly. Wearily William began to pull on his outer clothing again.

"Saddle a pony for me," he said. "I'll carry the mail on."

"You'd never make it," he was told. "Snow's drifting now. If a man was fresh, he might get through, seeing the wind's at his back going east. But you're a kid. You're played out now. You haven't got a chance."

"Get that pony ready," commanded William fiercely. "I'm going to make it. The mail's got to go through."

Of that long, wearisome ride William never afterwards had any very clear recollection. He knew only that he rode, trusting to the animal under him to keep to the trail, that he dozed in the saddle, waking up to change horses at the two remount stations and falling asleep again as soon as he was in the saddle. Then he felt his pony stopping, forced open his eyelids, and found they were at the ferry. He slept again as it bore him across the river, and was pounded into wakefulness on the other side. He realized that it was broad daylight, and had been for hours.

Slowly up the path to the settlement William rode. He fell off his horse in front of the office of Russell, Majors and Waddell, pushed open the door, staggered inside, tossed his saddlebags at the feet of Mr. Majors, and said thickly:

"The mail has come through, sir!"

Many hours later he awoke to find that it was another day. Beside his bunk stood his employer.

"William," he said, "the train from the East is due in two hours. Do you think you can be ready to carry the mail on the first relay west?"

The boy struggled upright, full of amazement and joy.

"What do you mean, sir?" he managed to ask.

"This," said Mr. Majors; "if you still want to ride for the Pony Express, there's a job waiting for you."

NOTES AND QUESTIONS

1.  The list below gives the main points of this story. But they are not in the right order. Write them down in correct order so that you could begin with the first point and tell the story as it is told in your book.

> William's everyday work at St. Joseph
> The plan of the Pony Express
> The wounded express rider
> Choosing the first rider
> William's reward
> The first rider from St. Joseph
> William with the supply train
> William's brave ride

2.  Which one of the sentences below tells you the most important thing about William?

(*a*) He knew all about life on the Plains.

(*b*) He was faithful in both big things and little things.

(*c*) He was brave.

(*d*) He knew all about horses.

3.  The author of this story has used some words especially to help you feel and see things. For example, on page 36, "glowed with excitement," "racing madly," and "yelled joyfully." Make a list of five other groups of words that helped you feel and see what happened.

4.  On an outline map of the United States put New York, St. Joseph, Missouri River, Rocky Mountains, San Francisco, Atlantic and Pacific Oceans. Draw a line to show how far the railroad went, and a dotted line to show the Pony Express.

Other stories of Uncle Sam's mail are: "The Pony Express Rider" and "The Fast Mail," Walker (in *How They Carried the Mail*); "The Pony Express," Evans (in *America First*); "Flying Ponies," Fox (in *Uncle Sam's Animals*).

# LINDBERGH, PIONEER AIR SCOUT

## Laura Antoinette Large

For hundreds of years men have wished that they could fly like the birds. Men first made balloons, but they could only drift with the winds. Then, just a few years ago, Orville and Wilbur Wright made an airplane. When they first tried it, they could keep it up only about a minute. It could fly only a quarter of a mile. But that was only the beginning. We shall now see what a strong carrier of men and messages the airplane has become.

### OFF TO PARIS

It was a few minutes before eight o'clock on the morning of May 20, 1927. On most days the sun is up and shining in the city of New York long before that hour, but on that morning the sun was not shining. The sky was overcast with clouds, and there was a mist hanging over the city.

A tall slim young man stepped out of an automobile at the aviation runway on Roosevelt Field. A beautiful new airplane, with the name *Spirit of St. Louis,* stood near by. The tall young man stood still a moment. He looked up into the sky toward the east and northeast. The weather was bad around New York. What was the weather out on the ocean over which he was to travel? What would it be later in the day? What might it be that night after darkness had set in?

This young man had planned to fly from New York

to Paris!   Such a flight had never been made before.
It was a very dangerous undertaking.   One might not
have been surprised if there had been fear upon the
man's face, but there was no fear.   This man was
ready to go.

Into the cockpit of the airplane the youth climbed
hastily.   He started the motor.

"How does it sound?" he asked a man who stood
near.   The man was the field engineer for the Wright
Company, which had built the motor.

"She sounds mighty good to me," the man replied.

The tall youth listened a moment longer.

"Don't you think I might as well go?" he asked.

"Yes, I guess you had better," was the answer.

The roar from the motor filled the air.   The tall
young man waved his hand to the people who had
gathered about the field, and started on the long journey.

It seemed hard for the plane to rise from the ground because it was so heavily loaded. People held their breath for fear the great undertaking might end even before it was well under way. Once off the ground, the airplane barely passed over some trees near by. It flew dangerously near some electric wires. Up—up—higher and still higher it went! Yes, it was really off at last. *Charles Lindbergh was on his way to Paris!*

People all over the world were hoping and wishing and praying that the brave young man would reach his journey's end safely. "Will his engine prove strong and steady enough to make the 3610 miles that lie between New York and Paris?" they asked one another.

"Will the young man be able to remain awake until he reaches the city toward which he is headed?" It might be thirty-five hours. It might be as long as forty hours!

"He will become so tired that he cannot control the ship properly," some predicted. "The steady roar of the motor may cause him to fall asleep," others said.

Then there was the weather about which to wonder. "What was going on out over the ocean?" "Were there many storms?" "Would ice gather upon the wings of the airplane and force it down?" This had happened many times before, and had been the cause of the death of more than one brave man of the air.

And while people talked, Charles Lindbergh proceeded on his way. Up along the northeastern coast of the United States the great air-bird was seen from time to time during the day. At 9:05 o'clock it passed over East Greenwich, Rhode Island. At 9:40 o'clock it was sighted at Halifax, Massachusetts. At 12:25 P. M. it flew over Meteghan, Nova Scotia. At 1:05 o'clock in the afternoon Springfield, Nova Scotia, was passed. Finally at 7:45 P. M., just before dark, Lindbergh guided the *Spirit of St. Louis* like a messenger from another world over the Atlantic Ocean, and on into the great adventure.

### CROSSING THE ATLANTIC

No sooner had Lindbergh left Newfoundland than he ran into a cold fog. He was prepared for this, however, for he had put on a warm fur-lined coat. His enclosed cockpit helped to protect him from the cold as well as from the strong wind and rain. Lindbergh pointed the nose of his airplane upward until he had reached a height of ten thousand feet, or about two miles. Below him was a low light fog through which tall icebergs could be seen. This fog kept growing thicker and higher until it reached the very edge of the area through which he was flying. There was no moon at first. It was very dark. People wonder just what Charles Lindbergh's thoughts were as he flew alone above the tossing waves of the Atlantic Ocean all through that long dark night. Perhaps he had in mind just one thought—*"To Paris!"* And on—on—Lindbergh flew.

The moon came out after a while, and the flying was

easier than it had been. But the storm clouds and fog areas were present most of the time.

While making his way through one thick storm cloud, ice formed upon the wings of his airplane. He had to turn back to a clear region and then fly around the cloud. Then other storm clouds appeared. Each time Lindbergh flew around or over them.

At 1 A. M., New York time, the first signs of dawn appeared. With the coming of the day there was perhaps a little more hope than before. The air was warmer for a time, and the small amount of ice which had begun to gather upon the plane melted away.

After a time the sun came up, and all the while the *Spirit of St. Louis* was roaring on and on toward its distant goal!

There was more fog, there were more storm clouds to pass through or get around, but much of the traveling was in clear weather now. A part of the time Lindbergh found a place not more than ten feet above the water. At this distance there is a cushion of air through which an airplane can travel most easily.

At one time during the morning flight Lindbergh had to direct his plane up fifteen hundred feet to get away from heavy fogs. Even then he ran into storm clouds again, through which he had to travel because he could not get away from them. To tell which way to go, Lindbergh had to watch his compass. Without this he might have gone many miles out of his way.

Some fishing vessels upon the water gave Lindbergh the first sign of land. He lowered his plane until he was down very close to one of the vessels, but he could see no men aboard. In the window of a second fishing boat a man's head appeared. Lindbergh lowered his plane again and quieted his motor as much as he could when just a few feet from the man in the boat.

"Ahoy, there!" he called. "Which way to Ireland?" Perhaps the fisherman could not understand English. Perhaps he was too surprised to answer. At any rate he did not reply, and Lindbergh directed his plane upward again and continued on his way.

After traveling several hours more, he could see a rough coast line that was partly mountainous. He thought that this must surely be the southeastern coast of Ireland, and soon found that he was really this far on his way toward Paris.

How hopeful he must have been at this time, and how thankful!

### PARIS AT LAST——MESSAGES OF GOOD-WILL

In a little over two hours the coast of England appeared. Then across the English Channel the brave flier made his way. At last Cherbourg on the ·French coast was reached, and not long after, the beacons of the Paris-London airway could be seen. It was dark again—almost 10 P. M. (5 P. M. New York time). Flares had been lighted at the landing field of Le Bourget to

attract Lindbergh's notice as he neared Paris. He saw
these flares, but traveled a few miles farther to make
sure this really was the right landing place, and then
he turned back again. He noticed lines of autos crowd-
ing the roads near the field, and he could make out the
long lines of hangars.

At last Lindbergh brought his plane down upon the
aviation field at Le Bourget. He had arrived at the very
place for which he had set out just thirty-three and a
half hours before!

A great shout went up from the crowd of people which
had gathered. Lindbergh had to get out of his plane
quickly in order to save it from being damaged by the

vast throng which was pressing upon it. For half an hour Lindbergh was carried about upon the shoulders of different men of the crowd. No one carried him very far or seemed to want to take him away. He was just carried around and around within a very small area. Every one shouted and hurrahed, and there was such an uproar it was impossible to hear anyone speak.

At last the French military fliers took charge. One of them quickly removed Lindbergh's helmet and placed it upon the head of an American newspaper reporter who happened to be near.

"Here is Lindbergh!" the Frenchman cried.

At once the reporter was lifted up and carried away, followed by great crowds of people. The reporter did not like this at all, and tried to explain, but it was no use! What he said could not be heard. In the meantime the real Lindbergh, without any helmet upon his head, escaped from the crowd and was taken away by our American ambassador, Myron T. Herrick, in order that he might have a good night's rest.

When Lindbergh arose the next day, the streets of Paris were crowded with people eager to welcome him and do him honor. And from that day on, gifts and honors of all kinds, such as the world had never given to one person, were heaped upon him. Almost every noon there was a dinner with important persons present, and almost every night there was a banquet.

He seemed greatly pleased with it all. He smiled in

a way that made people like him even better than ever,
and spoke in a way that made friends for himself and for
his country as well.   Lindbergh extended the friendship
of his country, the United States, to the country of
France first, and later to the English and Belgian gov-
ernments.   "We want to be your friends," was his
message to each country.

### AMERICA HONORS THE HERO

By this time the people of the United States were
beginning to be eager to see their own American hero.
The President and all the people were proud of what
Lindbergh had done.   They were delighted because of
the message of good-will which he had taken to the
foreign countries across the water.   The President showed
what he thought of Lindbergh by sending the United
States warship, *Memphis,* to bring him back home to
America.   The *Spirit of St. Louis* could be carried back
on the same boat, Lindbergh was told.

Thus in a short time Lindbergh was home again in the
United States—and what a welcome awaited him!   As
in Europe, he was awarded medals of all kinds.   The
President of the United States presented him with the
Distinguished Flying Cross on the first day of his arrival
in the city of Washington.   Mrs. Evangeline Lindbergh,
his mother, was present at this ceremony, and a very
happy and proud woman she must have been.

When the city of Washington had conferred all its

honors upon Lindbergh, he went to visit New York City, where they planned the biggest celebration ever given any visiting hero!

When the festivities were over in New York, Lindbergh was invited to St. Louis. This was his home city —the city for which his monoplane, the *Spirit of St. Louis,* had been named. It was also the city in which money had been raised to pay for the making of the airplane and for other expenses of the trip. St. Louis could not turn out so many millions of people to see Lindbergh as did New York City. But there was a hearty welcome and a spirit of pride for what Charles Lindbergh had been able to do.

Paris, Brussels, London, Washington, New York, St. Louis, Chicago! Why did so many cities do their best to honor Lindbergh? This is easy to answer. Charles Lindbergh was brave; he had skill and good health; he was friendly and kind to other people and knew how to make them friendly toward him. Charles Lindbergh was ready to do a great work, and when the time came, the great work was done.

## NOTES AND QUESTIONS

1. How far did Lindbergh fly?
2. How many hours was he in the air?
3. Was he in the air about one day, a day and a half, or two days?
4. Give four dangers that Lindbergh faced on his flight.
5. How is a compass helpful in guiding a person?

6. What land across the ocean did he first see?

7. What message did Lindbergh carry to the people of Europe?

8. Here is a list of nine words, and nine sentences with letters in them. Write the letters (*a*) to (*i*) on your paper. After each letter write the word that belongs where that letter is in the sentence.

overcast          hangars          uproar
cockpit           airway           throng
beacons           flares           skill

....(*a*).... means being able to do something very well.

When the sky is cloudy, we say it is ....(*b*).....

Airplanes are kept in ....(*c*).....

Lights to guide people at night are called ....(*d*).... or ....(*e*).....

A crowd of people is called a ....(*f*).....

The route over which airplanes travel is called an ....(*g*).....

An aviator sits in the ....(*h*).... of his plane.

A mixture of many loud noises is called an ....(*i*).....

9. On a map of the world find New York, Nova Scotia, Newfoundland, Ireland, England, the English Channel, Cherbourg, and Paris. Be ready to show on a wall map just where Lindbergh flew.

You will enjoy reading "New York to Paris," Lindbergh (in *We*); "Through the Storm," Collins (in *Skyward Ho!*, Mathiews); *Picture Book of Flying*, Dobias.

## AIR MAIL

### Gordon Hillman

Every night when the clock strikes eight
And the stars are out and it's very late,
And the moon is dim in the western sky
I watch to see the mail go by.

You can hear it whirring over the hill
When the sun has set and the wind is still,
And if you are looking straight overhead
You see its lights all green and red,

And its motor plays a little tune
As a shadow swoops across the moon
Just beneath the stars and across the sky,
I watch the mail go roaring by.

# A BACKWARD LOOK

AIRPLANES, radios, dog-teams, horses, trains—we have read about all these ways of carrying men or sending messages. We perhaps understand a little better how man has made the world smaller. There are other ways, too.

Make a list of all the ways men send messages.

Make another list of the ways they travel.

Write down the different ways you have traveled and sent messages.

Your class might like to gather pictures of ways of traveling and sending messages. These pictures could be put on a bulletin board.

There was a time when traveling almost always meant danger—danger from wild animals, from cold and hunger and thirst, from savage people. Now in most parts of the world we travel in comfort and safety, and our messages speed on their way to our friends. But there are still parts of the world where travel is hard, and where men wait days and even weeks for news they are eager to get.

Name five places where this is true. One of the stories in this Part tells you of such a place.

The four stories you have just read are only a few of many just as interesting. Did they show you how progress in transportation and communication makes the world grow smaller? Men have dug canals for boats, strung thousands of miles of wire for messages, built roads over and through mountains for trains and automobiles, and spent long hours of patient work to invent the radio and the airplane. Many books have been written about these men. You will find some very interesting ones in the list on page 431.

# PART TWO
# · THE OUTDOOR WORLD ·

## I LOVE ALL OF OUT-OF-DOORS

CLINTON SCOLLARD

I love all of out-of-doors;
Music that the robin pours,
And the wren-talk, and the low
Warble of the vireo
And the "spink-a-chink-a-chink"
Of the merry bobolink!

Then I love the brook, and love
Cloud-ships floating far above;
Love the gentle rain-song that
On the pane sounds "pit-a-pat";
Love the lion wind that roars;
Love just all of out-of-doors!

# ALL THE WORLD IS A ZOO

IT IS FUN to watch the lions and tigers and monkeys in a zoo. Probably you have many times begged your parents to take you to see the animals. But did you ever stop to think that all the world is a zoo? Close about you are wild things of nature that are just as interesting as tigers and monkeys. Do you know the names of all the kinds of birds that nest near your home? How many kinds of wild flowers can you name?

Perhaps there are some wild animals near your home that you never dreamed lived there. One fifth-grade boy never knew there were weasels near his home until they killed his pet guinea pigs one night. His sister found a little gray-furred baby that had fallen from its nest. She carried it home and took care of it until it grew into a lively flying squirrel. She had never seen any flying squirrels; so she looked them up in a book. There she found that they come out only at night.

Yes, the wild things of the out-of-doors are so interesting that all over the world today thousands of men and women are studying them. And they are writing books and stories of the wonderful things they see and learn. You are now going to read some of these stories. Three Boy Scouts will tell you how it feels to be surrounded by lions at night. Mrs. Bradley will tell you about Pembe Kubwa, a wise and wicked elephant. Mr. Rutledge will explain why birds and animals need our help in this day of farms and cities. As you read some of these stories and observe the outdoor life around you, perhaps you will learn, too, that while some outdoor things should be protected, others must be destroyed.

# A MIDNIGHT LION HUNT

### ROBERT, DAVID, AND DOUGLAS

Mr. and Mrs. Martin Johnson are famous for the moving pictures of wild animals they have taken in many parts of the world. On one of their trips to Africa they had as their guests three Boy Scouts: Robert Douglas, Jr., of Greensboro, North Carolina; David Martin, Jr., of Austin, Minnesota; and Douglas Oliver, of Atlanta, Georgia.

In this story these boys tell you of "the most exciting adventure" they had on the trip.

## WAITING FOR THE LIONS

We all came home agreed about the most exciting adventure of our trip; it was the night we spent in the truck surrounded by hungry lions.

The sides of our truck were of heavy wire. As it had a good top, only the front and back had to be closed. These were made secure by lashing poles across both openings. After we got into the truck, we wired poles across the front, and thus shut off the seat from the rest of the truck.

We knew that we were safe from lions, yet we all felt a little nervous when Mr. Johnson left us. We changed to our sleeping clothes while it was still light, and ate the lunch which Mrs. Johnson had prepared for us. Just as we started to eat, Dave said something about this being our last meal on earth. We all laughed, but little remarks like that at such a time make one feel rather uneasy. To

From "Midnight Thrills" in *Three Boy Scouts in Africa* by Robert D. Douglas, Jr., David R. Martin, Jr., and Douglas L. Oliver. Courtesy of G. P. Putnam's Sons, Publishers, New York and London.

be sure, we had arranged with Mr. Johnson to fire the
rifle twice if we needed him, but what good would that do
if he were quite a distance away and the lions only a few
feet?

After eating lunch in a silence broken only by a few
strained whispers, we crawled under the blankets. We had
been told that if the lions heard a human voice they would
instantly run. It was likely, though, that even if the animals were not afraid, we would have whispered because
we were all so excited. Douglas said something about getting a lion into the truck and then jumping out. This
started Dave laughing. He buried his head in the pillow
and laughed until we thought he was crying. When he
called out, "You fellows will kill me yet!" we all began
laughing, at the same time trying not to make a sound.

### TAKING THE LION'S PICTURE

We had been turned in about half an hour when we
suddenly heard a bone crack. We slowly rose up and
peeped out between the poles across the opening in the
rear. Instead of the hyenas we had expected, we saw an
old lion. He had a short mane, but he was a big fellow.
When we saw him, we all started shaking. It was not so
much the fright as it was seeing a big lion just a few
feet away.

As we watched, he started eating away on the zebra
that had been placed there for bait. Now and then he
snarled and growled deeply in his throat. We turned the

flashlight on him; but instead of running away, he only crouched down behind the zebra. For several minutes we watched him. After a while he got over his fear of the light and began once more to eat. Mr. Johnson says that he thinks the lions believe the flash of a hand-light or of a flare to be only lightning in the sky. Whatever this one thought, he showed no fear.

Finally we started whistling to make him hold his head up. When we first whistled, he ran off a few feet but soon returned. We whistled again, and he just looked up at us. Now Dick caught hold of the two wires which controlled the flares. To set them off the wires had to be touched together. The lion looked up just then, but he was not in the right position. Dick was going to whistle once more, but just as he drew in his breath, the flare went off with a loud report and a blinding flash. His hands had been shaking so that the wires had touched without his knowing it. We teased Dick about that for the rest of the trip. But from the way the truck was shaking at the time, our hands and bodies were trembling as much as his.

Then this conversation took place.

Dick said: "I bet the lion wasn't even in the picture."

Douglas answered: "I expect Mr. and Mrs. Johnson think we are crazy, taking a picture at this time of night."

In a few minutes we heard Mr. Johnson calling. Douglas whispered: "I bet they are laughing at us. They're saying, 'Those boys probably photographed a hyena, mistaking it for a lion.' "

Mr. Johnson called: "What did you get?"

"Only a lion," we answered in a careless way.

"Well, go to sleep," he yelled back. "We'll see in the morning."

We all crawled under our blankets, thinking it was all over for the night. This was about eight o'clock. We remained awake for half an hour; then dropped off to sleep.

### MORE LIONS COME

Several hours later we were awakened by a violent shake of the truck. We heard growling outside. After some minutes of lying in bed, shivering with both fright and excitement, we got up enough courage to shine our lights out the back. Just under us was an old lioness calmly chewing on a tire. Twenty-five feet away on the bait, we saw four other lions. And as we watched, two more joined in. Then the old lioness went back to the group. There were three big ones with manes, three smaller ones, and one toto, or young one. Surely we believe it was the most exciting moment of our lives, and also one of the most interesting.

In spite of their fierce looks, the lions were exactly like a bunch of cats quarreling over a meal. They lay there, one at the head of the zebra, two at the back, two at the side, and one on the haunches. The toto stood off a few feet, watching his chance to slip into the feast. Our light seemed not to bother them, for they just looked up now and then and blinked. However, the one whom we had made the picture of before seemed a bit suspicious. When we moved the light, he would crouch down behind the zebra. Perhaps he had been frightened by the flash of the camera flares. But he soon got over his fright, and took his place among the others.

After a while the toto crawled up beside one of the big fellows. As long as he kept to his place, he was allowed to eat. But once when he got up too close and started for the same bit of meat as one of the others, the big lion rose up and gave him a slap. It seemed a light blow, but it sent the youngster sprawling into the grass. He jumped up and ran over to the other side of the zebra, where he lay down beside a lioness, probably his mother.

After we had watched them for some time by the light of our flashlights, we noticed that one of the cameras had been knocked down. We were just discussing this in whispers when one of the big lions left the zebra, walked over to the fallen camera, and began chewing on it. Then he grabbed it in his mouth and started dragging it away. Suddenly in some way one of the legs of the tripod flew up and hit him. He jumped almost twenty feet. In a few minutes he came back to it; slowly at first, but when he saw it did not move, he pounced on it.

We felt that there was nothing we could do. None of us would have got out of the truck for any three-hundred-dollar camera. In a few minutes one of the lions left the zebra and came over to the other camera, which was still standing. She rubbed her head against it and chewed the wires connecting the cameras with the flares. We whistled and hissed to frighten her from it, but it did no good.

Finally Dick yelled, "Scat, you heathen, scat!" Then Douglas shouted, "Get away! We've told you twice!"

The sound of our voices finally frightened the lioness from the camera and scared the others away for a while. They soon returned, however, and continued their meal.

We watched them for about an hour before we lay down again. But just as we decided to go to sleep, we heard a slight noise up in the front of the truck. Dick grabbed his flashlight and crawled up to the poles that separated the front seat from the body of the truck. Shining his light out through the bars, we saw the head of a lioness not

three feet away! She had one foot on the fender and one on the floor board, and she had stuck her head up to the seat. When she saw the light, she only blinked her eyes and crawled back down.

We said not a word. It was the first time we had ever seen a lion try to drive a truck, and the sight gave us quite a shock. We came back to our blankets and waited several minutes before we felt like turning in again. We all lay perfectly still for a while and at last dropped off to sleep.

### THE RETURN TO CAMP

In the morning when Mr. Johnson came over and woke us, we told him about the night. He laughed for half an hour. The loss of one of his cameras did not seem to worry him. He said that our experience was worth it if the picture of the first lion was good. Of course the plate in the smashed camera was ruined, but the one in the other was all right. He and Mrs. Johnson had heard the lions roaring and growling over on our bait, but they had never suspected there were seven.

When we returned to camp, we were all very sleepy. So after breakfast we lay down for a while. But we were soon up again.

Mrs. Johnson, active and energetic as usual, spent the morning out hunting for lions with her native guide. She was not going to shoot, but just find them for picture making. In the meantime, Mr. Johnson developed the picture made the night before. About the middle of the morning he called us over to where he was developing. He let out a whoop and we came running. We found that there was nothing the matter; he just wanted us to see the proof of the picture we had made. We had been afraid that the lion was not in the right position; but when we saw the picture, we were satisfied. We had caught the lion broadside, standing over the zebra, a good likeness of the King of Beasts himself.

## NOTES AND QUESTIONS

1. Find the lines that tell what you think was the most exciting part of this adventure. Be ready to read them.

2. Find a part that you think was funny, and be ready to read it. You may not all agree.

3. Would you rather hunt animals with a gun or with a camera? Give reasons for your answer.

4. Is it more dangerous to hunt with a camera or with a gun? Give reasons for your answer.

5. Be ready to read or tell something about how the lions acted.

6. Have you ever felt as the boys did—a little nervous even though you knew you were safe? Tell about it.

If you enjoyed this story, you will like to read "Doug Gets His Lion," in *Three Boy Scouts in Africa,* the book which the boys wrote and from which this story was taken.

# PEMBE KUBWA, THE BIG TUSKER

## Mary Hastings Bradley

Mrs. Bradley, whose home is in Chicago, has made a number of trips to Africa to study the wild animals and the tribes of people who live there. In this story she tells of a very wise and a very wicked elephant—how he won and kept the leadership of the herd.

### WHEN KUBWA WAS YOUNG

Pembe Kubwa was a very wise and wicked elephant. He was so big that he stood shoulders high over the rest of the herd and so old that his tusks had grown to such a length that they were crossed in front of him.

He had no idea how old he was—perhaps a hundred, perhaps two hundred years old, but he was still so strong that he was the leader of the herd, and no bull had dared turn against him now for a long, long time.

As a matter of fact, his tusks were not so dangerous in a fight now as when they were shorter and he could thrust deeper with them, but no elephant had fought with him for so long that none of the herd had found this out. However, he suspected it himself.

Kubwa did not remember very much about his young days. He knew that he had trailed about with his mother in a big herd, and he knew that he had given his mother a good deal of trouble, because her temper was often very short with him. He had a way of straying off that particularly provoked her, and he did remember very clearly one day when she finally grabbed him with her trunk and just boosted him along, bumpity bump, through the forest trail.

It was good luck for him that he did not get into trouble, because at first he did not learn except from his own experience. Elephants and people who depend upon experience alone often get into trouble.

After a time, because as I said, he was a wise elephant even when he was young, he learned from the experiences of others, from those he saw and those he heard about. But in the beginning it was just luck that saved him. For instance, there was the adventure with the crocodile. Ever since he could remember, his mother had always been cautioning him not to put his trunk in the river to drink until he had looked out for crocodiles. His mother always used to wade in the stream and cast her bright beady eyes upstream and down and thrash around a bit; then she would put her trunk swiftly into the river and drink in the delicious water.

But Kubwa never saw any sense in waiting for something he wanted. So one day he scrambled out of the line of march and ran on ahead toward the river. Another little elephant ran along with him, because a bad example is as contagious as the measles. Down to the bend in the stream went Kubwa, and in went his trunk. Down went the other elephant, and in went *his* trunk. And suddenly the other elephant gave a gurgling cry of

fright and then a shrill, terror-stricken squeal. Something under water had seized that trunk in its firm jaws and was pulling him in.

The little elephant, squealing for all he was worth, pulled and pulled, until it seemed that his trunk would come off, but the crocodile was the stronger, and the baby elephant was forced out farther and farther into the water. Then his trunk was hurting so much that, to avoid the pain, he took more steps forward into the deeper water.

Kubwa didn't know what on earth to do! They had gone so far ahead of the herd that it seemed as if help would never come. However, he heard the wild, far-away trumpeting of the other baby's mother who had

recognized his voice.  He had jerked his own trunk out
of the water as if it had been stung and held it high
above his head, galloping out of the water as fast as his
frightened legs could carry him.  Now he wrapped his
trunk about the hind legs of his friend and pulled with
all his strength, and suddenly the two elephants began
to go backward and with them, drawn against its
braced feet, showed the head and body of a long and
powerful crocodile.

. And then, snap! the crocodile fell back with his mouth
full of one bite of the elephant's trunk, and the elephant
himself was saved.

Just at this moment the herd came tearing down the
trail.  The angry cow, the mother of the injured baby,
was in the lead.  She was so grateful to see her child
alive and so angry with him for his disobedience and
for scaring her nearly to death that she promptly began
to spank him for dear life with her trunk.

As for Kubwa, she had nothing but praise for his
strength and help!  She said nothing at all about his
disobedience, because if he had not been there, her child
could not have been saved.  However, Kubwa's mother
had some ideas of her own about that.  After that she
did not need to warn Kubwa any more about crocodile
waters.

He remembered that he used to play about a good
deal with a big ball of mud that he and the other youngsters rolled up for themselves.  He liked getting up

games, and he was always stirring about and disturbing the elders of the herd when they were taking a noonday forty winks.

But one day of his youth seemed very much like the next. Life was not really exciting until he began to get his strength and discovered that he could bully the others and have his way with them.

### LEADING HIS OWN HERD

It was not only Kubwa's strength that made him win, for often he tackled elephants who were really stronger than himself. But he was quick to think and could get into action before the other fellow had decided on his plan of attack. As Kubwa got bigger and bigger, he got deadlier and deadlier in action.

The time came when he only snorted when his mother spoke to him, and he threw dust in his older brother's eyes, which was not a respectful thing to do. Finally he fought his uncle, who started out to teach him his place, and gave his uncle such a horrid poke in the shoulder with his long sharp tusks that the old leader went off in a huff. Several of the older ones went with his uncle, but the others stayed and listened politely and lazily to this energetic young boss, and Kubwa began to lead his own herd.

Kubwa adored commanding! He said when it was time to go into the swamp, and when into the forest, and he led the way to the grazing grounds and sampled all the best places for miles around. Soon he began bullying any strangers or any small groups that wandered into the grazing grounds when he was there; mild-mannered elephants, who wanted a quiet life and good food, began to come and join his herd in order to get the benefit of his protection and his leadership.

Year by year, too, more little elephants were added to the herd. Now, some fathers have a way of slipping off into the forests when the youngsters are trotting around, letting the mothers have all the bother of bringing up the children, but Kubwa was too much of an overlord for that. He never left his herd. He bossed the mothers, and he saw to it that the mothers bossed the children. None of the tricks that he used to play on his mother for *him!*

Every year he grew bigger and stronger, and his tusks grew heavier and longer. They were very long for their weight, sharp and fierce like swords, and very curving, growing toward each other. He used to thrust them into an enemy with such wicked force that no elephant would stand up to him. After a time they grew so long that they began to cross in front of him. They were about seven feet long when they began to cross, and they grew so long that they extended about two feet more beyond the crossing.

He could do a great deal with two feet of tusks, but not nearly so much as he wanted the other elephants to keep on believing he could. That crossing would stop his thrust short!  He lost all the seven-foot length behind it.  He knew this, and he wondered if the other elephants of the herd ever thought of it.  Those crossed tusks of his gave him a good deal of secret uneasiness as he grew older and older.

### OLD KUBWA'S WICKED TRICKS

The first real fear he had ever known was this terrible fear that some elephant would be able to defeat him.  He made up his mind that he would never be driven away.  He told himself that he would die first.  He began to watch out for rivals.  Whenever he met any elephant that he thought might prove of danger to him, he began to plot against that elephant.  And always the elephant came to an unlucky end.

There was a big, broad-backed fellow who had talked back to him and showed in several ways that he felt himself to be a coming champion.  Kubwa let the big fellow walk ahead one day, and he fell into an elephant pit.  Kubwa led the others carefully around the pit, chuckling quietly to himself.  He was a wicked old fellow, as I said, for he did not stop to put down his trunk and try to give the other a lift out.  He had known all about that pit for years.  Every year the natives covered it with fresh branches, hoping he would forget and fall into it, but he never forgot.

There was another elephant who began to think himself more than a match for Kubwa.  He had sharp,

wide-apart tusks, and a very hasty, irritable temper. Kubwa told him about a fruit tree one day in the forest, and the elephant hurried over to it and walked between two little trees in front of it. Between the trees a poisoned spear fastened to the end of a log arm fell down and put an end to him. Kubwa had known all about that trap.

There was very little about the natives' way of doing things that Kubwa did not know. He had taken a liking to their food, especially to their bananas, and he used to make a business of raiding the villages. He knew the difference between a fire on the ground that stayed there, and one in the hand that could be thrown; he knew all about spears and about sharp sticks stuck in the ground; and whenever the natives played any of those tricks on him, he used to tear down the huts of the villages and trample the fields under foot, just for revenge.

After a while he got to trampling just for the fun of it. When he was in the banana groves at night, he used to chuckle over the way the youngsters were smashing over the young trees not bearing fruit. It was wasteful, but it was good fun, and the natives could always plant others. Altogether he lived a lordly life, helping himself to what he liked and taking care to keep what he got; his herd was the biggest in the country, and his name was the most feared by elephants and natives.

## Notes and Questions

1. What happening does Mrs. Bradley tell about to show that Kubwa at first never learned by what was told him?

2. What kept Kubwa from being such a good fighter as he grew older?

3. When he could not fight so well, how did he get rid of his rivals?

4. Tell three things Kubwa did for the herd that made him a good leader.

5. From what this story tells, which word do you think best describes elephants? *wicked    savage    wise*

6. Name three kinds of traps the natives used to catch elephants.

7. Write or tell of ways in which elephants are useful to men.

8. Name two other kinds of animals that run in herds and have a leader. Perhaps you can name more than two.

9. Write or tell of a wise thing some other animal has done.

Other good elephant stories are *Kari the Elephant,* by Mukerji; "The Elephant's Child," Kipling (in *Just So Stories*); and *Jungle Joe,* by Hawkes.

# THE LITTLE AMERICAN WOODCUTTER

### Clarence Hawkes

Clarence Hawkes, the author of this story, has been blind for many years, yet boys and girls in all parts of our country have seen nature through his unseeing eyes. While he was a boy, he learned to know and love the wild things of the out-of-doors. When he became blind, he began to write stories of the animals and birds he had known. Here he tells us of the beaver—the first American woodcutter.

The beaver is the first American woodcutter; he is also a famous dam builder. He cuts the wood both for food and building material for his dam. He builds the dam in order to flood the country around his house, and thus protect himself from his many enemies. The bear, the wildcat, the wolverine, all love beaver meat; so he has to look to it that his house is well protected.

The beaver is a wonderful builder. Not only does he select with great care the place where he will build his dam, but he also builds it most skillfully. He usually selects a spot in a valley which has steep hills or banks on each side at the lower end. There the dam will be placed. Then, if luck is with him, there will be a large tree standing on either side of the stream.

These trees he fells toward each other, so that, if possible, their tops meet. When this is done, he has the backbone for his dam. Then he fills in with stakes and small logs and finally plasters up all the holes with mud and sod. When he has finished, it is as tight as any man-made dam.

But if trees are not available, he can do without them; he can cut logs, roll them into place, and make a dam wholly out of logs. The beaver seems to understand how powerful moving water is. At any rate, his dam usually curves upstream in the middle, and every engineer knows that a dam built in this way is the strongest. The beaver also provides a waste waterway which runs around one end of the dam. So, when the water is high, it flows around the end instead of washing away the top of the dam. He is very watchful of the dam, and if it begins to leak, he investigates at once.

When the dam is finished, the water spreads back, and there is a beautiful woodland lake. Many of the trees which were in the valley will now be standing in the water. This causes them to rot, so that they gradually decay and fall into the lake. It was in this way that the beaver did most of his land-clearing for the white man. He caused a small valley to become flooded by his dam; this rotted the timber, causing it to die; and thus the land was cleared. Then the spring freshets brought down rich mud and plastered it all over the bottom of the lake.

When the white man came, he trapped and killed the beaver and broke down his dam, causing the water to flow out. Behold, there was his farm all cleared free of

timber and enriched by the mud which had been collecting for many years.

When the beaver has finished his dam and it is filled
with water, there is usually an island in the woodland
lake which he has formed; it is upon such an island
that he builds his house.  It is cone-shaped and made
with a skeleton of sticks or rafters, but the chief building materials used by the beaver are sod and mud. These
are plastered very skillfully on the framework. When
the house is finished, the little builder lays in his supply
of winter food. He goes upstream and cuts many small
trees.

These trees he cuts into logs about three feet long and

floats them down to the dam, where he piles them up.
Then when the great freeze comes, most of this wood
will be frozen under the ice where the beaver can get at
it. Day after day he comes out and gets a stick, carries
it into his house, and eats the bark. When it is stripped
clean and white, he puts it back on the dam and gets
another stick. Thus he and his family live under the ice
all winter long. His mud house by this time has frozen
until it is as hard as steel, and it would take a strong
enemy to break into it, although the top still shows above
the ice and snow.

Today the beaver has nearly disappeared from the
United States. He is sometimes protected in the Adiron-
dack region and in the State of Maine, but the timber-
men soon get angry because of his destruction of their
trees. Then the law is again repealed, and the beaver
again disappears. Away to the Northwest, in Idaho and
Montana, he is probably still found in his wild state enjoying his freedom. But he is almost sure finally to disappear, like all his wild kindred whose fur is valuable or
whose hides or bones can be made useful to man. So the
beaver will go the way of the bison and the American
Indian. He was most useful before the coming of the
white man in clearing his beautiful meadows and in making them ready for the farmer, but he has served his day
and done his work; so he disappears just as many other
beautiful and wonderful creatures have done.

I always think of the beaver with gratitude and affection and sorrow when I remember that soon his sleek coat will wholly disappear, not only from the fur market, but from his own plump body where God first placed it. Good-by, little American. We are grateful to you for all you did for us even before we came to your wilderness.

## NOTES AND QUESTIONS

1. Give two reasons why the beaver cuts wood.

2. To see whether you know how a beaver builds a dam, answer these questions:

   (*a*) Where does he build it?

   (*b*) What does he use for materials?

   (*c*) In what two ways does he keep it from being swept away by the water?

3. What two things did the beaver lakes do to help the settlers of our country?

4. To see what you know about a beaver's house, tell what word belongs where each letter is in the sentences below.

   The beaver builds his house on an ....(*a*).....

   He uses ....(*b*).... and ....(*c*).... plastered on a framework of ....(*d*).....

   His house is especially strong in ....(*e*).....

5. Why do men hunt beavers?

6. Name three other animals hunted for the same reason.

7. Don't forget to use the Glossary. Did you know the meaning of *available, decay, freshets, repealed, sleek?*

Other beaver stories are "In Beaver-land," Hawkes (in *Trails to the Woods and Waters*); "Shaggycoat and the Nimble Otter," Hawkes (in *Child-Library Readers, Book Five*); and "The Industrious Beaver," Seton (in *Wild Animals I Have Known*).

# WASTE LAND: A WILD-LIFE PRESERVE

## ARCHIBALD RUTLEDGE

Once upon a time there were thousands of beautiful birds called passenger pigeons. Now they are gone. Herds of graceful antelope used to roam the prairies of the West. They are disappearing. Mr. Hawkes has told us that the beaver is in danger. In this story Mr. Rutledge tells us how we can help save these wild children of Nature.

Mr. Farmer, don't keep your place too clean. Leave that patch of scrub growing over yonder by the creek; leave that fence row filled with briars. Your best friend of the great bird kingdom, bob-white, can't live with you if you take away all his cover. Keep most fields clean, if you like, but leave some places untidy for the sake of those who will leave you if you clean away their shelters.

Wild creatures will take what we leave. They will rejoice to live on our waste lands. There is no place so impossible for the home of man that it cannot be made into a home for wild life. It looks, then, as if in the years to come, man will take all the *choice* lands for himself. Then he will set aside *waste* lands for the wild children of the woods and the waters and the air.

There is a valley in southern Pennsylvania which shows that whatever man gives up wild life takes. In this valley, some eighteen miles long and two miles wide, almost all the land up to the foot of the mountain was

years ago cultivated.  But one after another the hillside
farms and the creek-bottom pastures have been deserted.
People have moved to the towns.  In this whole valley
now there are not more than eight or ten homes.  Nature, in her quiet, joyous way, has re-taken land that in
pioneer days was taken from her and from the Indians.

Wild things have helped to recapture their home of
pioneer days.  Here in a deserted orchard, where a few
apple trees still are bearing, deer munch the fallen fruit.
In this old upland field where some volunteer buckwheat
has sprung up, wild turkeys feed.  Beside a pathway
leading from a deserted mountain home down to the
spring, ruffed grouse can be seen.  Along the creek in
the shellbark hickory trees which farm boys used to
raid for nuts, gray squirrels now gather their winter
supply of food.  In the creek itself wade migrating ducks
on their way to the South for the winter.

All that wild life seems to want is a bare chance.  They
cannot occupy and increase in the face of rifles, traps, and
shotguns; neither could man.  But they are swift and
brave, and will return when the chance of getting killed
is lessened, even slightly.

What has happened in this wild valley of Pennsylvania would lead us to believe that there should be no
such thing as waste land.  Whatever places man is too
proud or too lazy to occupy, wild creatures will humbly
rejoice in.

It frequently happens that a place which is attractive

to wild life can be made even more attractive by a little intelligent planning on the part of the land-owner. Such a place is a duck preserve near Oakley, South Carolina, some thirty miles up the Cooper River. On both sides of the river are waste rice fields, long since abandoned. Those fields, now grown to marsh and duck oats instead of to rice, are thronged by thousands of wild ducks who joyously feast there. They tip up in the warm shallow water, and hail all passing flocks with the glad tidings that the true paradise for wild fowl has at last been discovered. In these days of hunters and improved firearms such a sight is amazing.

"Three things have done it," the owner of the place

said. "These fields, you see, were worthless to me for planting purposes. But ducks have always come here. At a small expense, I arranged to have the fields hold water when once the water had flowed over them. A duck isn't going to light on dry land, not if there's water within reach of his wings. The third thing was the matter of feed. I went to Washington, D. C., and spent two or three days at the Department of Agriculture finding out just what wild food would grow here, things that the ducks liked best. They recommended to me duck oats, water lilies, and the American lotus. This last is probably the most successful food I have tried. The bloom has a seed-holding disk like a sun-flower. The seeds themselves are like hard black acorns, and the ducks are very fond of them.

"Yes, these old fields were worthless, but in these days there is no such thing as waste land if a man will turn over to wild things those parts of his lands which he cannot use himself. And if he will encourage the wild life just a little, he will have it coming in abundance. Reasonable quiet and protection, water, food— get these three things in this part of the country, and you will have all the ducks you want."

The setting aside of lands where wild life is protected always has the same effect; that is, the immediate increase in wild life. But the effect is much more far-reaching than might be imagined. There are huge tracts of wild country in Pennsylvania, in Virginia, in Maryland, and in the Carolinas, which ten years ago were practically dead so far as game birds and animals were concerned. Now they are alive again. Such tracts of waste land provide a wonderful home for wild life.

Very simple, indeed, is the requirement for having beautiful wild life on any place. *Don't kill it and don't clean away every trace of that wild home that Nature provides for all wild things. We must not rob them of their homes.*

## Notes and Questions

1. Below are four statements. Which one best answers the question, "Why did Mr. Rutledge write this story?"

   (*a*) To tell us about the habits of wild animals and birds.

   (*b*) To get us never to kill wild animals.

   (*c*) To save wild animals and birds by giving them homes.

   (*d*) To tell us how useful wild animals and birds are.

2. The title of this story is "Waste Land: A Wild-Life Preserve." Think of another name for the story that would be just as good, or better.

3. What three things do wild animals need if they are to stay with us?

4. Make a list of all the birds and animals that are found near your home.

You will enjoy reading "Little Gustava," Thaxter (in *Poetry's Plea for Animals,* Clarke); and "Man and Dog and Horse and Tree," Wynne (in *For Days and Days*).

# DUNCAN'S BIRD TENANTS

### ERNEST HAROLD BAYNES

Mr. Rutledge told you that birds and animals will come to live with us if we give them a home. Duncan, a fifth-grade boy, found that Mr. Rutledge was right.

It was the fifteenth of March, and Duncan was exactly eleven years old. His parents had given him a tool chest for a birthday present, and as he walked proudly out of the back door into the morning sunshine, he was wondering what he should make first with the new tools. He had hardly gone as far as the pump when he heard a soft, gurgling bird voice from the old apple tree in the yard, and a bluebird fluttered down almost to his feet. In an instant he decided to make a bird house, and he walked off to find his father and talk the matter over with him.

His father gladly agreed to help him and suggested that they build a house suitable for both bluebirds and tree swallows, and for purple martins, too, if they wished to come, though martins had not nested in Meriden for many years. First they wrote to the Department of Agriculture in Washington for a pamphlet called *Homes for Birds,* and with this as a guide they went to work. Early in April the little dwelling was ready to put up. In appearance it was like an old-fashioned, two-story New England farmhouse, painted white, and it was fastened to the end of a stout pole about eighteen feet long.

The bluebirds had already chosen a hole in the apple tree for their first home; so for the present they were not interested in any other. But on the telephone wire sat a pair of tree swallows, their steel-blue coats and white shirt fronts glistening in the sunlight. As soon as Duncan and his father began to raise the pole into the air, the swallows left their perch, and twittering excitedly, flew round and round the little bird house as if they knew that it was for them. It had barely come to rest as the end of the pole dropped into the hole which had been dug for it, when the swallows alighted boldly on the roof and took possession as its first tenants.

During the next few days Duncan noticed that the

swallows were very busy. Much of their time was spent in looking over their new home, creeping first into one room, then into another as if trying to decide which they liked best. Then they would sit on the telephone wire in full view of the bird house, perhaps admiring it, and ready to attack and drive away any other bird which came near. And of course they never neglected their regular work of darting back and forth to catch the insects which they needed for their daily food.

At last one of the rooms was selected, and the birds began to gather bits of hay to make a nest, and then followed swift visits to the poultry yard for feathers with which to line it. One morning when Duncan opened the door of the henhouse and let out the hens, he was surprised and amused to see the swallows swoop down, pluck soft feathers from an indignant old hen, and bear them home in triumph.

Five white eggs had been laid when a flock of English sparrows arrived. One tree swallow was in the nest and the other on guard outside. A fierce but one-sided battle took place, and the nest and eggs might have been thrown to the ground, had not Duncan protected his tenants by driving the sparrows away.

In about two weeks the eggs were hatched, and the parents were on the wing from daylight until dusk, scooping up in their wide mouths many hundreds of flies to feed their babies. In about two weeks the young swallows, dressed very much like their parents, came out on the roof to be fed. A few days later they left their little home forever, and were soon hunting insects over the fields and through the barnyard.

But the bird house was not long unoccupied. The bluebirds had reared their first brood, and about a week after the swallows had left, Duncan saw new tenants inspecting the little dwelling. A few busy days of nest building, and then the male, in sky-blue coat and reddish vest, perched on the roof, singing softly to his hidden mate, who sat on four blue eggs in a simple nest of hay. Still busier times followed when the eggs were hatched, and every day the parents made scores of trips to the fields near by for caterpillars and other insects to feed four gaping mouths.

About a fortnight later the youngsters began to show their heads and their speckled breasts at the doorway, and presently they attempted to fly to the roof. Three of them succeeded, but the fourth fluttered to the ground; and Duncan's mother, who happened to be watching, was just in time to save it from a neighbor's cat. The hired man got a ladder and put the young bird back in the nest, and very soon the little family got safely away.

Duncan was so much encouraged by his success that he began to plan for the following season. He built smaller, single-roomed houses for the bluebirds and tree-swallows, and put them up in the fall. He saved the larger house for the martins this time, by blocking the doorways with strips of wood until it was about time for them to return.

Just as he had hoped, the first bluebirds built in one of

the smaller boxes, and a pair of tree swallows in the other. But when he spoke of trying to get the purple martins, most of the neighbors shook their heads and laughed. Nevertheless, about the third week in April, Duncan removed the strips of wood and hoped and waited.

At last, on the first of May, a bright warm morning, he leaped from his bed at the sound of strange, sweet bird voices outside. There they were, the longed-for purple martins, sailing gracefully around the bird house, singing as they sailed. They examined the little dwelling inside and out, and a small colony of them, five pairs, decided to nest in it. Duncan had scored a triumph. The purple martin, largest and noblest of American swallows, after an absence of many years, had come back to Meriden.

## Notes and Questions

1. Read again the sentence at the beginning of the story; then tell in one sentence how Duncan found out that Mr. Rutledge was right.

2. Find a part of the story which shows that Duncan learned much about tree swallows, and make a list of at least five things he learned. Maybe you can find more than five. Start like this: *1. Swallows eat insects.*

3. If you have bird houses in your yard or near your home, write or tell what birds nest in them.

Other good bird stories and a poem are "The Purple Martin," Ball (in *Bird Biographies*); "Purple Martins," Meigs (in *Child Life,* Nov., 1926); "Trees to Let," Wynne (in *For Days and Days*).

# THE BROWN THRUSH

### Lucy Larcom

There's a merry brown thrush sitting up in a tree—
  He's singing to me! he's singing to me!
And what does he say, little girl, little boy?
  "Oh, the world's running over with joy!
    Don't you hear?  Don't you see?
    Hush!  Look!  In my tree
I'm as happy as happy can be!"

And the brown thrush keeps singing—"A nest do you see,
  And five eggs, hid by me in the juniper-tree?
Don't meddle! don't touch! little girl, little boy,
  Or the world will lose some of its joy.
    Now I'm glad!  Now I'm free!
    And I always shall be,
If you never bring sorrow to me."

So the merry brown thrush sings away in the tree,
  To you and to me, to you and to me;
And he sings all the day, little girl, little boy—
  "Oh, the world's running over with joy;
    But long it won't be,
    Don't you know, don't you see,
Unless we're as good as can be?"

# THE FEATHERED MASTERS OF THE AIR

### Floyd Darrow

Think of it! A frail little bird with no compass to guide it flies twice every year across two thousand four hundred miles of ocean. Another bird travels twenty-two thousand miles every year. Men have their airplanes, but Mr. Darrow tells you why the birds are still the Masters of the Air.

By October the migration of the birds to their winter homes in the southlands is well under way and has been going on for some time. In fact, some of these feathered masters of the air begin their southward jaunts as early as the middle of July. When the nesting season is over and the young are able to care for themselves, the old birds turn their thoughts toward their favorite winter resorts of the tropics.

But why should birds thus migrate twice a year? Why should they build their nests and rear their young in the north, and then, often long in advance of autumn's chilly blasts, fly hundreds and sometimes thousands of miles to other homes? What guides them so truly on these long flights? These are questions which men have always asked, and yet we are but little nearer to their answers than when the quest began. Mystery still surrounds the birds and their journeyings.

Talk of transatlantic flights! The golden plover makes a non-stop flight of 2400 miles from Nova Scotia to the

northeast coast of South America, and has been doing it for centuries without ever getting a line of publicity in the newspapers. The night-hawk nests in the Yukon and winters in Argentina, 7000 miles away. Nineteen species of shore-birds rear their young north of the arctic circle and then fly to South America, six of the species even penetrating Patagonia, 8000 miles from their northern nesting grounds. The far-famed bobolink of New England migrates to Brazil, making a transoceanic flight of 700 miles from Cuba to the South American coast. So also do the purple martins, cliff-swallows, barn-swallows, and some thrushes.

The bird which holds the world's record for long-distance flying is the arctic tern, which you see in the picture. It builds its nest within seven and one-half degrees of the north pole, remaining but a brief period in the "land of the midnight sun," when it flies away to the icebergs of the antarctic continent, a distance of 11,000 miles. Although thousands of these birds make this round trip every year, no one has yet been able to map the route by which they travel. For nearly half the year they are in flight.

Still, some birds go but a short distance from their northern homes. Such birds as the grouse, quail, cardinal, and Carolina wren do not migrate. The bob-white remains throughout his life close to his first home. Meadow-larks migrate but a very short distance. The pine-warbler and the black-headed grosbeak do not venture in winter south of the country in which they rear their young. The robin does not go far away.

Talk of mystery, what becomes of the chimney-swifts during the winter months? Drifting southward in autumn, they become an innumerable host on the northern coast of the Gulf of Mexico. Then, of a sudden, as though swallowed up by the sea, they disappear—no one knows where. The last week in March sees them return; a gladsome twittering high in the air announces their coming, but where they have been in the meantime is a puzzling mystery, known only to the swifts themselves.

Winter's cold and lack of food, of course, cause birds to move south. But why should most of them go so far?

And why do many of them leave their northern haunts while skies are still sunny and food abundant? We do not know.

### Notes and Questions

1. What do you think is the most wonderful fact about the long-distance flight of a bird?

2. What wonderful knowledge do the birds seem to have about the seasons of the year?

3. Make a list of five birds, where they go, and the distance they fly. Thus:

*Golden Plover     Nova Scotia to South America     2400 miles*

Put them in order with the longest flight first.

4. Name three birds that leave your neighborhood in the fall. Perhaps you can name more.

5. Be ready to show on a wall map the flights of these birds. Or make an outline map of North and South America and draw lines to show the flights. You can put the bird's name and the distance on the line, too.

Two interesting stories about bird migration are "Sandy, the Swallow," Patch (in *Holiday Pond*) and "Snowflakes," Patch (in *Holiday Meadow*). There are some fine bird pictures in "Bird Banding: the Tell-Tale of Migratory Flight," Nelson (in *National Geographic Magazine*, Jan., 1928).

# THE PINE CATERPILLAR
## JEAN HENRI FABRE

Nature has stories to tell—the story of the beaver, the story of the strange flights of birds, and countless others. Jean Henri Fabre, a French school teacher, spent many, many hours of his life listening to Nature's stories. Then he began to write of what he had learned, and he became famous for his books about butterflies, grasshoppers, bees, and other insects.

You hungry little caterpillars, if I let you have your way, I should soon be robbed of the murmur of my once leafy pine trees. But I am going to make a bargain with you. You have a story to tell. Tell it to me; and for a year, for two years or longer, until I know more or less about it, I will leave you undisturbed.

The result of my bargain with the caterpillars is that I soon have some thirty nests within a few steps of my door. With such treasures daily before my eyes, I cannot help seeing the pine caterpillar's story unfolded at full length. These caterpillars are also called the processionaries, because they always go out in a procession.

First of all, there is the egg. During the first half of August, if we look at the lower branches of the pine trees, we shall discover, here and there on the foliage, certain little whitish cylinders spotting the green. These are the pine moth's eggs; each cylinder is the cluster laid by one mother. The cylinder is like a tiny muff about an inch long and a fifth or sixth of an inch wide, wrapped around the base of the pine needles, which are grouped in twos. This muff has a silky appearance and is white, slightly tinted with reddish brown. It is covered with scales that overlap like the shingles on a roof.

The scales, soft as velvet to the touch and carefully laid one upon the other, form a roof that protects the eggs. Not a drop of rain or dew can get underneath it. Where did this soft covering come from? From the mother moth; she has stripped a part of her body for her children. Like the eider duck, she has made a warm overcoat for her eggs out of her own soft down.

If one removes the scaly fleece with pincers, the eggs appear, looking like little white, shiny beads. There are about three hundred of them in one cylinder. Quite a family for one mother! They are beautifully placed, and remind one of a tiny ear of Indian corn. Nobody, young or old, could help exclaiming, on seeing the pine moth's pretty little spike of eggs, "How handsome!"

The eggs hatch in September. If one lifts the scales of the muff, one can see black heads appear, which nibble and push back their coverings. The tiny creatures come out slowly all over the surface. They are pale yellow, with black heads twice as large as their bodies. First they eat the pine needles on which their nest was placed; then they eat the near-by needles.

From time to time, three or four, who have eaten as much as they want, fall in line and walk in step in a little procession. This is practice for the coming processions. If I disturb them, they sway the front half of their bodies and wag their heads. The next thing they do is to spin a little tent at the place where their nest was. The tent is a small ball made of gauze, resting on some leaves. Inside it they take a rest during the hottest part of the day. In the afternoon they leave this shelter and start feeding again.

In less than an hour, you see, after coming from the egg, the young caterpillar shows what he can do. He eats leaves, he forms processions, and he spins tents.

In twenty-four hours the little tent has become as large as a hazelnut, and in two weeks it is the size of an apple. But it is still only a summer tent. When winter is near, they will build a stronger one. In the meantime, the caterpillars eat the leaves around which their tent is stretched. Their house gives them at the same time meals and lodging. This saves them from going out for food when they are so young and so tiny.

When this tent gives way, owing to the caterpillars' having nibbled the leaves that hold it, the family moves on and erects a new tent higher up on the pine tree. Sometimes they reach the very top of the tree.

In the meantime the caterpillars have changed their dress. They now wear six little bright red patches on their backs, surrounded with scarlet bristles. In the midst of these red patches are specks of gold. The hairs on their sides and underneath are whitish.

In November they begin to build their winter tent high

up in the pine tree at the tip of a bough. They surround
the leaves at the end of the bough with a network of silk.
Leaves and silk together are stronger than silk alone. By
the time this shelter is finished, it is as large as a half-
gallon measure and about the shape of an egg.

In the center of the nest is a milk-white mass of thickly-
woven threads mingled with green leaves. At the top are
round openings, the doors of the house, through which the
caterpillars go in and out. There is a sort of veranda on
top made of threads stretched from the tips of the surrounding leaves where the caterpillars come and doze in
the sun, heaped one upon the other with rounded backs.
The threads above are an awning, to keep the sun from

being too warm for them. The inside of the caterpillars'
nest is not at all a tidy place; it is full of rags, shreds of
the caterpillars' skins, and dirt.

The caterpillars stay in their nest all night, and come
out about ten o'clock in the morning to take the sun on
their veranda. They spend the whole day there, dozing,
motionless, heaped together, and from time to time show
their bliss by nodding and wagging their heads. At six or
seven o'clock, when it grows dark, the sleepers awake, stir
themselves, and go out over the surface of the nest.

Wherever they go, they strengthen the nest or enlarge
it by the threads of silk that come out of their mouths and
trail behind them. More green leaves are taken in, and the
tent becomes bigger and bigger. They are busy doing this
for an hour or two every evening. So far, they have known
nothing but summer; but they seem to realize that winter
is coming. They work away at their house in a manner
which seems to say: "Oh, how nice and warm we shall be
in our beds here, nestling one against the other, when the
pine tree is lighted with frost. Let us work with a will!"

After the day's work comes their dinner. The caterpillars come down from the nest and begin eating on the
pine-needles below. It is a magnificent sight to see the red-
coated band lined up in twos and threes on each needle
and in ranks so closely formed that the green sprigs of the
branch bend under the load. The diners, all motionless, all
poking their heads forward, nibble slowly in silence. Their
black foreheads gleam in the rays of my lantern. They

eat far into the night. Then they go back to the nest, where for a little longer they continue spinning on the surface. It is one or two o'clock in the morning when the last of the band goes indoors.

To guide them as they wander about their tree, the caterpillars have their silk ribbon, formed by threads from their mouths. They follow this on their return to the nest. Sometimes they miss it and strike the ribbon made by another band of caterpillars. They follow it and reach a strange dwelling. No matter! There is not the least quarreling between the owners and the new arrivals. And all, when bedtime comes, start for the nest, like brothers who have always lived together.

### NOTES AND QUESTIONS

1. From the sentences below, choose two that you think best tell what this story teaches us.

(a) How pine caterpillars destroy pine trees.

(b) How pine caterpillars live.

(c) How pine caterpillars are valuable to man.

(d) Why pine caterpillars are called processionaries.

(e) That interesting things are near at hand in Nature.

2. Prove that Mr. Fabre studied the caterpillars carefully, by telling four things he learned that could only be learned by closest study. Perhaps you can tell more than four.

3. Name any other insects that you know spin threads.

You would like also to read "The Processionaries," "The Caterpillars as Weather Prophets," and "The Pine Moth," Fabre (in *Insect Adventures*); and "The Adventures of a Meadow Caterpillar," Patch (in *Holiday Meadow*).

## FOUR-LEAF CLOVERS
### ELLA HIGGINSON

I know a place where the sun is like gold,
    And the cherry blossoms burst with snow;
And down underneath is the loveliest nook,
    Where the four-leaf clovers grow.

One leaf is for hope, and one is for faith,
    And one is for love, you know;
But God put another in for luck—
    If you search, you will find where they grow.

But you must have hope, and you must have faith;
    You must love and be strong; and so,
If you work, if you wait, you will find the place
    Where the four-leaf clovers grow.

From *When the Birds Go North Again* by Ella Higginson, copyright 1898 by The Macmillan Co.

# THE WEATHER QUESTION

ANNA BIRD STEWART

I wonder how the weather's made?
And where the factory stands?
And if our weather merchants trade
In all the foreign lands?

I wonder where they get the things
To make the snow and storm,
And winds that howl and winds that sing,
And days so bright and warm?

And just what sort of things they are
Is what I wonder most.
Are they expressed from very far?
Or sent by Parcel Post?

Suppose a weather famine came,
And every bit had fled—
I wonder who would get the blame?
What could we use instead?

## THE LAKE AND THE SKY

MARY BARTON

The lake and sky, it seems to me,
Are friendly as two things could be,
For when the sky is smiling blue,
The lake is always happy too,
And when the lake is dull and gray,
The sky seems never to be gay.

The lake and sky are such good friends
That I can't tell where either ends,
And when I sit upon the sands,
And gaze 'way out where they join hands,
I wonder which it is that goes
To meet the other one.
                  Who knows?

# THE GLADNESS OF NATURE
## William Cullen Bryant

Is this a time to be cloudy and sad,
   When our Mother Nature laughs around,
When even the deep blue heavens look glad,
   And gladness breathes from the blossoming ground?

There are notes of joy from the hangbird and wren,
   And the gossip of swallows through all the sky;
The ground squirrel gayly chirps by his den,
   And the wilding bee hums merrily by.

The clouds are at play in the azure space,
   And their shadows at play on the bright green vale,
And here they stretch to the frolic chase,
   And there they roll on the easy gale.

There's a dance of leaves in that aspen bower;
   There's a titter of winds in that beechen tree;
There's a smile on the fruit, and a smile on the flower,
   And a laugh from the brook that runs to the sea.

And look at the broad-faced sun, how he smiles
   On the dewy earth that smiles in his ray,
On the leaping waters and gay young isles;
   Ay, look, and he'll smile thy gloom away.

# A BACKWARD LOOK

Suppose your father or your mother or your big brother or sister said to you, "I see you have been reading some stories about animals and birds. Did you like them?" What would you say? If they asked which story you liked best, what would you tell them? Could you tell why you liked it best?

If someone asked you what interesting facts you learned from these stories, what four or five things would you tell?

Do you know enough about the birds and animals and flowers of your neighborhood so that you could give a talk on "The Wild Life Near Us"? You might try now to make a list of animals, a list of birds, and a list of flowers that are found near your home or city. Then your class can get together and put all the different kinds into a big class list of birds, another of animals, and another of flowers. You may be surprised at what some of your classmates have seen in the out-of-doors, and they may be surprised at what you have seen.

Have you ever done anything to help the birds and animals, or do you know of anything that is being done near where you live? You might like to tell the class about it.

Perhaps you have had an adventure or an interesting experience with wild life that would be worth telling to the class. Or maybe you have gone on a journey to a different part of our country and have seen some strange animals or flowers. The class would like to hear about it.

If someone asked you for a list of good stories and books about the out-of-doors, what would you put in your list? Perhaps you would put down some of the stories named in this part and in the list on pages 431 and 432.

# PART THREE
## · STORIES WE ALL SHOULD KNOW ·

## MY STORY BOOK

### ANNETTE WYNNE

My book holds many stories, wrapped
    tightly in itself,
And yet it never makes a noise, but waits
    upon my shelf
Until I come and take it; then soon my
    book and I
Are sailing on a fairy sea or floating in
    the sky.

From "My Book Holds Many Stories." Re-
printed by permission from *For Days and Days:
A Year-round Treasury of Verse for Children* by
Annette Wynne, copyright 1919, by Frederick A.
Stokes Company.

# "TELL ME A STORY!"

JUST ABOUT as soon as you were old enough to put words together into sentences, you probably began to bother your father and mother by saying, "Tell me a story 'bout lions 'n tigers 'n everything." And when you did this, you were acting just like a grown-up person, because grown-up people like stories as much as boys and girls. And for thousands of years they have liked them.

Even savage people who cannot read or write have story tellers. These story tellers are really the books for those people. When the old story teller dies, a younger man takes his place, and he goes on telling the stories the old man told—stories of the great deeds of his people and of strange things that have happened. Famous stories that have been read in books by millions of people were first told for hundreds of years before they were written. No one knows who started them.

But now our story tellers write for us. They carry us on journeys to far lands where we should love to go, but cannot; they take us through exciting adventures that we should really be a little afraid to go through ourselves; they tell us of interesting things that are happening to other people; they make us laugh.

Now you are going to read a few stories—just a few— of the hundreds and hundreds that you would surely like. There are countless other good stories. Wouldn't it be fun to read some of these other stories, too, so that you can become a good story teller? Some of them are listed on page 432. Your teacher and your library will help you find others.

# GUILLAUME'S FLUTE

GERTRUDE CROWNFIELD

In the southeastern part of France, near the Mediterranean Sea, is a region of hills and mountains called Provence. Here in the village of Maussane lived a little shepherd boy, Guillaume. He was very, very shy, but in his heart was a great longing to play the flute as his grandfather had played it at the Christmas celebrations in the little village.

Very mellow was the flute of old Guillaume. With it, for many years, he had led the procession of the Adoration of the Shepherds, playing, as none but he could play, the music of the noels.

But the flute of old Guillaume had long been silent, for old Guillaume was no longer living in this world, and François, another shepherd, played at the Feast of Noel. Yet still the people of Maussane, and even François himself, would say regretfully at every Christmas-tide, "Ah, if we could but hear once more the flute of old Guillaume!"

Meanwhile the flute lay upon the high shelf in his son's cottage, with none in the house who had the skill to draw music from it. His grandson, little Guillaume, looked at it often, his fingers itching to hold it, his heart hungering to put it to his lips to see whether he could draw from it at least one pure and beautiful note.

Yet little Guillaume was shy, and could not bring him-

117

self to ask for such a privilege. Every day he led his father's sheep to feed upon the hillsides. Every day before he went, he lifted his eyes longingly to the high shelf where lay the coveted flute.

At last his mother said to him, "Why dost thou look so earnestly upon thy grandfather's flute, my little Guillaume? Dost think thou couldst play upon it as he played? Ah, my child, to do that, one must have a great gift, indeed."

Guillaume hung his head, and made no answer. He had no belief that he could play upon it, yet he would give much to try. He was about to pass out of the door, but he turned back before he did so, for a last look at the flute.

"Come then, my little one, thou shalt hold it in thy hand for a moment. Perhaps that will satisfy thee." The good woman took it down, and dusted it carefully, while Guillaume waited, quivering with eagerness.

As she gave it to him, and his fingers touched it, such a thrill of strange happiness rushed through him that he grew bold. "Mother," he whispered entreatingly, "let me carry it with me today, to the hill."

"To the hill!" cried his mother, raising her brows with astonishment. "Nay, nay, Guillaume, thou art far too young to be permitted to do that. Some harm might happen to it there."

"Nothing shall hurt it—I will take great care! See, I will keep it safely—here—in my breast." His words

came fast and imploringly, and his mother, although she feared to trust it to his keeping, could not resist the longing in his eyes.

"Remember, my Guillaume," she warned him, "it was thy grandfather's. There is no other flute so fine in Maussane. See that thou dost bring it back unhurt."

Guillaume promised, and with the instrument lodged securely in his breast, rushed like a whirlwind to call his flock. Off to a lonely hill he took them, where they could browse contentedly upon the thick short grass, and where none could overhear him while he tried the flute.

His fingers shook, and his breath came fast as he pressed the instrument to his lips, and drew out a feeble note. It was shrill, and thin, and unlovely. Guillaume winced with disappointment. Nevertheless, he knew that beautiful sounds dwelt in the flute, and he was determined to call them out. So he persevered. Over and over he breathed carefully into the slender tube. Over and over he pressed his fingers now upon this hole, now upon that, to make the notes. At last, to his delight, one pure mellow note rewarded him.

Each morning after that he pleaded to be allowed to take the instrument with him. His mother, having discovered that he always brought it back uninjured even by a single scratch, humored him, saying from time to time, "Some day, my little Guillaume, thou shalt learn of Francois how to play upon it—some day when thou art older."

Yet already little Guillaume, alone with his sheep, had taught himself far more than Francois knew. Patiently, faithfully, he labored, until he had mastered every note. Before the summer had passed, there was not a noel known in Provence that he could not play with a quite touching beauty, for the rare gift that had been old Guillaume's lived again in his grandchild.

Although little Guillaume had accomplished all this, no one but himself knew, for he was too shy to speak of it, or to summon up the courage to play before others.

The Feast of Noel was approaching. Francois was expected to lead the procession of the shepherds as usual. Guillaume, making music to his sheep upon the slopes where the grass had now become dry and thin, told himself that some day, when he was grown, he might perhaps be permitted to take the place in the procession that had been his grandfather's.

Then came a wintry evening when he trudged beside Francois as the sheep ran down from the pastures to their folds, and Francois said, with a heavy sigh, "It is a pity, little Guillaume, that you have not the power to play upon the flute as your grandfather could, for my fingers, that I wounded at the sheep-shearing in the spring, have become stiff, and I can no longer make the notes sound as they should. It is too bad. Who is to play the noels at the Feast? There is none to do it in Maussane. This very evening I must go in to Monsieur le Cure, and tell him that for me it is now quite impossible."

Even in spite of this, Guillaume could not speak for shyness; he could only walk by Francois's side with a choking in his throat, and a swifter beating of the heart. Soon they reached the priest's house. Francois knocked at the door; it opened, and he went in.

Guillaume stood outside as one whose feet are chained. Through the half-open window he could hear the grave voices of Monsieur le Cure and Francois. Although he could not hear a word they said, he knew as well as if he had done so, what disappointment they felt. Surging up from the depths of his being was a desire to draw out his grandfather's flute from his breast, to play upon it, to show them that the Feast of Noel need not go by, after all, without the music that had always helped to make it beautiful.

Several times he took out the flute cautiously, set it to his mouth, and almost breathed into it, but each time timidity seized him, and he slipped it back into his breast. While he hesitated thus, and Francois tarried, night fell. Guillaume knew that he must go home, for his mother would become anxious.

A single step he took in that direction, and then, driven by a feeling which he had no power to resist, he turned back quickly, snatched out the flute, and brought from it a deep full note. This much done, little Guillaume immediately forgot everything but his music. Now, borne upon the evening air to the startled ears of the priest and Francois, came the strains to which the shepherds of Maussane had always marched at the Feast of Noel, played as none but old Guillaume had ever played them.

"The flute of old Guillaume!" exclaimed Monsieur le Cure, leaping to his feet in amazement. "Aye, the flute of old Guillaume, and the music for the shepherds," stammered the puzzled Francois. "But whence comes it? Who can play it thus?"

Monsieur le Cure did not stop to wonder. He went directly to the window, and looked out. There, with his back to the wall of the house, was Guillaume, playing his very best.

"Guillaume," breathed Monsieur le Cure softly, "little Guillaume."

At the sound all Guillaume's bashfulness suddenly returned. The music ceased instantly, and he stood crestfallen and trembling at his daring.

"Come in, little Guillaume," invited Monsieur le Cure. "I would speak with thee."

Guillaume obeyed.

"Thou hast given us the music for the shepherds well," commended Monsieur le Cure, drawing the boy to him. "Canst thou not play for me, also, a noel or two?"

Encouraged by this, and encircled by the protecting arm of the priest, Guillaume played them every one. When he had finished, Monsieur le Cure spoke. "Thou hast had none to teach thee, my child—that I know, and yet thou hast learned to play most sweetly. Wilt thou not play in the church, then, for the shepherds at the Feast of Noel? Our good Francois can do so no more, because his fingers have become too stiff to make the notes."

Guillaume, his flute clutched tightly to his breast, was too overcome with happiness to answer in words, but he nodded his head slowly, and the kindly priest understood.

"And now, my child," continued Monsieur le Cure, smiling upon him, "we will say nothing of this to anyone, but will keep it to be a surprise to the people of Maussane at the Feast of Noel."

Surprise it was to them, in truth. When through the

open door of the church on Christmas Eve floated such rich, such tender, such melodious tones as the people of Maussane had not heard in many a year, they turned their ears swiftly to the sound, in awe and wondering delight.

"Hark, hark!" they whispered excitedly, each to each. "Is not that the flute of old Guillaume? There is none other like it. And yet—and yet—how can it be?"

"But see!" cried one. "Who could have believed it! See! It is the little Guillaume who plays!"

Yes, it was indeed little Guillaume, moving at the front of the procession, the flute of old Guillaume in his hands, and as he came, his head no longer drooped shyly upon his breast, but was lifted in a rapture of adoration, while not from his lips alone, but from his very heart streamed forth the glorious notes of praise and worship of the Babe of Bethlehem.

## Notes and Questions

1. What is the French name for Christmas?

2. What is a noel? Do you know the names of any noels? If you do, tell two or three of the names.

3. Make up names for the pictures in the story.

4. What other happening in the story would make a good picture?

5. Which one of these reasons best tells why Guillaume wanted to play the flute?

　(a) To honor his grandfather
　(b) To have a big part in the celebration
　(c) Because he loved the music of the flute.

6. Miss Crownfield has used certain words especially to make you feel and see things; for example, on page 117, *draw music, fingers itching, heart hungering.* Find six other words or groups of words that helped you to feel and see things.

7. On your paper write the words in the first column. Then for each word in the first column choose a word or group of words in the second column that means about the same thing. For example, *mellow* means *soft and gentle;* so your paper would read: *1. mellow—soft and gentle.*

|     |                |                        |
|-----|----------------|------------------------|
| (1) | mellow         | bashful                |
| (2) | tarried        | trembling              |
| (3) | shy            | soft and gentle        |
| (4) | coveted        | sudden, sharp feeling  |
| (5) | quivering      | much desired           |
| (6) | thrill         | feed                   |
| (7) | imploringly    | stayed on              |
| (8) | browse         | kept on trying         |
| (9) | winced         | unusual                |
| (10)| persevered     | beggingly              |
| (11)| pleaded        | shrank                 |
| (12)| rare           | kept on asking         |

This story was taken from a book, *The Feast of Noel*, by Miss Crownfield. There are five other stories in the book. You would probably like also to read "The Knights of the Silver Shield," by Alden (in *Child-Library Readers, Book Five*), and "The Little Brown Bowl," by Bowman (in *The Little Brown Bowl and Other Stories*).

# THE GOLDEN TOUCH

NATHANIEL HAWTHORNE

Nathaniel Hawthorne, one of our first great American story-tellers, was born and lived in the old town of Salem, Massachusetts. He loved boys and girls and liked to tell them stories. One summer he wrote a book in which he retold some old stories. Even before the book was printed, his three children knew the stories by heart. "The Golden Touch," which you will now read, is taken from this book.

## KING MIDAS AND HIS LOVE FOR GOLD

Once upon a time there lived a very rich king whose name was Midas. He had a little daughter, whom nobody but myself ever heard of, and whose name I either never knew, or have entirely forgotten. So, because I love odd names for little girls, I shall choose to call her Marygold.

This King Midas was more fond of gold than of anything else in the world. He valued his royal crown chiefly because it was made of that precious metal. If he loved anything better, or half so well, it was the one little maiden who played so merrily around her father's footstool. But the more Midas loved his daughter, the more did he desire and seek for wealth. He thought, foolish man, that the best thing he could possibly do for this dear child would be to give her the largest pile of yellow, glistening coin that had ever been heaped together since the world was made.    Thus, he gave all his thoughts and all his time to this one purpose.    If ever he happened to gaze for an instant at the gold-tinted clouds of sunset, he wished that they were real gold and that they could be squeezed safely into his strong-box. When little Marygold ran to meet him, with a bunch of buttercups and dandelions, he used to say, "Pooh, pooh, child!    If these flowers were as golden as they look, they would be worth the plucking!"

And yet, in his earlier days, before he was so entirely possessed of this foolish desire for riches, King Midas had shown a great taste for flowers.    He had planted a garden in which grew the biggest and sweetest and most beautiful roses that anyone ever saw or smelled.    These roses were still growing in the garden, as large, as lovely, and as fragrant as when Midas used to pass whole hours gazing at them and inhaling their perfume.    But now, if he looked at them at all, it was only to imagine how much the garden would be worth if each of the many rose-petals were a thin plate of gold.

At length Midas had become so exceedingly foolish that he could scarcely bear to see or touch any object that was not gold.    He made it his custom, therefore, to pass a large part of every day in a dark and dreary apartment, underground in the basement of his palace.    It was here that he kept his wealth.    To this dreary hole— for it was little better than a dungeon—Midas betook himself whenever he wanted to be particularly happy.

Here, after carefully locking the door, he would take a bag of gold coin, or a gold cup as big as a washbowl, or a heavy golden bar, or a peck-measure of gold-dust, and bring them from the dark corners of the room into the one bright and narrow sunbeam that fell from the narrow window. He valued the sunbeam for no other reason but that his treasure would not shine without its help. And then would he count the coins in the bag; toss up the bar, and catch it as it came down; sift the gold-dust through his fingers; look at the funny image of his own face in the polished surface of the cup; and whisper to himself, "O Midas, rich King Midas, what a happy man art thou!"

Midas was enjoying himself in his treasure-room one day as usual, when he saw a shadow fall over the heaps of gold; and, looking suddenly up, what should he behold but the figure of a stranger, standing in the bright and narrow sunbeam! It was a young man with a cheerful and ruddy face. King Midas could not help fancying that the stranger's smile had a kind of golden look.

As Midas knew that he had carefully turned the key in the lock, and that no one could possibly break into his treasure-room, he of course thought that his visitor must be an unusual being. Midas had met such beings before now, and was not sorry to meet one of them again. The stranger's manner was so good-humored and kindly that it would have been unreasonable to suspect him of intending any mischief. It was far more probable that

he came to do Midas a favor. And what could that favor be, unless to multiply his heaps of treasure?

The stranger gazed about the room, and when his bright smile had glistened upon all the golden objects that were there, he turned again to Midas.

"You are a wealthy man, friend Midas!" he said. "I doubt whether any other four walls on earth contain so much gold as you have piled up in this room."

"I have done pretty well—pretty well," answered Midas. "But, after all, it is but a trifle, when you consider that it has taken me my whole life to get it together. If one could live a thousand years, he might have time to grow rich!"

"What!" exclaimed the stranger. "Then you are not satisfied?" Midas shook his head.

"And pray what would satisfy you?" asked the stranger. "I should be glad to know." Midas paused and thought deeply for a while. He had a feeling that this stranger, with such a golden, good-humored smile, had come with the power to grant his wishes. Therefore, he had but to speak in order to obtain whatever thing it might come into his head to ask. So he thought and thought and thought without being able to imagine anything big enough. At last, a bright idea occurred to King Midas. It seemed really as bright as the glistening metal which he loved so much.

Raising his head, he looked the stranger in the face.

"Well, Midas," observed his visitor, "I see that you

have at length hit upon something that will satisfy you. Tell me your wish."

"It is only this," replied Midas. "I am weary of collecting my treasures with so much trouble, and beholding the heap so small after I have done my best. I wish everything that I touch to be changed to gold."

"The Golden Touch!" exclaimed the stranger. "You certainly deserve credit, friend Midas, for striking on so brilliant an idea. But are you quite sure that this will satisfy you?"

"How could it fail?" said Midas.

"And will you never regret the possession of it?"

"I ask for nothing else to make me perfectly happy," said Midas.

"Be it as you wish, then," replied the stranger, waving his hand in farewell. "Tomorrow, at sunrise, you will find yourself gifted with the Golden Touch."

The figure of the stranger then became exceedingly bright, and Midas was forced to close his eyes. On opening them again, he beheld only one yellow sunbeam in the room, and, all around him, the glistening of the precious metal which he had spent his life in storing up.

Whether Midas slept as usual that night, the story does not say. Asleep or awake, however, his mind was probably like that of a child to whom a beautiful new plaything has been promised in the morning. At any rate, day had hardly peeped over the hills when King Midas was wide awake and, stretching his arms out of bed, began to touch the objects that were within reach. He was anxious to prove whether the Golden Touch had really come, according to the stranger's promise. So he laid his finger on a chair by the bedside, and on various other things, but was disappointed to find out that they remained exactly the same as before.

### THE GIFT OF THE GOLDEN TOUCH

All this while, it was only the gray of the morning, with but a streak of brightness along the edge of the sky, where Midas could not see it. He lay in a very unhappy mood and kept growing sadder and sadder, until the earliest sunbeam shone through the window and gilded the ceiling over his head. It seemed to Midas that this bright yellow sunbeam was shining in rather a strange way on the white covering of the bed. Looking more closely, he found that this linen fabric had been changed to what seemed a woven texture of the purest and brightest gold! The Golden Touch had come to him with the first sunbeam!

Midas started up joyfully, and ran about the room grasping at everything that happened to be in his way. He seized one of the bed-posts, and it became a golden pillar. He pulled aside a window-curtain, and the tassel grew heavy in his hand—a mass of gold. He took up a book from the table. At his touch the leaves became a bundle of thin golden plates. He hurriedly put on his clothes, and was delighted to see himself in a magnificent

suit of gold cloth, which kept its softness, although it
burdened him a little with its weight.

Wise King Midas was so excited by his good fortune
that the palace seemed not large enough to contain him.
He therefore went downstairs and smiled to see that the
railing of the staircase became a bar of burnished gold
as his hand passed over it on his way down. He lifted
the door latch (it was brass only a moment ago, but
golden when his fingers left it) and went into the garden.
Here he found beautiful roses in full bloom, and others
in all the stages of lovely bud and blossom.

But Midas knew a way to make them far more precious, according to his way of thinking, than roses had ever

been before. So he took great pains in going from bush to bush, and used his magic touch freely until every flower and bud, and even the worms at the heart of some of them, were changed to gold. By the time this good work was completed, King Midas was called to breakfast; and, as the morning air had given him an excellent appetite, he made haste back to the palace.

What was usually a king's breakfast, in the days of Midas, I really do not know. To the best of my belief, however, on this particular morning, the breakfast consisted of hot cakes, some nice little brook trout, roasted potatoes, fresh boiled eggs, and coffee for King Midas himself, and a bowl of bread and milk for his daughter Marygold. At all events, this is a breakfast fit to be set before a king; and, whether he had it or not, King Midas could not have had a better.

Little Marygold had not yet made her appearance. Her father ordered her to be called, and, seating himself at the table, awaited the child's coming, in order to begin his own breakfast. Midas really loved his daughter, and loved her much more this morning on account of the good fortune which had befallen him. It was not a great while before he heard her coming along the passage crying bitterly. This surprised him, because Marygold was one of the cheerfulest little people whom you would see in a summer day, and hardly shed a thimbleful of tears in a twelvemonth. When Midas heard her sobs, he determined to put her into better spirits by an agreeable surprise; so, leaning across the table, he touched his daughter's bowl and turned it to gleaming gold.

Meanwhile, Marygold slowly and sadly opened the door, and showed herself with her apron at her eyes, still sobbing as if her heart would break.

"How now, my little lady!" cried Midas. "Pray what is the matter with you this bright morning?"

Marygold, without taking the apron from her eyes, held out her hand in which was one of the roses which Midas had so recently changed.

"Beautiful!" exclaimed her father. "And what is there in this magnificent golden rose to make you cry?"

"Ah, dear father!" answered the child, as well as her sobs would let her, "it is not beautiful, but the ugliest flower that ever grew! As soon as I was dressed, I ran into the garden to gather some roses for you, because I know you like them, and like them the better when gathered by your little daughter. But, O dear, dear me! What do you think has happened? All the beautiful roses, that smelled so sweet and had so many lovely blushes, are blighted and spoiled! They are grown quite yellow, as you see this one, and have no longer any fragrance! What can have been the matter?"

"Pooh, my dear little girl, pray don't cry about it!" said Midas, who was ashamed to confess that he himself had brought about the change which so greatly troubled her. "Sit down and eat your bread and milk! You will find it easy enough to exchange a golden rose like that (which will last hundreds of years) for an ordinary one, which would wither in a day."

"I don't care for such roses as this!" cried Marygold. "It has no smell, and the hard petals prick my nose!"

The child now sat down to table, but was so occupied with her grief for the blighted roses that she did not even notice the wonderful change of her china bowl. Perhaps this was all the better.

Midas, meanwhile, had poured out a cup of coffee; and, as a matter of course, the coffee-pot, whatever metal it may have been when he took it up, was gold when he set it down. He began to be puzzled with the difficulty of keeping his treasures safe. The cupboard and the kitchen would no longer be a safe place for articles so valuable as golden bowls and coffee-pots.

Amid these thoughts, he lifted a spoonful of coffee to his lips, and, sipping it, was astonished to find that it became molten gold, and the next moment hardened into a lump!

"Ha!" exclaimed Midas, rather terrified.

"What is the matter, father?" asked little Marygold, gazing at him, with tears still standing in her eyes.

"Nothing, child, nothing!" said Midas. "Eat your bread and milk before it gets quite cold."

He took one of the nice little trout on his plate, and touched its tail with his finger. To his horror, it was immediately changed from a well-fried brook trout into a gold fish. Its little bones were now golden wires; its fins and tail were thin plates of gold; and there were the marks of the fork in it.  A very pretty piece of work, as you may suppose; only King Midas just at that moment would much rather have had a real trout in his dish.

"I don't quite see," thought he to himself, "how I am to get any breakfast!"

He took one of the smoking hot cakes, and had scarcely broken it, when it took on the yellow color of Indian cornmeal.  Almost in despair, he helped himself to a boiled egg, which immediately underwent a change similar to that of the trout and the cake.  The egg, indeed, might have been mistaken for one of those which the famous goose in the story-book was in the habit of laying, but King Midas was the only goose that had had anything to do with the matter.

"Well, this is a puzzle!" thought he, leaning back in his chair, and looking with envy at little Marygold, who was now eating her bread and milk with great satisfaction.  "Such a costly breakfast, and nothing that can be eaten!"

King Midas next snatched a hot potato, and attempted to cram it into his mouth, and swallow it in a hurry.  But the Golden Touch was too nimble for him.  He found his mouth full, not of mealy potato, but of solid metal, which so burned his tongue that he roared aloud, and, jumping up from the table, began to dance and stamp about the room, both with pain and fright.

"Father, dear father!" cried little Marygold, who was

a very affectionate child. "Pray, what is the matter? Have you burned your mouth?"

"Ah, dear child," groaned Midas. "I don't know what is to become of your poor father!"

And, truly, did you ever hear of such a pitiable case in all your lives? Here was the richest breakfast that could be set before a king, and its very richness made it good for nothing. The poorest laborer, sitting down to his crust of bread and cup of water, was far better off than King Midas, whose food was really worth its weight in gold. And what was to be done? Already, at breakfast, Midas was very hungry. Would he be less so by dinnertime? And how great would be his appetite for supper, which must consist of the same kind of food as that now before him! How many days, think you, would he survive the use of this rich fare?

These thoughts so troubled wise King Midas that he began to doubt whether, after all, riches are the one desirable thing in the world, or even the most desirable. But this was only a passing thought. So pleased was Midas with the glitter of the yellow metal that he would still have refused to give up the Golden Touch for so small a matter as a breakfast. Just imagine what a price for one meal! It would have been the same as paying millions and millions of money for some fried trout, an egg, a potato, a hot cake, and a cup of coffee!

"It would be quite too dear," thought Midas.

Nevertheless, so great was his hunger that King Midas

groaned aloud.  Pretty Marygold could endure it no longer.  She sat a moment gazing at her father, and trying with all her might to find out what was the matter with him.  Then, with a sweet and sorrowful desire to comfort him, she ran to him and threw her arms lovingly about his knees.  He bent down and kissed her.  He felt that his little daughter's love was worth a thousand times more than the Golden Touch.

"My precious, precious Marygold!" cried he.

But Marygold made no answer.

Alas, what had he done?  The moment the lips of Midas touched Marygold's forehead, a change had taken place.  Her sweet rosy face, so full of affection as it had been, became a glittering yellow color with yellow tear-drops hardening on her cheeks. Her beautiful brown ringlets took the same tint. Her soft and tender little form grew hard and stiff within her father's arms. O terrible misfortune! Little Marygold was a human child no longer, but a golden statue!

Yes, there she was, with the look of love, grief, and pity hardened into her face. It was the prettiest and most woeful sight that anyone ever saw. All the features of Marygold were there, even the beloved little dimple in her golden chin. It had been a favorite habit of Midas, whenever he felt particularly fond of the child, to say that she was worth her weight in gold. And now the phrase had become really true. And now, at last, when it was too late, he realized how much greater value had a warm and tender heart that loved him than all the wealth that could be piled up betwixt the earth and sky!

Midas began to wring his hands and bemoan himself; he could neither bear to look at Marygold, nor yet to look away from her.

### WHAT KING MIDAS LEARNED

While he was in this despair, he suddenly beheld a stranger, standing near the door. Midas bent down his head, without speaking, for he recognized the same figure which had appeared to him the day before in the treasure-room, and had bestowed upon him this unlucky power of the Golden Touch. The stranger's face still wore a smile, which seemed to shed a yellow luster all about the room.  It gleamed on little Marygold's statue, and on the other objects that had been changed by the touch of Midas.

"Well, friend Midas," said the stranger, "pray how do you succeed with the Golden Touch?"

Midas shook his head.

"I am very miserable," said he.

"Very miserable, indeed!" exclaimed the stranger. "And how happens that?  Have I not faithfully kept my promise with you?  Have you not everything that your heart desired?"

"Gold is not everything," answered Midas.  "And I have lost all that my heart really cared for."

"Ah!  So you have made a discovery since yesterday?" asked the stranger.  "Let us see, then.  Which of these two things do you think is really worth the more— the gift of the Golden Touch, or one cup of clear cold water?"

"Oh, blessed water!" exclaimed Midas.  "It will never moisten my parched throat again!"

"The Golden Touch," continued the stranger, "or a crust of bread?"

"A piece of bread," answered Midas, "is worth all the gold on earth!"

"The Golden Touch," asked the stranger, "or your own little Marygold, warm, soft, and loving, as she was an hour ago?"

"Oh, my child, my dear child!" cried poor Midas, wringing his hands. "I would not have given that one small dimple in her chin for the power of changing this whole big earth into a solid lump of gold!"

"You are wiser than you were, King Midas!" said the stranger, looking closely at him. "Your own heart, I see, has not been entirely changed from flesh to gold. Were it so, your case would indeed be hopeless. But you have come to understand that the commonest things, such as lie within everybody's grasp, are more valuable than the riches which so many men sigh and struggle after. Tell me now, do you really desire to rid yourself of this Golden Touch?"

"It is hateful to me!" replied Midas.

A fly settled on his nose, but immediately fell to the floor, for it, too, had become gold. Midas shuddered.

"Go, then," said the stranger, "and plunge into the river that glides past the bottom of your garden. Take likewise a vase of the same water, and sprinkle it over any object that you may desire to change back again from gold into its former substance. If you do this in earnestness and sincerity, it may possibly undo the mischief which your greed for gold has caused."

King Midas bowed low; and when he lifted his head, the stranger had vanished.

You will easily believe that Midas lost no time in snatching up a great earthen pitcher (but, alas! it was no longer earthen after he touched it) and in hastening to the riverside. As he hurried along forcing his way through the shrubbery, it was marvelous to see how the leaves turned yellow behind him, as if the autumn had been there, and nowhere else. On reaching the river's brink, he plunged headlong in, without waiting so much as to pull off his shoes.

"Poof! poof! poof!" snorted King Midas, as his head came up out of the water. "Well, this is really a refreshing bath, and I think it must have quite washed away the Golden Touch. And now for filling my pitcher!"

As he dipped the pitcher into the water, it gladdened his very heart to see it change from gold into the same good, earthen vessel which it had been before he touched it. He felt, also, a change within himself. A cold, hard, and heavy weight seemed to have gone out of his bosom. Seeing a violet that grew on the bank of the river, Midas touched it with his finger, and was overjoyed to find that the delicate flower kept its purple hue, instead of turning yellow. The curse of the Golden Touch had, therefore, really been removed from him.

King Midas hastened back to the palace; and, I suppose, the servants knew not what to make of it when they saw their royal master so carefully bring home an earthen pitcher of water. But that water, which was to undo all the mischief that his folly had wrought, was more precious to Midas than an ocean of melted gold could have been. The first thing he did, as you need hardly

be told, was to sprinkle the water by handfuls over the golden figure of little Marygold.

No sooner did it fall on her than you would have laughed to see how the rosy color came back to the dear child's cheek!—and how she began to sneeze and splutter!—and how astonished she was to find herself dripping wet, and her father still pouring more water over her!

"Pray, do not, dear father!" cried she. "See how you have wet my nice clean frock, which I put on only this morning!"

For Marygold did not know that she had been a little golden statue; nor could she remember anything that had happened since the moment when she ran with out-stretched arms to comfort poor King Midas.

Her father did not think it necessary to tell his beloved child how very foolish he had been, but contented himself with showing how much wiser he had now grown. For this purpose he led Marygold into the garden, where he sprinkled all the remainder of the water over the rose-bushes, and with such effect that about five thousand roses recovered their beautiful bloom. There were two things, however, which, as long as he lived, used to put King Midas in mind of the Golden Touch. One was that the sands of the river sparkled like gold; the other that little Marygold's hair had now a golden tinge, which he had never noticed in it before she had been changed by the effect of his kiss. This change of hue was really an improvement, and made Marygold's hair richer than in her babyhood.

When King Midas had grown quite an old man, and used to trot Marygold's children on his knee, he was fond of telling them this marvelous story, very much as I have now told it to you. And then would he stroke their glossy curls and tell them that their hair, likewise, had a rich shade of gold like their mother's.

"And to tell you the truth, my precious little folks," quoth King Midas, trotting the children all the while, "ever since that morning I have hated the very sight of all other gold except this!"

## Notes and Questions

1. On page 142 the stranger says to Midas, "So you have made a discovery since yesterday." What had Midas discovered?

2. If you heard or read of someone who was called "a Midas," what kind of person would you think he was?

3. Hawthorne said he picked Marygold for a name because he liked unusual names. Do you think he had some other reason? What was it?

4. What good way to teach a person a lesson is shown in this story?

5. Make up a name for each of the pictures in this story.

6. Find and be ready to read a very foolish thing that King Midas said.

7. Find lines that seem to show that the stranger knew Midas was making a mistake. Be ready to read them.

8. Find lines in which King Midas showed that he had really learned his lesson.

This story was taken from *A Wonder Book for Boys and Girls*. Other famous stories that you would enjoy are "The Garden of Tears and Smiles," Meigs (in *The Kingdom of the Winding Road*); "St. George and the Giant," Esenwein (in *Child-Library Readers, Book Five*); and "The Selfish Giant," Wilde (in *The Happy Prince and Other Fairy Tales*).

# THE NUREMBERG STOVE

## Louise de la Ramee

Because a boy loved a grand old stove, he did a brave thing that caused his dream to come true. Louise de la Ramee, a famous English story-teller, tells us about the boy, and about the stove that had a name.

## AUGUST'S HOME

August lived in a little town in Europe called Hall. It is on a wide river which has green meadows and great mountains all about it. It has paved streets and charming little shops and a grand old church. Then there is the Tower, looking down on a long wooden bridge, and the broad, rapid river.

August's mother was dead, his father was poor, and there were many mouths at home to feed. He had been sent on a long errand one afternoon and had been delayed. He was half-frozen, but he kept up his courage by saying over and over again to himself, "I shall soon be at home with dear Hirschvogel." He went on through the streets and at twilight reached his father's house.

At his knock the door was opened, and the boy darted in, and shouted, "Oh, dear Hirschvogel, except for the thought of you, I should have died!"

It was a large room into which he rushed with so much pleasure. At one end of it, sending out warmth and color together, as the lamp shed its rays upon it, was a big

148

stove of porcelain, shining with all the hues of a queen's jewels. On the stove were the letters A. R. H., for it was the work of a great potter, Augustin Hirschvogel, who always signed his work in that way. The stove no doubt had stood in palaces; it was a royal thing. Yet it had never been more useful than it was now in this poor room, sending down comfort into the troop of children, tumbled together on a wolfskin at its feet, who received August with shouts of joy.

"Oh, dear Hirschvogel, I am so cold, so cold!" said August, kissing its gilded lion's claws. "Is father not in, Dorothea?" he said, speaking to his oldest sister.

"No, dear. He is late, but he says we are never to wait for him; we will have supper, now you have come home," said Dorothea.

After supper Dorothea drew her spinning-wheel near to the stove and set it whirring, and the little ones got August down upon the wolfskin and asked him for a picture or a story. For August was the artist of the family. He had a piece of smooth board that his father had given him, and some sticks of charcoal, and he would draw a hundred things he had seen in the day, wiping each out when the children had seen enough of it.

"Tell us a story, August," they cried, when they had seen charcoal pictures till they were tired. And August did as he did every night, nearly—looked up at the stove and told the children what he imagined of the adventures of the man who was pictured on the panels.

The stove was a very grand thing.  It was of great height and breadth, with all the shining colors that Hirschvogel had learned to give to his enamels.  There was the statue of a king at each corner, modeled with much skill.  August's grandfather had dug the stove up out of some ruins where he was working, and finding it without a flaw, had taken it home.  That was now sixty years past, and ever since then the stove had stood in this room, warming his children and his grandchildren.

Once a traveling peddler had told them that the letters on it meant Augustin Hirschvogel, and that Hirschvogel had been a great potter and painter.  He said that Hirschvogel had made many such stoves, all wonders of

beauty, putting all his heart and his soul and his faith
into his work, and thinking but little of gold or praise.

So the stove had come to be called Hirschvogel. All
the children loved the stove, but August loved it most
of all. He used to say to himself, "When I am a man,
I will make such things, too, and then I will set Hirschvogel in a beautiful room in a house that I will build."

August lay now in the warmth of the stove and told
the children marvelous stories. In the midst of their
chatter and laughter a blast of freezing air reached them
even in the warmth of the old wolfskin and the great
stove. The door had opened; it was their father who had
come home. The father answered the welcome of his
children very wearily, and sat down heavily.

"Take the children to bed," he said, and Dorothea
obeyed. August stayed behind, curled up before the
stove. Dorothea came down from putting the little ones
into their beds, and then sat down to her spinning.

### THE STOVE IS SOLD

Suddenly August's father struck his hand on the
table. "I have sold Hirschvogel," he said; and his voice
was husky and ashamed. The spinning-wheel stopped.
August sprang up.

"I have sold it to a traveling trader in such things
for two hundred florins. I owe double that. He saw it
this morning when you were all out. He will take it
away tomorrow."

"O father!" August cried, throwing himself on his knees at his father's feet, his face very white. "Sell Hirschvogel! You could not do such a thing—you who have always been gentle and good, and who have sat in the warmth here with our mother. Oh, listen; I will go and try to get work tomorrow! There must be something that I could do, and I will beg the people we owe money to, to wait; they will wait for it. But sell Hirschvogel!—Oh! Never, never, never!"

"Get up and go to bed," said his father harshly, as the children had never heard him speak before. "The stove is sold. There is no more to be said. Be thankful I can get bread for you."

Sorrowfully August left the room. All that night he lay tossing on his bed. In the morning, while it was yet dark, the three elder brothers came down, each bearing his lantern and going to his work in the stone-yard and timber-yard and salt-works.

August had not slept, but he arose and went down to take a last look at the beautiful stove, just in time to hear loud blows made by the heavy iron knocker of the house-door. A strange voice called out, "Let me in! There is no time to lose! Do you hear? I have come to take the great stove."

As his father came into the room and opened the door, August sprang up, screaming, "You shall never touch it!"

"Who shall prevent us?" laughed a big man, amused at the fierce little figure.

"I!" said August. "You shall never have it! You shall kill me first!"

"You are like a little mad dog," said the big man.

So his father put the boy out from the back entrance, and the buyers of the beautiful stove set to work to pack it and bear it out to an ox-cart which was waiting to carry it to the railway station.

August stood for a time, leaning sick and faint against the back wall of the house.

### AUGUST GOES WITH THE STOVE

August remained leaning against the wall; his head was buzzing and his heart fluttering with a new idea. "Why not go with Hirschvogel?" he thought. How he managed it he never knew clearly himself, but when the freight-train carrying Hirschvogel moved out of Hall, August was hidden behind the stove. He was close to Hirschvogel, and presently he meant to be closer still. For he meant to get inside Hirschvogel itself.

Being a shrewd little boy, and having a few pieces of money in his pocket, earned the day before by chopping wood, he had bought some bread and sausage at the station, and this he ate in the darkness.

When he had eaten, not as much as he wanted, but as much as he thought wise (for who could say when he would be able to buy anything more?), he set to work like a mouse to make a hole in the bands of straw which wrapped the stove. He gnawed and nibbled and pulled, making his hole where he guessed the opening of the stove was—the opening through which he had so often thrust the big oak logs.

He had hard work getting through the straw and twisted ropes; but get through them he did, and found the door of the stove. He slipped through, as he had often done at home for fun, and curled himself up there. Air came in through the brass fret-work of the stove. With great care he leaned out, drew the hay and straw together, and replaced the ropes. Then he curled himself up again, and, being safe inside dear Hirschvogel and very cold, he fell asleep.

The slow train took the short winter's day and the long winter's night and half another day to go over the ground that the mail-trains cover in a forenoon. Happily for August, the thick wrappings of the stove protected him from the cold, else he must have died—frozen. He still had some of his loaf and a little of his sausage. But he began to suffer from thirst, and this frightened him more than anything else.

At last the train stopped with a jar and a jerk, and he could hear men crying the name of some town. Then he felt himself carried on the shoulders of men, rolled along on a truck, and set down, where he knew not; only he knew he was thirsty—so thirsty!

"I shall not unpack it till Anton comes," he heard a man's voice say; and then he heard a key turn in a lock. By the stillness he knew he was alone, and ventured to peep through the straw and hay. What he saw was a

square room filled with pictures, carvings, old blue jugs, old steel armor, shields, daggers, Chinese idols, china, Turkish rugs, and all the articles of a bric-a-brac dealer's.

It seemed a wonderful place to him; but, oh! was there one drop of water in it all? That was his single thought; for his tongue was parching, and his throat felt on fire. There was not a drop of water, but there was a window, and beyond the window was a stone ledge covered with snow. August darted out of his hiding-place, ran and opened the window, and crammed the snow into his mouth again and again. Then he flew back into the stove, drew the hay and straw over the place by which he had entered, tied the cords, and shut the brass doors on himself.  He had brought some big icicles with him, and by them his thirst was quenched.

### THE STOVE IS SOLD AGAIN

By and by the key turned in the lock of the door.  He heard heavy footsteps and the voice of the man who had said to him, "You are like a little mad dog."  The voice said, "Now you shall see what I have bought for two hundred florins.  Never did you do such a piece of work."

Then they began to strip the stove of its wrappings. Soon they uncovered it; that he knew by the exclamations of wonder which broke from the man who had not seen it before.

"A right royal thing!  Magnificent!  Matchless!"

After praising and marveling, the men moved to a distance and began talking of sums of money.  All August could make out was that the king—the king— the king was used very often as they talked.  After a while they seemed to agree to something, and were in great glee.  He had made out from their talk that they were going to show Hirschvogel to some great person.

Presently the door opened.  He could hear the two dealers' voices and the voice of another person, clearer and softer, close by the boy's ear, which exclaimed, "Beautiful!"

"Beautiful!" said the stranger a second time, and then examined the stove in all its parts.  After a while the

men went away, leaving August and Hirschvogel to pass
the night there.

August awoke with a start, just as the clocks of the
city struck six in the morning. All was dark around him.
Was it still night, or had morning come? Tramp, tramp,
came a heavy step up the stair. Then the dealers began
to wrap up the stove once more in its straw and cords.
Presently they called up their porters, and the stove was
carried on the shoulders of six strong men down the stairs
and out into the street. Even behind all those wrappings
August felt the icy bite of the cold air.

The carriers tramped through the city to the railway
station. August recognized the railway noises, and
thought, "Will it be a long journey?" For his stomach
had an odd shrinking, and his head felt light and swim-
ming. Whether for a long or a short journey, the stove
was this time not left alone. The two dealers and the
six porters were with it. In his darkness August knew
that, for he heard their voices.

In three hours more the train came to a stop, and the
stove was lifted out. August heard one of the dealers
say to the porters, "Now, men, for a long mile and a
half!" They shouldered the stove, grumbling at its
weight, but little dreaming that they carried within it
a small, trembling boy, for August began to tremble now
that he was about to see the owner of Hirschvogel.

"If he seems to be a good, kind man," he thought, "I
will beg him to let me stay with Hirschvogel."

Then he heard voices, but could not understand what was being said. His bearers paused for a time, then moved on again. Their feet went so softly he thought they must be moving on carpet, and as he felt warm air come to him, he knew that he was in some heated rooms.

They must have gone through a great number of rooms, he thought, for they walked on and on, on and on. At last the stove was set down.

### AUGUST BEFORE THE KING

Soon August heard a step near him, and he heard a low voice say, close to him, "So!"

Then the same voice said, after a long pause, "It was well bought; it is very beautiful!  It is undoubtedly the work of Augustin Hirschvogel."

Then the hand of the speaker started to open the brass door, and the heart of the little prisoner within grew sick with fear. The door was slowly drawn open, someone bent down and looked in, and the same voice that he had heard praising its beauty called in surprise, "What is this in it?  A live child?"

Then August sprang out of the stove and knelt before the speaker. "Oh, let me stay!  Pray, sir, let me stay!" he sobbed. "I have come all the way with Hirschvogel!"

"My child, how came you here, hidden in this stove? Be not afraid; tell me the truth.  I am the king."

August looked bravely up at the king; he was too much in earnest to be in any way afraid.

"Oh, dear king!" he cried, in a clear voice, "Hirschvogel was ours; we have loved it all our lives; and father sold it. And when I saw that it did really go from us, then I said to myself I would go with it; and I have come all the way inside it. And I pray you to let me live here with it, and I will go out every morning and cut wood for it and you, if you will only let me stay beside it. No one but me ever has fed it with fuel since I grew big enough."

Then breath failed him, and as he lifted his eager, pale face to the king's, tears were falling down his cheeks.

"What is your name?" asked the king.

"I am August Strehla. I live in Hall; and Hirschvogel has been ours so long—so long!" His lips trembled with a broken sob.

"And have you truly traveled inside this stove all the way from Hall?"

"Yes," said August. "No one thought to look inside."

"Who bought the stove of your father?" asked the king.

"A traveling trader," said August, "and he sold it to some art dealers."

"What sum did the trader pay your father, do you know?" asked the king.

"Two hundred florins," said August. "It was so much money, and he is so poor, and there are so many of us."

The king turned to his companions. "Did these art dealers come with the stove?"

When he was told that they had done so, he ordered them to be brought before him.

"You are pale, little one. When did you eat last?"

"I had some bread and sausage with me. Yesterday afternoon I finished it."

"You would like to eat now?"

"If I might have a little water, I should be glad. My throat is very dry."

The king had water brought for him, and cake also; but August, though he drank eagerly, could not eat anything. His mind was in too great trouble.

"May I stay with Hirschvogel?—May I?" he said.

"Wait a little," said the king, and then he asked, "What do you wish to be when you are a man?"

"A painter. I wish to be what Hirschvogel was—I mean the artist that made my Hirschvogel."

"I understand," said the king.

Then the two dealers were brought before the king. They were frightened and trembling. And they were so surprised, too, at a child's having come all the way from Hall in the stove, that they looked very foolish.

"Did you buy this stove of this little boy's father for two hundred florins?" the king asked them; and his voice was no longer soft and kind as it had been when speaking to the child, but very stern.

"Yes, your Majesty," murmured the trembling traders.

"And how much did the man who purchased it for me give you?"

"Two thousand ducats, your Majesty," muttered the dealers, frightened out of their wits.

"You will give to this boy's father the two thousand gold ducats that you received, less the two hundred florins that you paid him," said the king. "Be thankful you are not more greatly punished."

August heard, and felt dazed. Two thousand gold ducats for his father! Why, his father would never need to go any more to the salt-works! And yet, whether for ducats or for florins, Hirschvogel was sold just the same; and would the king let him stay with it?—Would he?

The king looked down on the child, and as he did so, smiled once more. "Will I let you stay with your Hirschvogel? Yes, I will; you shall stay at my court, and you shall be taught to be an artist, and you must win all the prizes at our schools of art. If, when you are twenty-one years old, you have done well, I will give you your porcelain stove again. You shall light a fire every morning in Hirschvogel, but you will not need to go out and cut the wood."

The king smiled and stretched out his hand. August was so happy that he dropped to his knees and kissed the king's feet. Then he fainted away from hunger.

Sometimes August goes back for a little visit to Hall, where the gold ducats have made his father comfortable. In the old room there is a large white porcelain stove, the king's gift to Dorothea.

August never visits his home without going into the

great church and saying his thanks to God, who blessed his strange winter's journey in the porcelain stove.

## NOTES AND QUESTIONS

1. Here is a list of the main things that happened in the story. But they are not in the right order. Put them in the right order so that you could tell the story from them.

> The king finds August.
> August's father sells the stove.
> The stove is sold to the king.
> August comes home to the family and the stove.
> August's dream comes true.
> August goes with the stove.

2. Read again the list in Question 1. Choose the happening that you think is the most important one in the story.

3. What was the most exciting part of the story?

4. Which one of these three reasons best tells why August loved the stove?

> (*a*) He knew it was very valuable.
> (*b*) The family needed it to keep them warm.
> (*c*) It was beautiful.

5. Which one of these four reasons best tells why Hirschvogel made such wonderful stoves?

> (*a*) He was a great potter and painter.
> (*b*) He could sell them and make much money.
> (*c*) He liked to have people praise his work.
> (*d*) He loved his work.

Another story which tells of strange and exciting journeys is *The Little Lame Prince and His Traveling Cloak*, Mulock.

# HIAWATHA'S CHILDHOOD

Henry W. Longfellow was another great American story-teller, but he told his stories in poetry. You are now going to read part of a long poem about Indian life. In this poem Longfellow tells for us many of the old stories or legends that the story-tellers of the tribes passed on from one to another down through the years.

By the shores of Gitche Gumee,
By the shining Big-Sea-Water,
Stood the wigwam of Nokomis,
Daughter of the Moon, Nokomis.
Dark behind it rose the forest,
Rose the black and gloomy pine-trees,
Rose the firs with cones upon them;
Bright before it beat the water,
Beat the clear and sunny water,
Beat the shining Big-Sea-Water.

There the wrinkled, old Nokomis
Nursed the little Hiawatha;
Rocked him in his linden cradle,
Bedded soft in moss and rushes,
Safely bound with reindeer sinews;
Stilled his fretful wail by saying,
"Hush! the Naked Bear will get thee!"
Lulled him into slumber, singing,

"Ewa-yea! my little owlet!
Who is this that lights the wigwam,
With his great eyes lights the wigwam?
Ewa-yea! my little owlet!"

Many things Nokomis taught him
Of the stars that shine in heaven;
Showed the broad, white road in heaven,
Pathway of the ghosts, the shadows,
Running straight across the heavens,
Crowded with the ghosts, the shadows.

At the door on summer evenings
Sat the little Hiawatha;
Heard the whispering of the pine-trees,

Heard the lapping of the water,
Sounds of music, words of wonder;
"Minne-wawa!" said the pine-trees,
"Mudway-aushka!" said the water.

Saw the firefly, Wah-wah-taysee,
Flitting through the dusk of evening,
With the twinkle of its candle
Lighting up the brakes and bushes;
And he sang the song of children,
Sang the song Nokomis taught him:
"Wah-wah-taysee, little firefly,
Little, flitting, white-fire insect.
Little, dancing, white-fire creature,
Light me with your little candle,
Ere upon my bed I lay me,
Ere in sleep I close my eyelids!"

Saw the moon rise from the water
Rippling, rounding from the water;
Saw the flecks and shadows on it;
Whispered, "What is that, Nokomis?"
And the good Nokomis answered:
"Once a warrior, very angry,
Seized his grandmother, and threw her
Up into the sky at midnight;
Right against the moon he threw her;
'Tis her body that you see there."

Saw the rainbow in the heaven,
In the eastern sky, the rainbow;

Whispered, "What is that, Nokomis?"
And the good Nokomis answered:
" 'Tis the heaven of flowers you see there.
All the wild-flowers of the forest,
All the lilies of the prairie,
When on earth they fade and perish,
Blossom in that heaven above us."

When he heard the owls at midnight,
Hooting, laughing in the forest,
"What is that?" he cried in terror;
"What is that," he said, "Nokomis?"
And the good Nokomis answered:
"That is but the owl and owlet,
Talking in their native language,
Talking, scolding at each other."

Then the little Hiawatha
Learned of every bird its language,
Learned their names and all their secrets—
How they built their nests in summer,
Where they hid themselves in winter—
Talked with them whene'er he met them,
Called them "Hiawatha's Chickens."

Of all beasts he learned the language,
Learned their names and all their secrets—
How the beavers built their lodges,
Where the squirrels hid their acorns,
How the reindeer ran so swiftly,

Why the rabbit was so timid;
Talked with them whene'er he met them,
Called them "Hiawatha's Brothers."

Then Iagoo, the great boaster,
He the marvelous story-teller,
He the traveler and the talker,
He the friend of old Nokomis,
Made a bow for Hiawatha;
From a branch of ash he made it,
From an oak-bough made the arrows,
Tipped with flint, and winged with feathers,
And the cord he made of deerskin.

Then he said to Hiawatha:
"Go, my son, into the forest,
Where the red deer herd together;
Kill for us a famous roebuck,
Kill for us a deer with antlers!"

Forth into the forest straightway
All alone walked Hiawatha
Proudly, with his bow and arrows;
And the birds sang round him, o'er him,
"Do not shoot us, Hiawatha!"
Sang the robin, the Opechee,
Sang the bluebird, the Owaissa,
"Do not shoot us, Hiawatha!"

Up the oak-tree, close beside him,
Sprang the squirrel, Adjidaumo,

In and out among the branches,
Coughed and chattered from the oak-tree,
Laughed, and said between his laughing,
"Do not shoot me, Hiawatha!"

And the rabbit from his pathway
Leaped aside, and at a distance
Sat erect upon his haunches,
Half in fear and half in frolic,
Saying to the little hunter,
"Do not shoot me, Hiawatha!"

But he heeded not, nor heard them,
For his thoughts were with the red deer;
On their tracks his eyes were fastened,
Leading downward to the river,
To the ford across the river;
And as one in slumber walked he.

Hidden in the alder-bushes,
There he waited till the deer came,
Till he saw two antlers lifted,
Saw two eyes look from the thicket,
Saw two nostrils point to windward,
And a deer came down the pathway,
Flecked with leafy light and shadow.
And his heart within him fluttered,
Trembled like the leaves above him,
Like the birch-leaf palpitated,
As the deer came down the pathway.

Then, upon one knee uprising,
Hiawatha aimed an arrow;
Scarce a twig moved with his motion,
Scarce a leaf was stirred or rustled,
But the wary roebuck started,
Stamped with all his hoofs together,
Listened with one foot uplifted,
Leaped as if to meet the arrow,
Ah! the singing, fatal arrow;
Like a wasp it buzzed and stung him!

Dead he lay there in the forest,
By the ford across the river;

Beat his timid heart no longer.
But the heart of Hiawatha
Throbbed and shouted and exulted,
As he bore the red deer homeward;
And Iagoo and Nokomis
Hailed his coming with applauses.

From the red deer's hide Nokomis
Made a coat for Hiawatha;
From the red deer's flesh Nokomis
Made a banquet in his honor.
All the village came and feasted;
All the guests praised Hiawatha,
Called him Strong-Heart, Soan-ge-taha!
Called him Loon-Heart, Mahn-go-taysee!

## Notes and Questions

1. Read aloud or tell the legend of the moon.
2. Read aloud or tell the legend of the rainbow.
3. What is "the broad, white road in heaven"? What did the Indians think it was?
4. Who was Iagoo? Read the lines that tell about him.
5. How did Hiawatha feel toward the wild animals?

You will like to read *Indian Boyhood* and *Indian Heroes and Great Chieftains*, Eastman; "Little Turtle of the Miamis," and "Little Turtle Fears the Big Wind," Sabin (in *Boy's Book of Indian Warriors*); and *Chi-Wee*, Moon.

# A BACKWARD LOOK

GUILLAUME the flute player, King Midas and Marygold, August, and Hiawatha—do you see that you have become acquainted with some people you had never met before? You will perhaps find that your father and mother knew them years ago. It is strange how the boys and girls and men and women in stories become so well known. Almost anywhere you might go in our country you would find someone who knew of King Midas and of Hiawatha.

As you think back over these four stories you have read, which one did you like best? Can you give some good reasons why you liked it best? What happenings in the stories can you see almost as if you had been there? If you had to choose one of these stories to tell, which one would it be? Did any of these stories teach a good lesson? Which one was it, and what was the lesson?

Of course, there are many other stories you ought to read. And you will want to read them because it will be fun to do so. If you liked "The Golden Touch," there are Hawthorne's *Tanglewood Tales* and his *Wonder Book*. "Hiawatha's Childhood" is only a small part of the whole poem, *The Song of Hiawatha*. Did you get time to read any of the other five stories in Miss Crownfield's book *The Feast of Noel?* If one of your classmates were ill, and you wanted to take him some stories to read, what four or five would you choose?

If you have already found the list of other "Stories We All Should Know" on page 432, you have had many happy hours with these books. Wouldn't you like to tell the class some good story that you have found?

# PART FOUR
## ·YOUNG AMERICAN CITIZENS·

## SONG OF OUR LAND

ANNETTE WYNNE

Mountainland, fountainland, shoreland, and sea,
God's land thou art surely—His gift to the free;
How blest are thy children wherever they roam
To claim thee their country, their hope, and their
    home.

I love thee, my country, O great be thy fame;
I love thy dear banner—I honor thy name;
I'll live for thee, die for thee, serve no land but thee:
My country forever, great land of the free!

Reprinted by permission from *For Days and
Days: A Year-round Treasury of Verse for Children*
by Annette Wynne, copyright 1919, by Frederick
A. Stokes Company.

# WHAT IS A GOOD CITIZEN?

M ANY hundreds of years ago, Athens, in the country that we now call Greece, was the most beautiful and the most famous city in the world. Its people loved it and were proud of it. When the Athenian boys became about your age, they were taught a pledge to their city. This is the promise they made:

> We will never bring disgrace to this our city by any act of dishonesty or cowardice, nor ever desert our comrades. We will respect and obey the city laws, and do our best to get others to respect and obey them. We will ever strive to teach others to be loyal and true. Thus, in all these ways, we may make this city greater, better, and more beautiful.

One more thing the Athenian youth was taught: to keep himself strong and healthy.

What do you think of the pledge of the Athenian youth? Could you take it for your own pledge to your city and your country? To be honest, to be brave. Never to betray your friends. To respect and obey the laws. Always to try to make your home, your city, and your country greater, better, and more beautiful. To keep yourself healthy and strong.

Now you are going to read stories about some young American citizens—Paul Seabury, who did a dangerous thing in order to save his comrade; Josie Dawn, who was loyal and true to the team and to her brother; George Washington and Robert E. Lee. Read to see which of them you would want to put on an honor roll for a Good American Citizens' Club.

# A HERO FOR A FRIEND

## Joseph B. Ames

Can a person be afraid and still be brave? Perhaps you will be able to answer this question after you have read this story of an adventure that Paul Seabury and Bill Hedges had while they were skiing one afternoon.

### PAUL MEETS HIS HERO

Opening the door of the long, low-ceiled library, Bill Hedges paused in surprise. He had expected to find the library as deserted as were all the other rooms of the boarding-school since the Christmas vacation had begun four days before. Instead, on the hearth a log fire burned cheerfully. Curled up in an easy chair close by was the slight figure of Paul Seabury, who, like himself, lived at too great a distance from school to go home for the holidays.

"Hello!" said Bill in surprise. "You have surely made yourself comfortable here. I thought you were upstairs."

He dragged a chair up to the hearth and plumped down into it. "What are you reading?" he asked.

Paul's eyes brightened. *"Robinson Crusoe,"* he answered eagerly. "It's awfully exciting. I've just got to the place where—"

"Never read it," interrupted the larger fellow. Lounging back against the leather cushions, he surveyed the slim, rather pale-faced boy with curiosity. "Do you read all the time?" he asked.

"Why, no—not all the time," Paul answered slowly. "But just now there's nothing else to do."

Bill grunted. "Nothing else to do! Gee-whiz! Don't you ever feel like going for a tramp or something? I suppose you can't snowshoe, or ski, but I shouldn't think you would want to stay in the house all the time."

A faint, nervous smile curved the boy's lips. "Oh, I can ski and snowshoe all right. Everybody does where I live in Canada. Often it's the only way to get about."

"Oh, I see." Bill's tone was no longer curt, and a sudden look of interest had flashed into his eyes. "But don't you *like* it? Doesn't this snow make you want to try some stunts? Come on out and let's see what you can do."

Paul hesitated; he did not feel at all inclined to leave his comfortable chair and this interesting book. On the other hand, he wanted to have Bill Hedges think well of him. From the first he had regarded this big, strong fellow with a secret admiration, the sort of admiration he felt for certain heroes in his favorite books. When Bill had made some showy play on the athletic field or performed a thrilling stunt on the skating-rink, Paul, watching from the side-lines, became breathlessly excited. He had often wondered what it would be like to have such a person for a friend. But until this moment Bill Hedges had paid little attention to him, and Paul

Seabury was much too shy to make advances, even when they had been thrown together for the holidays in the loneliness of the empty school.

"I—I haven't any skis," Paul said at length.

Bill sprang briskly to his feet. "That's nothing; I will fix you up. We can borrow Marston's. Come ahead."

### OFF FOR A TRAMP

Swept along by Bill's enthusiasm, Paul closed his book and followed him out into the hall and down to the locker room. Here they got out sweaters, woolen gloves and caps, and Bill calmly turned over to Paul the skis belonging to the absent John Marston.

Coming out finally into the open, Paul shivered a little as the keen wind struck him. By the time he had adjusted the leather harness to his feet and pulled on his gloves, his fingers were blue, and he needed no urging to set off at a swift pace. In saying that he could ski, the boy had told the truth. He was, in fact, so perfectly at home upon his skis that he glided along with an easy grace.

"You're not *much* good on skis, are you?" Bill commented after watching Paul closely for a time. "I suppose you can jump any old distance and do all sorts of fancy stunts."

Paul laughed. "Nothing like that at all," he answered. "I can jump some, of course, but I'm really not much good at anything except just straight-away going."

"Huh!" grunted Bill. "I'll bet you could beat any of the fellows here. Well, what do you say to taking a little tramp? Let's go up Hogan Hill."

Paul agreed, though he was not altogether thrilled at the thought of such a climb. Hogan Hill rose steeply back of the school. A few hay-fields covered its lower level, but above them the timber growth was fairly thick, and Paul knew from experience that skiing on a wooded slope was far from easy. But Bill had no intention of tackling the steep slope directly. He knew of an old wood-road which led nearly to the summit by many twists and curves. It was his idea that they take this old road as far as it went and then ski back down its winding length.

By the time they were half-way up, Paul was getting rather breathless. It was the first time he had been on skis in nearly a year, and his muscles were soft from lack of exercise. He made no complaint, however, and presently Bill himself proposed a rest.

"I wish I could handle skis as easily as you do," he commented. "You just glide along as if you were on skates."

"I may glide, but I haven't any wind left," confessed Paul. "I've used skis ever since I was a little kid, and compared to some of the fellows up home, I am rather poor. Do you think we ought to go any farther? I felt some snow on my face just then."

"A little snow won't hurt us," said Bill, "and we can ski down in no time at all. Let's not go back just yet."

Presently they started on again. It seemed to Paul wiser to turn back at once, but he was afraid to suggest it again lest Bill think him a quitter. A little later, still mounting the narrow, winding trail, they came upon a deserted log hut, with a sagging half-open door; but the two boys did not stop to investigate it. Every now and then during the next half mile, little gusts of stinging snowflakes whirled down from the sky, beat against their faces, and scurried on. Paul's nervousness increased, but Bill merely laughed, saying that the trip home would be all the more interesting for a little snow.

The words were scarcely spoken, when from the distance there came a curious wailing of the wind, rising swiftly to a dull, threatening roar.   Startled, both boys stopped abruptly and stared up the slope.   As they did so, something like a white curtain surged over the crest of the hill and swept rapidly toward them.   Almost before they could draw a breath, it was upon them, a dense, blinding mass of snow, which whirled about them and blotted out the landscape in a flash.

"Wow!" gasped Bill.   "Some speed to that!   We had better hurry home while there is still time."

The boys had gone perhaps a quarter of a mile down the trail when a sudden heavier gust of stinging flakes blinded them both.   Paul instantly put on the brake and almost stopped.   When he was able to clear his eyes, Bill was out of sight.   An instant later there came a sudden crash, a startled, muffled cry, and then—silence!

### PAUL MAKES A DECISION

Horrified, Paul instantly jerked his staff out of the snow and sped forward.   At first, he could barely see the tracks of his companion's skis, but presently the storm lightened a trifle and suddenly he realized what had happened.   Bill had misjudged a sharp curve in the trail, and instead of following it, had plunged off to one side and down a steep slope thickly grown with trees.   At the foot of this little slope Paul found him lying, a twisted heap, face downward in the snow.

Sick with horror, the boy bent over that silent figure. A moment later his heart leaped as Bill stirred, tried to rise, and fell back with a stifled groan. Bill's left foot was twisted under him, and the front part of his ski was broken off. As Paul freed the other's feet from the skis, Bill made a second effort to rise, but his face turned quite white, and he sank back with a grunt of pain.

"I—I believe my ankle's sprained," he muttered.

For a moment or two he sat there, face screwed up, arms gripping his knees. Then he looked up at the frightened Paul, a wry smile twisting the corners of his mouth. "It looks as if we are in a mess, doesn't it?"

Paul nodded, still unable to trust himself to speak. But Bill's coolness soothed his nerves, and presently a thought struck him.

"That cabin back there!" he exclaimed. "If we could only manage to get that far—"

"Good idea," Bill agreed promptly. "I'm afraid I can't walk it, but I might be able to crawl."

"Oh, I didn't mean that. If we only had some way of fastening my skis together, you could lie down on them and I could pull you."

A gleam of admiration flashed into the older boy's eyes. "You have your nerve with you, old man," he said. "Do you know how much I weigh?"

"That doesn't matter," was Paul's reply. "It's all down hill; it will not be so hard. Besides, we can't stay here, or we'll freeze."

And it was true. Already Paul's teeth were chattering, and even Bill could feel the cold through his thick

sweater. He tried to think of some other way, but finally agreed to try Paul's plan. His heavy high shoes were laced with rawhide thongs, which could be used to bind the two skis together. There was no possibility, however, of pulling them. The only way they could manage was for Bill to seat himself on the hastily made toboggan while Paul trudged behind and pushed.

It was a toilsome and painful method of progress for them both and often jolted Bill's ankle, which was already badly swollen. Paul, wading knee-deep in the snow, was soon breathless, and by the time they reached the cabin, he felt completely exhausted.

"Couldn't have kept that up much longer," grunted

Bill, when they were inside the shelter with the door closed against the storm. His alert gaze traveled swiftly around the hut. There was a rough stone chimney at one end, a shuttered window at the back, and that was all. Snow lay piled on the cold hearth, and here and there made little ridges on the logs where it had filtered through the many cracks and crevices. It was not much better than the out-of-doors, and Bill's heart sank as he glanced at Paul, leaning exhausted against the wall.

"It is sure to stop pretty soon," he said hopefully. "When it lets up a little, we might—"

"I don't believe it's going to let up." Paul straightened up suddenly with an air of determination. "We've got to do something, and do it immediately."

Bill stared at him, amazed at the sudden change in Paul's manner.

"You're not thinking of pushing me all the way down the road, are you?" he protested. "I don't believe you could do it."

"I don't believe I could, either," agreed the other, frankly. "But I could go down and bring back help."

"Gee-whiz! You—you mean ski down that road? Why, it's over three miles, and you'd miss the trail a dozen times."

"I shouldn't try the road," said Paul, quietly. "If I went straight down the hill back of this cabin, I'd land close to the school, and I don't believe the whole distance is over half a mile."

Bill gasped. "You're crazy, man! Why, you'd kill yourself trying to ski through those trees."

Paul cut short his protests by buttoning his collar tightly about his throat and testing the laces of his shoes.

"I'm going," he stated stubbornly; "and the sooner I get off, the better."

### SKIING FOR HELP

And go he did, with a curt farewell which astonished his companion. Back of the cabin, poised at the top of the slope, with the snow whirling around him, he had one horrible moment when he was on the point of turning back. But with a tremendous effort he fought down that feeling. He could not bear the thought of facing Bill as a coward and a quitter. An instant later a thrust of his staff sent him over the edge, to glide downward through the trees with swiftly increasing speed.

Strangely enough, he felt that the worst was over. After he had successfully steered through the first hundred feet or so of woods, growing confidence in himself helped to strengthen his courage. After all, except for the blinding snow, this hill was no worse than some of the wooded slopes back there at home in Canada.

At first he managed, by a skillful use of his staff, to hold himself back a little and keep his speed within a reasonable limit. But just before he left the woods, a sudden side-turn to avoid a clump of trees nearly flung him off his balance. In struggling to recover it, the end of his staff struck against another tree and was torn

instantly from his grasp. There was no stopping now. A moment later he flashed out into the open and shot down the steep incline.

Long before he expected it, the snow-covered bulk of a stone wall seemed to leap out of the blinding snow-curtain and rush toward him. Almost too late he jumped, and soaring through the air struck the slope again a good thirty feet beyond.

He tried to figure where he was coming out and what hindrances he might yet encounter, but the effort was useless. He knew that the highroad, bordered by another stone wall, ran along the foot of the hill, with the school grounds on the other side. But the lightning speed at which he was traveling made thought almost impossible. Again, with the same terrible swiftness the final barrier loomed ahead. He leaped, and, at the very take-off, a gasp of horror was jolted from his lips by the sight of a two-horse sledge moving along the road directly in his path!

It was all over in a flash. Helpless to avoid the collision, Paul nevertheless twisted his body toward the left. The next instant he landed badly, his feet shot out from under him, and he fell backward with a stunning crash.

His first knowledge was of two strange faces bending over him and of hands lifting him from where he lay half buried in the snow. For a moment he was too dazed to speak or even to remember. Then, with a rush of immense relief, he realized what had happened, and gaining speech, he blurted out the story of Bill Hedges' injury and the need for help.

His rescuers were woodsmen, perfectly familiar with the Hogan Hill trail and the old log cabin. Paul's skis were taken off, and he was helped into the sledge and driven to the near-by school. Stiff and sore, but otherwise unhurt, he wanted to go with them, but his request was firmly refused; and pausing only long enough to get some rugs and a heavy coat, the party set off. Little more than two hours later they returned with the injured Bill, who was carried at once to the infirmary to be treated for a severe cold and a badly sprained ankle.

## TRUE FRIENDS AT LAST

Bill's strong body and good health soon conquered the cold, but the ankle proved more stubborn; so Christmas dinner had to be eaten in bed. But somehow Bill did not mind that very much, for Paul Seabury shared it, sitting on the other side of a folding table drawn up beside the couch. When they had eaten everything in sight and reached that state of fullness without which no Christmas dinner is really perfect, the two boys relapsed for a space into a friendly sort of silence.

"Not *much* on skis, are you?" Bill commented, presently, glancing teasingly at his companion.

Paul flushed a little. "I wish you wouldn't," he protested. "If you had any idea how scared I was, and—and—why, the whole thing was just pure luck."

Bill snorted. "Luck! You will never make me believe that. Now, as soon as I'm around again," he added, "you must come out and give me some points. I thought I was fairly decent on skis, but I guess after all I am not so good."

"I'll show you anything I can, of course," agreed Paul, readily. He paused an instant and then went on hesitatingly: "I—I am going to do a lot more of that sort of thing from now on. It was simply disgusting the way I got winded so soon and all tired out."

"That's the way to talk," nodded Hedges, promptly. "You need to take more exercise and stop moping around by yourself so much. But we will fix that up all right from now on." He paused. "Aren't you going to read some more in *Robinson Crusoe?*" he asked expectantly. "That's a good book, believe me! What with you and that and everything, I'm not going to mind being laid up at all."

NOTES AND QUESTIONS

1. Of what was Paul most afraid?
   (*a*) Getting lost in a storm.
   (*b*) Hurting himself.
   (*c*) Being a quitter and a coward.
2. What three things made Bill respect and admire Paul?
3. Some of the words below describe Paul, and some describe Bill. Write the names "Paul" and "Bill." Under each name write the words that you think belong there. Perhaps some of the words belong under both names.

| | | |
|---|---|---|
| strong | nervous | cool-headed |
| liked to read | shy | liked to be with people |
| slender | jolly | a good leader |
| liked outdoor games | brave | a good friend |

4. What valuable lesson did Paul learn from this ski trip?
5. In what did Bill become interested because of Paul?
6. What was the most exciting moment in the story?
7. Write titles for the three pictures.
8. Make a list of seven words or groups of words that the author used to help you see and feel and hear the things in this story—words like *scurried, curious wailing,* and *grunted.*

Some other stories about young American citizens are: "The Boy Who Saved the Settlement," Trowbridge, and "The Oyster Farmer and the Pirates," Robins (in *Child-Library Readers, Book Five*).

# BETSY FINDS A WAY

DOROTHY CANFIELD FISHER

Mrs. Fisher is one of our best story-tellers today. She writes stories for grown-up people and for boys and girls, too. Here is one of her stories. It is about a little girl who, like Paul Seabury, just had to find a way to do something.

## BETSY'S BIRTHDAY

Betsy was to celebrate her tenth birthday by going to Woodford to the County Fair. Aunt and Uncle Putney, with whom she lived, weren't going to the Fair that year. But the Wendells, on the next farm, said they could make room for the two little girls; for of course Betsy's little friend, Molly, was going along.

When they arrived at the Fair, the two little girls were allowed to wander about as they pleased until noon, and they thoroughly enjoyed the many sights and sounds and smells of their first County Fair. At noon they met the Wendells in front of Industrial Hall for a picnic lunch. As they ate, the children talked happily of the merry-go-round, the balloon-seller, and the popcorn stands. The Wendells had met some cousins who wished to ride home with them.

"Betsy, could you and Molly go home with the Vaughans?" Mrs. Wendell asked. "They're here in their big wagon. You could sit on the floor with the Vaughan children."

Betsy and Molly thought this would be great fun.

"All right, then," said Mrs. Wendell. She called to a young man who stood inside the building, near an open window: "Oh, Frank, Will Vaughan is going to be in your booth this afternoon, isn't he?"

"Yes, ma'am," said the young man. "His turn is from two to four."

"Now, Betsy," said Mrs. Wendell, "you go to Frank's booth at two o'clock and ask Will Vaughan what time they're going to start home. Be sure not to keep them waiting a minute."

"I'll be sure to be there on time," said Betsy.

She and Molly still had twenty cents to spend out of the forty they had brought with them, twenty-five earned by berry-picking and fifteen a present from Uncle Henry Putney. They now put their heads together to see how they could spend their four nickels. Molly wanted a big red balloon. While they were buying that, a man came along selling toy dogs with curled-wire tails. Betsy bought one done up neatly in a box.

### BETSY AND MOLLY LEFT ALONE

Now they had ten cents left, and they each decided to have a ride on the merry-go-round. But, glancing up at the clock-face in the tower, Betsy noticed that it was already half-past two; so she decided to go first and find out just what time the Vaughans would start for home. She found the booth, but William Vaughan was not in

it, nor was Frank. There was instead another young man, who said carelessly, in answer to Betsy's question: "Vaughan? Never heard the name." An older man leaned over from the next booth and said: "I heard somebody say the Vaughans had news that one of their cows was very sick, and they had to start home at once."

Betsy snatched Molly's hand. "Hurry! Quick! We must find the Wendells before they get away!"

In her fear she forgot how easily frightened little Molly was. "Oh, Betsy! Betsy! What will we do?" Molly gasped, as Betsy pulled her rapidly along.

"Oh, the Wendells can't be gone yet," said Betsy. To the horse-shed where Mr. Wendell had tied his horses she ran as fast as she could drag Molly's fat little legs. The horse-shed was empty!

Betsy stopped short; her heart seemed to be up in her throat so that she could hardly breathe. They were eight miles from home, much too far for Molly to walk, and neither of them knew the way. They had only ten cents left, and nothing to eat. The only people they knew in all that crowd of strangers had gone.

"What *will* we do, Betsy?" Molly wailed.

Betsy's head swam. "What would Aunt Abigail do if she were here?" she asked herself. One thing her aunt would be sure to do, of course; she would quiet Molly first of all.

At this thought Betsy sat down on the ground and took the frightened little girl in her lap. She wiped away the tears and said, "Now, Molly, stop crying this minute. I'll get you home all right."

"How will you ever do it?" sobbed Molly. "Everybody's gone and left us. We can't walk!"

"Never you mind how," said Betsy, though her under lip was quivering a little. "Come on back to the booth. Maybe Will Vaughan didn't go home with his folks after all."

When they found him again, the careless young man stopped his whistling only long enough to say, "No, Will Vaughan isn't anywhere around here."

"We were going home with the Vaughans," murmured Betsy in a low tone.

"Looks as though you'd better go home on the cars," advised the young man.

"How much does it cost to go to Hillsboro on the cars?" asked Betsy with a sinking heart.

"You'll have to ask somebody else about that," said the young man.

Betsy turned and went over to the man who had told her about the Vaughan's sick cow. Quite comforted, now that Betsy was talking to grown-ups, Molly trotted at her heels. Betsy would manage somehow. Then Betsy led Molly outdoors, where everybody was blowing on horns, waving plumes of colored tissue-paper, and eating popcorn and candy out of paper bags.

The popcorn reminded Molly that they had ten cents yet. "Oh, Betsy," she said, "let's buy some popcorn."

Betsy clutched at their little purse. "No, no, Molly. We must save every cent. I've found out that it costs thirty cents for us to go home on the cars. The last train goes at six o'clock."

"We have only ten cents," said Molly.

Betsy looked at her silently for a moment and then burst out, "I'll earn the rest! I'll earn it somehow! I'll have to! There isn't any other way!"

### BETSY EARNS MONEY FOR THE TICKETS

How *could* a little girl earn money at a country fair?

"Here, Molly, you wait here," Betsy said. "Don't you budge till I come back."

But Molly had only a moment to wait, for the man who was selling lemonade answered Betsy's shy question with a sharp "No! What could a child like you do!"

The little girls wandered on, Molly calm, trusting in Betsy; Betsy with a very anxious feeling. It was four o'clock. The last train for Hillsboro left in two hours, and she had not yet earned the price of the tickets. Although they were walking slowly, she kept feeling breathless and choked. Hearing something from one of the booths, she turned quickly.

"Oh, if I could only rest for an hour, I should feel much better."

The words, spoken to someone in a neighboring booth, came from a tired-looking woman who had home-made doughnuts, ginger ale, and lemonade for sale.

The weary voice went on: "I think I could keep on if I had only the selling to do, but there is a great pile of dishes that must be washed."

"Oh, please!" said a small voice. "I'll do it for twenty cents."

Betsy stood by the woman's elbow.

"Do what, child?" asked the tired woman in great surprise.

"Everything!" said Betsy. "Wash the dishes and tend the booth. You can go and rest. I'll do it for twenty cents."

The woman looked at the small, eager girl in surprise.

"I can wash dishes as well as anybody," said Betsy.

"Yes, I think she can," said the friend in the other booth. "And I am sure she can do the selling, too."

The tired woman waited no longer, but tied a long apron around Betsy's neck, gave her a few instructions, and left, saying she would be back shortly after five o'clock. So Betsy mounted a soap box and began joyfully to wash the dishes. She had never thought that she would ever in her life simply *love* to wash dishes.

"It's all right, Molly; it's all right!" she said. But Molly only nodded and asked if she might sit upon a barrel where she could watch the crowd go by.

"Two doughnuts, please," said a man's voice.

Somebody had come to buy! Whatever should she do! She came forward slowly. But the man laid down a nickel, took two doughnuts, and turned away. Sure enough, the sign read "2 for 5." She put the nickel up on the shelf and went back to her dishwashing.

Soon she began to find some fun in her new work, and when a woman with two little boys came up, she stepped forward to wait on her, feeling very important. "Two for five," she said in a business-like tone. The woman put down a dime, took up four doughnuts, and left.

"Oh, Betsy, see! The pig! The big ox!" cried Molly now, looking down the wide lane between the booths. Betsy turned her head to look over her shoulder, continuing to wash and wipe the dishes. The prize stock was being paraded around the Fair: the great prize ox, his shining horns tipped with blue rosettes; the prize

horses, four or five of them as glossy as satin, their
manes and tails braided with bright ribbon; the smaller
animals, the sheep, the calves, the colts, and the prize
pig waddling slowly along.

Betsy looked anxiously at the clock. It was nearing
five. Oh, what if the tired woman overslept! But in
a minute there she came, walking fast and looking
greatly rested.

"Have some doughnuts. Hold out your hands, both
of you," said the grateful woman as Betsy and Molly
prepared to leave.

"Oh, thank you so much," said Betsy. "We can eat
the doughnuts on the train." When the little girls had

left the booth, Betsy rushed back to say, "Some people came and bought things. The money is on the shelf."

The woman thanked her and said, "I wish I had a little girl just like you!"

## THE HOMEWARD JOURNEY

Molly and Betsy hurried out of the gate into the main street of the town and down to the station. Molly was eating doughnuts as she went. They were both quite hungry by this time, but Betsy could not think of eating till she had the railroad tickets in her hand.

She pushed her coins into the ticket-seller's window and said "Hillsboro." When she actually held the precious bits of paper in her hand, her knees shook so under her that she had to go and sit down on the bench. She drew a long breath and began rather slowly to eat a doughnut; she felt all of a sudden very, very tired.

She was tired still when they got out of the train at Hillsboro and started wearily up the road toward Putney Farm. Two miles lay ahead of them, miles which they had often walked before, but never after such a day of work as this. Molly dragged her feet as she walked and hung heavily on Betsy's hand. Betsy plodded along, her head hanging, her eyes all gritty with fatigue and sleepiness. A light buggy spun round the turn of the road behind them, the wheels rattling smartly. The little girls drew out to one side and stood waiting till the road should be clear again. When the driver saw them, he pulled the horse back so quickly that it stood almost straight up.  He looked at them through the twilight, and then with a loud shout sprang out of the buggy.

It was Uncle Henry Putney!  They wouldn't have to walk any farther!

He ran up to them, exclaiming, "Are you all right?"  He stooped and felt them over anxiously as though he expected them to be broken somewhere.  Then Betsy said, "Why, yes, Uncle Henry, we're all right.  We came home on the cars."  He took off his hat, wiped his forehead, and said, "Well, well, well!  And so here you are!  And you're all right!  A plucky little girl you are."

*—Adapted*

## NOTES AND QUESTIONS

1.  Why did Betsy feel especially that she had to be brave?
2.  Which do you think is the best way to quiet another person's fear?

(*a*)  To make fun of the other person's fear.
(*b*)  To act brave and quiet yourself.
(*c*)  To scold the person.

3.  Which of these things show that Betsy was a girl who planned things carefully?

(*a*)  She comforted Molly.
(*b*)  She found how much the tickets cost.
(*c*)  She asked for a job.
(*d*)  She worked hard washing dishes.
(*e*)  She found when the train left.

If you liked this story, you will want to read Mrs. Fisher's book *Understood Betsy,* from which this story was taken.

# GEORGE WASHINGTON

### NANCY BYRD TURNER

He played by the river when he was young,
He raced with rabbits along the hills,
He fished for minnows, and climbed and swung,
And hooted back at the whippoorwills.
Strong and slender and tall he grew—
And then, one morning, the bugles blew.

Over the hills the summons came,
Over the river's shining rim.
He said that the bugles called his name,
He knew that his country needed him,
And he answered, "Coming!" and marched away
For many a night and many a day.

Perhaps when the marches were hot and long
He'd think of the river flowing by,
Or, camping under the winter sky,
Would hear the whippoorwill's far-off song.
Boy and soldier, in peace or strife,
He loved America all his life!

# ROBERT E. LEE: FROM MANLINESS TO MANHOOD

Edith A. Heal

When Robert E. Lee had grown to manhood, he once wrote to his son that "duty" was the finest word in our language. Perhaps as you read this story, you will be able to tell whether, as a boy, he was faithful in doing the things that were his to do.

Robert E. Lee was born into an old Virginia family. The gentlemen of Virginia were proud of their homes, their horses, and their beautiful estates. They built their houses sturdily, so that many years later their sons and grandsons could still live in them.

It was in one of these famous old Virginia mansions that Robert E. Lee was born on January 19, 1807. Stratford House, the home of the Lees, stood high on a wooded hill overlooking the Potomac River in the county of Westmoreland. It was a grand old house. There were long halls with fine wainscoting and moldings brought over from England, beautifully furnished rooms, and broad stairways. Portraits of gallant soldiers recalled days that were gone, and it must have been easy for young Robert to imagine the time when gentlemen in white wigs and velvet breeches walked through the wide hallways. Wherever the boy looked, he was sure to see pictures and records of the deeds of the famous

Lee family.  He could not forget that he was one of a long line of brave Americans.

So young Robert Lee lived among inspiring surroundings.  Stratford House had done much to keep alive the glory of the Lee family.  Important men had lived beneath its roof.  There were Robert's cousins, the two brothers, Francis Lightfoot Lee and Richard Henry Lee, who had signed the Declaration of Independence.  And there was Robert's own father, General Henry Lee, the famous Light Horse Harry, as he was called, who had fought in the Revolutionary War by the side of General Washington when we won our freedom from England.

The boy was told that three generations of Lees had

lived at Stratford, and that the gates had always been open wide to their friends. Everyone was always welcome at Stratford, and the finest people of the land were proud to visit the distinguished family who lived there. The house stood for the best in all things. Its library was filled with fine books. Robert's father was a scholar as well as a soldier, and the boy always remembered him sitting in a big chair or at his desk writing an account of the battles he had fought with his beloved George Washington. The boy saw the brave spirit of the Lees still alive in his father, who was fighting constantly against ill-health. Robert himself had that same brave spirit, and he was to do even greater things than the others of his family had done.

Just as Robert loved the fine old rooms at Stratford House, rich in history, so he loved the fields and forests of the vast estate surrounding the house. He enjoyed roaming through the countryside and the cool woods. He was completely happy when he lay on the fragrant grass beneath the tall oaks and maples or raced along the river, where the rustling poplars grew. He learned early in his life to love the beauty and freshness of the out-of-doors, and this love stayed with him ever afterwards. He knew every inch of the grounds of Stratford, and years later when his own daughter wrote him of a visit to the old house, he answered her by saying:  "I am much pleased at your description of Stratford and your visit...... The horse-chestnut you mention in the garden was planted by my mother....... You did not mention the spring, one of the objects of my earliest recollections."

When Robert was still a young boy, the family moved to Alexandria, so that the children could go to school, but they still spent part of the time at Stratford. The Lees' first house in Alexandria was on Cameron Street near the old Christ Church, where George Washington himself had worshiped. Undoubtedly Robert's father told his son many stories of the great general, for in the days of the Revolution Mr. Lee had been a great favorite of Washington.

Life at Alexandria began very much like that at Stratford. Robert continued to love the out-of-doors, and his new surroundings were as beautiful as the old homestead they had left. When he was a grown man, Lee returned to Alexandria for a visit. He was found gazing over the fence at the garden in which he used to play. "I am looking," he said, "to see if the old snow-ball trees are still here. I should have been sorry to miss them."

But suddenly the carefree days ended. Robert's father was forced to leave his family and go to the West Indies for his health. The brave mother stayed at home to watch over her children, although she was an invalid much of the time herself. More and more Mrs. Lee turned to her small son. And when the boy's father died, she was able to depend entirely upon young Robert, although he was only eleven years old. His older brothers were away at school, and his sister was too small to be of any help.

The boy grew up almost over night. He became the young master of the house, carrying the keys, attending to the marketing, managing the outdoor tasks, and taking care of his mother's horses. The strong sense of duty that grew up in him at this time stayed with him all his life. Just as he stepped into his father's place and took charge of the household for his mother during his boyhood, so later in his life he became a great general.

The tasks that the boy undertook in his mother's household would have been hard work for a grown man. But his outdoor life had made him strong. His splendid health helped him to succeed. This same strength gave him an advantage over other men throughout his life. He was like a sturdy tree that could grow with little to eat and drink and could stand the harshest weather without noticing it.

While he was helping his mother, Robert went to school as well. His first teacher was an Irish gentleman, a Mr. Leary, with whom young Robert continued his friendship for many years. Later he prepared for West Point Military Academy at the school of Mr. Benjamin Hallowell, where he made a special study of mathematics. The famous teacher always spoke of him as a splendid student.

After school hours when other children played, Robert hurried home to take his mother driving. And now he had to pretend he was really grown-up to amuse the invalid. He told her that her ride would not make her better if she were not cheerful. When she shivered with the cold, he called to Nat, the coachman, to halt. Then he pulled out his big jackknife and some newspapers and made curtains to keep out the wind that whistled through the openings of the old family coach. His gay and happy efforts would soon cheer her.

Perhaps the happiest part of his early days at Alexandria was the time he spent in taking care of the horses. He learned to ride very well and followed the hunt for hours over the hills and valleys. So he came to love horses and to admire good riders. Long afterwards, when he had become a famous general, his love for his horse Traveller was known among all the soldiers. The horse—a handsome iron-gray, with black points and dark mane and tail—was as easily recognized as his master. In a letter to his daughter Agnes, General Lee once described this horse:

"If I were an artist like you, I would draw a true picture of Traveller—representing his fine proportions, muscular figure, deep chest and short back, strong haunches, flat legs, small head, broad forehead, delicate ears, quick eye, small feet, and black mane and tail."

Traveller was the great general's "patient follower" through the war, and in the end the gallant horse outlived his master. When Lee was in his last illness, the doctor tried to cheer him by saying, "You must make

haste and get well; Traveller has been standing so long in the stable that he needs exercise."

General Lee was both soldier and country gentleman. He had all the qualities of good leadership—devotion to duty, constant truthfulness, and a generous way of looking at every side of a question. He was the exact opposite of the city-bred boy who grows up to feel at home in crowds and lonely in the quiet country-side. Lee had learned at Stratford House that in the woods and the fields one can never be lonely. His own words, when he was a grown man, tell us this: "To be alone in a crowd is very solitary. In the woods I feel sympathy with the trees and birds, in whose company I take delight."

## Notes and Questions

1. In what state was Robert E. Lee born?
2. On what river was the Lee plantation?
3. About how long ago was Lee born—75 years, 125 years, or 200 years?
4. While he was a boy, what did he learn to love?
5. What outdoor sport did he like best?
6. What study did he like best in school?
7. Give two reasons why he had to take charge of the home in Alexandria.
8. Which three of these facts show that Lee could be a great and loved leader of men?

   (*a*) He loved horses.

   (*b*) He was faithful to his duty.

   (*c*) He knew that many of his family had been great men.

   (*d*) He loved the out-of-doors.

   (*e*) He was kind and thoughtful.

   (*f*) He was fair-minded and generous.
9. Find and be ready to read lines that show that Lee

   (*a*) was kind and thoughtful.

   (*b*) could be depended upon to do his duty.

   (*c*) could stand hard work.

Did you find some hard words in this story? Do you know the meaning of *wainscoting, inspiring, generations, distinguished, recollections?* Don't forget to use your Glossary.

Other good stories about Robert E. Lee are "Boyhood," Hamilton (in *The Life of Robert E. Lee for Boys and Girls*); "Father and Sons," Barnes (in *The Son of Light Horse Harry*); "Robert E. Lee," Evans (in *America First*).

# JOSIE'S HOME RUN

### Ruth Gipson Plowhead

It was lucky for Josie and the team that she was a twin,
and it was lucky that she needed a haircut just when she did.
But luck would not have been enough. What Josie did took
pluck as well as luck.

## I

Josie and Joe Dawn were twins—as like as two peas in
a pod, from their sturdy little bodies, up to their broad
smiling red mouths, freckled noses, and wavy red hair.

Josie had one deep trouble—she was not a boy. "Why,
oh, why, Mother, couldn't I have been a boy like Joe?"
she would question. "I can climb higher and run faster
than he, and I know I'd be a better ball player if I had a
chance." She was never so happy as when tagging after
Joe, dressed as nearly like him as possible in overalls,
sports blouse, and skull cap. Often she came home almost
in tears.

"Mother, Joe won't let me play with the ball team when
they are practicing. Why can't I, Mother?"

"Aw, Mother," Joe, who was very fond of his sister,
would reply, "I like to play with Josie, and the kids like
her. But you know, Mother, when there's a whole field
of boys and not another girl, it makes a fellow feel funny
if the girl's his sister. Sometimes the fellows say things."

"I think Joe is right, Josie, and you must come home if

the whole ball team is playing. When there are only two
or three of Joe's friends, you may play with them if they
want you."

Josie's face grew very red, and her curls seemed to
bristle like an angry pup's fur.

"I will make a ball team of my own," she said. But,
alas, for Josie! So many little girls preferred hopscotch
and jacks, paper dolls and tag, that she could not form a
team. Nevertheless, she managed to find a great many
chances to play ball. She found several girls who would
play at times, if she bribed them with "suckers" and pea-
nuts. She persuaded Father and Mother to pitch for her,
and many an evening she and Joe's friends spent playing
in the vacant lot across the street. She became a fair
pitcher, and she was surely a strong batter.

"Watch out for Josie when she bats," the boys would
laugh. "You may have to run all the way to China to
find the ball."

## II

The spring the twins were ten years old was an exciting
time in the Lowell school, which they attended. It seemed
as if all the boys in the town had gone ball mad, and each
room in each school had its own team. The different schools
had played each other, and the Lowell fifth-grade team,
of which Joe was a member, had only to beat the Whittier
school fifth-graders to become town champions. Better
still, the winning team was to go to Meridian, six miles
away, and play a match game there. An uncle and aunt of

the twins, who lived in Meridian, had been visiting in their home, and heard all about the excitement.

"If your team wins, Joe, and comes to Meridian, Aunt Emma and I will invite you all to a chicken dinner. And mind you, even if you don't let Josie play ball, she shall come and sit at the head of the table. Eh, Josie?"

Again and again Josie clenched her stout little hands over the thought that she could not play on the team. No one wanted to so much as she. How she would work! How she would run! How she would bat that ball so that it would fly even *beyond* China, if necessary! Every evening she worked with Joe, and sometimes he grew very cross when she insisted that he practice.

"You might let me alone a minute, Josie Dawn," he growled one night. "A fellow's got to do something in this world except play ball every minute."

"I won't let you alone until the game is over. If I can't play, my brother has to play well enough to make up for it."

### III

It was now Friday evening. The game was set for nine-thirty the following morning. The team had their last practice after school, and Joe did not come in until dinner time. Then he refused to eat, and sat hunched up in a shivering heap before the fireplace.

"I don't want any dinner," he said, when his mother called him to the table. "I'm not hungry."

"Why, what's the matter?" asked Josie in great alarm.

"Nothing. I'm just cold and tired. Can't a fellow rest a minute without everyone thinking something's the matter?" replied Joe crossly.

Nevertheless, although Joe insisted he was all right, Mother noticed that he shivered all evening, and went to bed very early. When she went for a last good-night look, he was tossing and mumbling in his sleep. By morning even Joe himself admitted that he could not get out of bed.

"Oh, Mother," he cried, the tears running down his cheeks, "the team needs me. What shall I do?"

Josie was crying, too. "Oh, brother, I am so sorry. What can I do for you? Shall I go and watch the game, or shall I stay with you?"

"You must go, Josie, and cheer for the boys just as loud as you can. They sometimes say your cheering helps as much as my playing. And take a pencil and paper and write down all the plays so that you can remember and tell me about each one. Just my luck!"

"Yes, you had better go," agreed Mother, "but you must hurry to the barber's before the game. Remember, I said you cannot go to Ernestine's party this afternoon unless you have your hair trimmed. Mike knows the way I like it cut."

"Perhaps if I have to wait at the shop I will go straight to the game from there. Esther and Eleanor are going with me. Oh, I wish you could go, brother. I will remember and tell you all about it."

"All right. Go by and tell the fellows, will you?"

## IV

A block from the house Josie met Jim Bane.

"Say, Josie," he roared, "did you hear of our tough luck? Bill hurt his ankle last night. He and Joe are our stars, and we need them both to win. Good thing we still have Joe, but even then we may not win."

Josie opened her mouth to tell about Joe. Then suddenly something stopped her. An idea was whirling in her brain; if she told the boys, they would probably spoil her plan.

"You needn't go by for Joe. He can't come now. I'll be there and yell for you at nine-thirty sharp." Josie ran like the wind, fearing she would be questioned by Jim. All the way to the barber shop she argued the problem in her mind. Should she do it? Should she not do it? Once in the chair, her mind was made up.

"Mike," she said, "cut my hair like Joe's. I'm going to have it cut the way I like it this time."

"I like it very short and shingled myself, Miss Josie, but your mother always seems to want your curls to show," said Mike doubtfully. He had in mind several very heated arguments upon this question which had proceeded from this very chair.

"Mother will like it this way, I am sure," said Josie. And she meant it. Mother was true blue. She had never failed them when it came to the question of helping one another, and, oh, what were curls compared to winning the game?

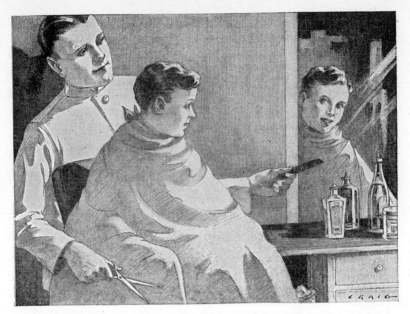

"If Mother knows I am doing this for Joe and the school, she will not care," argued Josie to herself. The shorn head felt delightful. She looked at herself with great satisfaction in the glass. "Oh, I look more than ever like Joe. I look so like him no one would know," she whispered to herself. She sped home like a scared little kitten, stopping only to stick her head into Esther's door and call, "Don't you and Eleanor wait for me."

It was easy to creep unseen into the little play-shed where all the twins' toys, bicycles, balls, bats, and outing garments were kept; it was also easy to slip into her little tweed knickers, so like Joe's, into her brother's red sweater, red stockings, and small, scuffed ball shoes.

With the red cap and visor pulled over her eyes, no one would have dreamed that it was not Joe who stepped jauntily into the ball park just before the game was called. Least of all did the team suspect. They had a yell for each of their players. When they saw Josie, they stamped their feet and chanted:

"Here's Joe—Joe—Joe!
Now the game will go—go—go!"

Thrills ran up and down Josie's back. She had never dreamed of anything so delightful. "I've got to make it go. I have to," she resolved. "If I play poorly, and the boys find out, they will tease me forever and ever."

### V

Now the game had started. Poor little Josie was so excited over it all that when her turn came to bat, she quickly fanned out.

"What's got into you, Joe? Forgotten that chicken dinner?" The boys guyed her well. After that she rallied and played a fair game, but it was not until the end of the last inning that her chance came. The game had been evenly balanced—the score went up and down like a seesaw. First the Lowells were ahead and then the Whittiers, next the Lowells and then the Whittiers—on through the whole game.

The score was now 15 to 14 in favor of Whittier; it was the last inning, two of the Lowell batters were out, there were three men on bases, and *Josie was at the bat*. Her heart thumped so that she feared everyone on the field must hear it. Her hands shook as she picked up the bat; never before in her short life had she so felt the need to do and win. Not for her own sake, but for the honor of the team, and for Joe.

"They think he has not played his best, and I mustn't go back on Joe. I must not lose this game." She dared not even think what would happen. Each little freckle stood out bravely on her face, like crowded blossoms on a pansy bed. She gripped the bat—the ball was coming.

Josie swung furiously and missed. "Strike one," called the umpire. Again the ball came, and again and again. "Ball one. Ball two. Strike two. Ball three." Only one more chance! Josie's courage came at last; she refused to be afraid. She swung the bat. There was a loud crack, and away the ball soared, high-higher-highest. As the ball flew, so flew Josie. Like frightened little rabbits were her feet, barely touching the ground. You would never dream that fat little legs could cover so much ground in so short a time.

First base! From the corner of her eye Josie saw Sam run in home. The score was even, 15 to 15. On she sped; the ball had landed in a patch of weeds, and the Whittier fielders were frantically hunting it. Second base, and Willie had gone home—now the game was won. On she went to third base, reaching there just as Jack touched the home plate. Josie, on third, saw the fielder pick up the ball. Could she make a home run? Wouldn't that be something to tell Joe? Breathless, panting, she ran on. The

fielder threw the ball. "Go it, Joe!" cried the spectators. "Beat the ball!  Good boy!  Run!"

Josie flew—the ball flew too, straight into the hands of the Whittier catcher. He fumbled, and down it rolled. Josie rolled also, just as she had seen the boys do many times. She reached forth her hands and touched the base, and lay there panting, almost sobbing for joy, too breathless to move. The score stood 18 to 15 in favor of Lowell.

## VI

"Hurrah for Joe!  Hurrah for Joe!  He made things go!" yelled the boys in a frenzy of joy. A tall man, passing, paused to see what was causing all the tumult. He was greeted by eager voices.

"Oh, Mr. Dawn," said the excited captain, "you ought to have seen Joe! He won the game for us. Just made the dandiest home run!"

"Joe made a home run? What do you mean? Joe is home in bed." He pushed his way through the crowd. His eye lighted on his red-faced, panting little daughter, still lying where she had fallen. He could always tell her from Joe by her sheepish little grin, and the funny dimple which appeared in one cheek when she was bothered.

"Josie," he gasped, "what does this mean? Get up out of the dust!"

Josie was still too exhausted to rise, but she had recovered enough breath to speak, and she panted, "I wanted the team to win. I can play as well as Joe, and he is one of the very best players. When he couldn't come, I thought I would take his place and not let anyone know. I was going to tell Joe, of course."

"Oh, Josie, Josie, what will you do next? Do you think your brother would be willing to take credit for what you did?"

Nevertheless, he laughed and laughed, for Josie looked so guilty and ashamed. The team yelled and cheered. Even the Whittier boys joined in the chorus.

"Don't scold her, Mr. Dawn. She won the game. Josie! Josie! Ring around a rosy!"

Well, this was the way the Lowell fifth-graders became champions. Perhaps I need not tell you that Josie was an honored guest at the Meridian game. Indeed, she yelled and cheered so loudly for Joe and his friends that I am sure she helped win the Lowell victory. She sat at the table when the chicken dinner was served, and if any member of the team ate more chicken and ice cream than Josie, I should like to know his name. For Josie liked to eat as well as she liked to play baseball.

## Notes and Questions

1. Give three reasons why Josie was so anxious to play well in the championship game.

2. Tell two ways in which she showed she was unselfish.

3. In what two ways did she show that she was loyal to the team?

4. Tell two ways in which she showed she was loyal to Joe.

5. The parts of this story are numbered but not named. Write the numbers I to VI on your paper, and make up a title for each part. Your first might be: *1. Josie's Love of Baseball.*

6. Which sentence best tells what this story is about?

(*a*) This is a story about a girl who loved to play base-ball and won a game by a home run.

(*b*) This story is about a twin sister who took her sick brother's place on a ball team and won the game by a home run.

(*c*) This is the story of a girl who had her hair cut short so that she could pretend she was a boy and play on a ball team.

You will like also to read "Grace Darling," Carey, and "Betty's Ride: A Tale of the Revolution," Canby (in *Child-Library Readers, Book Five*).

# HOW A BOY SCOUT BUILDS A CAMPFIRE

## E. V. Jotter

Boy Scouts have often been called upon to help in times of great danger from forest fires. But here is a story of a Boy Scout who did better than that: He told a man how to build a campfire so that there would be no danger of a forest fire. Perhaps this story will tell you some worth-while things, too.

> For want of a forest the stream went dry,
> For want of a stream the fish all die,
> For want of the fish the fishermen sigh—
> All caused by a fire when the brush was dry.
> —*John E. Gribble*

The Grayson family were taking their summer vacation. The new plan of traveling by automobile and camping out nights along the way they found most enjoyable. During the late afternoon of their third day's journey they came upon a National Forest. No one in their party had ever visited such a forest before, and the Graysons quickly decided to join the other families of tourists whose campfires here and there were already sending up curls of smoke into the evening air. Mr. Grayson had just started getting ready to build his own campfire when a Boy Scout, who had been watching him for several minutes, suddenly spoke up.

"Are you going to build your fire there, sir?"

"Why, yes," Mr. Grayson replied, "I guess it'll burn here."

"That's the trouble," the Scout came back with a quick flash; "it will burn too well. Where you have it in those pine needles, it's going to set fire to them and maybe to your camp. Of course, I wouldn't like that, but worse for us around here, it will set fire to the big forest. You see, I live just outside of the forest, and—"

"Has anything like that ever happened in this forest?" Mr. Grayson broke in.

"Yes, sir. Just last summer we had an awful fire that started from a campfire. A man built a big fire, the wind came up, and before the man and his wife could put it out, it had burned their tent and all their camp outfit.

"Another fire that a camper left burned into the forest and grew to be so big that it burned several ranch houses, and the people just got away in time. Another time—"

Impressed by the boy's earnestness, Mr. Grayson interrupted him.

"I'm new at this camping game, sonny, and I certainly do not want my fire to harm this wonderful forest. Will you tell me just how I can make a *safe* fire?"

It was a moment before the boy replied. Could the camper be making fun of him? Then, looking Mr. Grayson squarely in the face, he answered:

"Well, if you really want to know, sir, it's like this:

"First find a place away from a tree, a stump, or a log, and not near any underbrush or young trees.

"Then scrape away all the pine needles, the leaves, the grass, sticks—everything that will burn—even the partly rotted stuff—until you get down to the dirt where it will not burn at all.

"Make a cleared space about five or six feet across; then build a small fire, just big enough for cooking.

"When you leave the fire, put it out with water, sand, or dirt.

"Be sure to cover the fire with enough sand or dirt free from sticks or leaves, so that it will not get air enough to burn.

"Play safe by taking one last look at your fire to see that it is completely smothered. Otherwise it will just hold over, and maybe a little later the wind will blow some of the dirt away from it. The burning coals may burst into flame and set fire to the leaves and pine needles that might be blown across the fire by the wind."

When the Scout finished what he had to say about campfires, Mr. Grayson thanked him and then started off to find a safer place for his campfire.

### Notes and Questions

1. What four things should a person do in order to have a safe fire in the forest?

2. Give four losses that come from forest fires.

3. What is a National Forest?

4. Read the first line of the poem. Why will streams go dry if the forests are burned down?

5. Which one of these reasons best tells why Mr. Jotter wrote this story?

(a) To show us the dangers of forest fires.

(b) To let us know how valuable our forests are.

(c) To teach us how to build a safe campfire.

6. Why was this boy a good citizen?

A good story about Boy Scouts and a fire is "Chums," by Ames (in *Child-Library Readers, Book Four*).

# LET THE FLAG WAVE

CLINTON SCOLLARD

Let the flag wave!   Aye, let it wave on high,
Its red and white and blue against the sky!
From crest and casement, broad and bright and brave,
            Let the flag wave!

Let the flag wave!   Aye, let it wave above
The hills and valleys of the land we love,
And o'er the sea, to no mad tyrant slave,
            Let the flag wave!

Let the flag wave!   Aye, let its glory shine!
Let the flag wave, a symbol and a sign!
To guard our honor and to shield and save,
            Let the flag wave!

Let the flag wave!  Aye, wave in all men's sight,
Its stars unsullied as the stars of night;
Its stripes unblemished; only this we crave—
            Let the flag wave!

# A BACKWARD LOOK

Now read again the pledge of the Athenian boys. In what ways did the boys and girls in these stories live up to that pledge? Who would not desert his comrade? Who was loyal and true? Who was faithful to his duty? Who taught someone else to be careful?

You have probably been told many times that you should be loyal and brave, but have you ever stopped to think what loyalty and bravery are? Does loyalty mean unselfishness, too? Try to think of a way in which a person would have to be unselfish in order to be loyal. Does bravery mean not being afraid, or does it mean something more than that? Are there other kinds of bravery than daring to do something that may injure or kill you? Perhaps you can answer this by telling how Josie was brave.

It may be that you have never thought of yourself as a real citizen of the United States. You may have thought that you had to wait until you were grown up before you could be a citizen. But that is not true. You are a citizen just as much as your father and mother. Learning your lessons at school, playing games hard and fairly, doing the little jobs around the home faithfully and cheerfully, you are doing your part in making your home and your country a better and more beautiful place in which to live.

Did you read any of the stories that are named at the ends of the stories in this part? Did you find any names to add to your honor roll of Good Citizens? You may want to go on and read some more stories of boys and girls at work and at play. Your book list on page 433 will help you to find such stories.

# PART FIVE
## • BOYS AND GIRLS OF OTHER LANDS •

## TO EVERY CHILD OF EVERY LAND

### MADELINE BRANDEIS

To every child of every land,
    Little sister, little brother,
As in this book your lives unfold,
    May you learn to love each other.

# BOOKS CAN TAKE US TRAVELING

Books can take you traveling to lands far across the sea. In your own home, in a comfortable chair, you can explore places where very few men have ever been. You can live among people whose language you cannot speak, and who could not understand you if you talked to them. You can watch them work and play. You will be surprised at the strange things they do. Some of their ways of living will seem almost funny to you. Then, you will be just as surprised to learn that these people of far-away lands are in many ways like the people in our own land. The boys and girls have their lessons to learn; they have holidays to celebrate; they like to play and have good times.

Of course, it would be much more fun to travel and see these things ourselves. But not many of us can do so. Even in a lifetime we could not visit all the places and learn all the things that we find in travel books.

You have already been traveling in this book—with Admiral Byrd at the South Pole; on the snowy trail from Nenana to Nome; in Africa on a midnight lion hunt. Now you are going to read four more stories of other lands. Mrs. Crew will tell you of Mario, Fioretta, Annina, and Tino Bernado, whose land she has often visited; Caroline Mabry writes of Esteban and holiday celebrations in Porto Rico; Eunice Tietjens tells of Abdul Aziz, an Arab boy of North Africa; and Margaret Morley will take you high up in the Alps Mountains in Austria, and show you wood-carvers at work making toy horses, wagons, and dolls.

# GRANDMOTHER'S TRIP TO NAPLES

## Helen Coale Crew

Mrs. Crew, who wrote this story especially for this book, has many times traveled in countries across the sea, and she has always been interested in what the boys and girls of those lands do. She has written many stories about them.

Mrs. Crew is herself a grandmother; so she probably knows just how happy the grandmother in this story was over what the children did for her.

### I

Ugo and Margaretta Bernado had four children. There was Mario, the eldest, who was fifteen; grave Annina, who was thirteen; twelve-year-old Fioretta, gay and laughter-loving; and Tino, who was ten and full of mischief.

"Wife," said Ugo, seeing the four busy about their work and happy about their play, "I think we have wonderful children."

"Husband," said Margaretta, laughing, "did I not only yesterday hear you calling Tino a lazy little good-for-nothing? And last week did you not complain that Fioretta was always tearing her clothes?"

At this, Ugo began to talk about something else, and then went out to do some work upon the farm. It was a good farm, left to him by his grandfather, and not more than four miles from Florence, that lovely city of Italy

that is strung like a pearl upon the Arno River, and lies in a jewel-case of green hills whose lid is the sky.

Ugo was fortunate in owning his own farm, when so many of the farmers in Italy could only hire themselves out for farm work. A small stream ran through it; a little hill on which grew a few chestnut and mulberry trees rose up in one corner; and the earth gave good harvests of wheat and barley. The farmhouse was of stone, whitewashed over, and before it lay an old stone threshing-floor. The upper story held the big kitchen and two bedrooms, and below were the stables and barn.

Two creamy oxen with spreading horns stood in the

stalls; these oxen were the pride of Ugo's heart. With them he plowed his land, drew the wheat in his farm-cart from field to threshing-floor, and occasionally took the family to Florence. They always went, for example, to the Cathedral on Easter Day, each carrying a little pot of new-springing wheat, as a symbol of life in the springtime. Or they went at Christmas, to see the little wax image of the Christ Child in the manger and to sing carols, standing in the huge aisles.

Besides themselves and their children, there was Grandmother, old and bent, bright-eyed and busy, as she sat in her chair in the kitchen. There were six stools about the table, and one chair, an American rocking-chair sent over as a present to Grandmother by Uncle Matteo, who had gone to America to live. Anyone might sit on any of the six stools, but only Grandmother sat in the rocking-chair.

## II

There came an April when something seemed to be wrong with Grandmother. She still knitted stockings and mended garments, peeled potatoes for the stew and sliced apples for drying, but somehow she wasn't happy. For Grandmother to be unhappy was all wrong. It wouldn't do at all! Her eyes that had been so sharp and bright now quite frequently held tears, and there was a woebegone look on her deeply-wrinkled face.

It was one evening at the supper table that she asked, suddenly, "Ugo, do you think Naples is still there?"

"Still where, Grandmother?"

"By the sea."

"Yes, of course.  Why wouldn't it be?"

"I dream about the sea," said Grandmother.

It was at breakfast the next morning that she asked, "Margaretta, you don't think, do you, that Mount Vesuvius is gone?"

"Gone where, Grandmother?"

"Well," said Grandmother dreamily, "gone . . . . . away."

"Grandmother!" put in Mario, laughing.  "To be sure it is still there!  And the Bay of Naples is still there, and all of Italy, and Sicily, too!"

"I haven't seen the place where I was born for years and years," continued Grandmother wistfully.  Then they knew.  Grandmother was homesick.  And why should she not be, indeed?  It was sixty years since she had left Naples as a bride, and in all that time there was no money that could be spared to take her home for a visit.

"If I had not bought the oxen last spring—" began Ugo, but again Margaretta shook her head.  But if only they could send her, with one of the children to look after her, to spend a week or two with Uncle Tony and his family in Naples!  But where would the money come from?  It really couldn't be done.

Next morning, when the children went to the spring with buckets to fetch water, they talked it over.

## III

"Why," said Mario, "it is the simplest thing in the world.  Put the oxen to the cart and put Grandmother in the cart, and presto!  I'll drive her myself to Naples, just as *easy!*"

"Not at all," said Annina, who was practical.  "Where's the geography?"

Fioretta, the book-lover, ran back to the house on nimble feet and got the geography.  They gathered about the map of Italy eagerly.  Alas, Naples was nearly, or quite, or even more than, three hundred miles away, and the map between Florence and Naples was well-sprinkled with mountains and snaky black rivers.

Well, then, it would have to be by train.  But where was the money for the tickets?

"We must earn the money," said Annina.

"But how?" asked the rest in chorus.

Four young foreheads became wrinkled with anxious thought.

"Tino and I might raise silkworms and sell the cocoons," said Mario.  "There are the mulberry trees, and there is the little silkworm house where Mother used to raise them."

"But it is such hard work," said Fioretta.

"But it brings in good money," replied Mario.

"Annina and I can weave straw into hat braid and sell it at old Nello's shop.  Grandmother knows how, and can teach us," said Fioretta.

"But it will scratch and cut your hands," objected Mario.

"But it brings in good money!" said Fioretta with a saucy laugh at Mario.

All right then, they would begin as soon as school closed.  Of course it could be done!

When they told their plans to Margaretta, she approved promptly.  "It will not be any too easy," she warned them, "for you boys must help your father in the busy summer season, and the girls must help me as usual.  We will say nothing to Grandmother yet, until we see how things are going to turn out."

That very afternoon Margaretta wrote to Uncle Tony at Naples, asking if they would take in Grandmother and one of the children for a week or two in early September.  She told him how homesick Grandmother was, and how she longed to see Naples again.  After she had signed her name, she held her pen poised over the letter for some time.  Then she wrote, a little shamefacedly, "If Vesuvius isn't there, Grandmother will be disappointed."

When, some days later, a reply came, Uncle Tony said they would be much pleased to have Grandmother and one of the children visit them.  He, too, added a sentence after his name—"If Vesuvius isn't there, I'll fetch up Mount Aetna from Sicily; Grandmother shall not be disappointed."  Ah, that rascal Uncle Tony was laughing at her.

## IV

At once the boys set about giving the silkworm house —a tiny place with broad shelves along two walls—a thorough cleaning, whitewashing it inside and out. On the shelves they laid clean papers, and put a piece of netting at the window. There were a few bricks piled in one corner. Should a day threaten to be chilly, these would be heated in the kitchen oven and placed below the shelves to warm the air slightly. For silkworms are tender creatures, and must be cared for as though they were fretful babies.

Then the four, barefooted and bareheaded, and in their simple, home-made clothes, patched but clean, walked the four miles to Florence to buy both silkworm eggs and straw for the braiding. The eggs they bought at a little shop not far from the Ponte Vecchio, the oldest of the bridges over the river—the one that has a row of shops clinging on each side all the way across. For the straw, they went to the New Market, which, in spite of its name, is centuries old.

What a fascinating place it is, to be sure, with its arches holding up a great roof above its rows of stalls! And what a rainbow of colors is spread upon these stalls: purple of cabbages and plums, silver of onions and turnips, scarlet of tomatoes and peppers, green of beans and lettuce, white of celery, yellow of squash and pumpkins, earthy brown of potatoes. To the women and girls who go to market, there is a great charm in the straws of all

colors tied up in neat bundles.  These they may make into long pieces of braid and sell at the hat shop, where old Nello is so crabbed and yet so honest in his dealings with them.

The children, on the other hand, are equally pleased with the stalls where sticky sugar-candy is sold, and the fountain, where a great bronze boar spouts a lively stream of water from his mouth.  His bronze back has been polished by generations of small boys and girls who climb upon it and slide joyously off.

Home again over the four lovely miles, the Bernado children passed by great houses behind handsome wrought-iron gates; by stone walls over which April had thrown cascades of blossoming vines; by broad meadows carpeted with flowers; by stone pines and dark, pointed cypresses; across little streams over the round arches of ancient bridges; and at last reached the farm.

## V

Now their work began in earnest.  The silkworm eggs, which all winter had been kept in a cool place, now were put in a warm place to hatch, which they did in a few days.  At this Tino hurried off to the hill and brought back a basketful of the youngest and tenderest of the mulberry leaves.  At once the tiny jaws began to eat, and the worms grew so fast that one could almost see them growing.  Could their skins stand the strain?  No, they couldn't.  Twice they shed their too-tight skins, but not for long were the new ones loose and baggy; the little gluttons soon filled them up. The sound of their many little mouths chewing was like the sound of scratching on silk.

Meanwhile the girls, seated on the veranda, braided the rather brittle straws, which from time to time they moistened in bowls of water to keep them from splitting. Grandmother, in her rocking-chair near by, gave directions and was deeply interested. If she found a lumpy place, or a place too wide or too narrow, the girls would have to take it out and do it over better. There were some tears at first, and hands with many scratches, but as days passed, their braid grew smooth and even.

It was in the midst of all this busy work that Margaretta said that the one of the three older children doing the most faithful work and getting the best results should be the one to take Grandmother to Naples. This increased both care and speed, and Tino, who was too young to take care of Grandmother on the trip, and who might, therefore, if he wished, shirk his work, was faithful and eager in going four times daily to the mulberry trees to get fresh leaves for the little spoiled darlings of silkworms.

Both boys, indeed, worked so hard and fast that their mother reminded them of an old saying:

Of a mulberry leaf and a little patience silk is made.

Patience indeed! Nothing else would bring those tiny, spoiled little creatures to the point of spinning their cocoons. Mother said that silkworms had even been known to go on hunger strikes. Ah, what uncertain creatures they were!

In mid-July when cocoon-spinning time was approaching, the boys arranged branches and twigs upon the shelves, so that the silkworms might have something to which they could attach their silken threads. This was an anxious time, and, moreover, it was the time of wheat harvest, when Ugo, having cut the golden grain, needed the help of the boys to put it into shocks. Margaretta, too, gave a helping hand in the field one warm, sunny morning. The harvesters all sang as they worked; the two girls, busily braiding straw on the veranda, could hear the harvest song.

Very suddenly dark clouds massed themselves in the sky; thunder rolled along overhead. Following two vivid flashes of lightning, there came two heavy crashes of thunder. The boys hurried to the silkworm house. The worms were very much excited, and wove their lifted heads to and fro, refusing to eat. In a day or two some grew ill and died. This was a blow to Mario. He would not have as many cocoons as he had expected. And how he had longed to go to Naples and "see the world"!

Annina, by this time, had become almost perfect through care and practice. Her braid was even and firm, with no gaps in it. She could see very well that her work was better than Fioretta's. But Fioretta sang

happily as she worked, or broke out into delighted ac-
counts of what she would do and see in Naples if she
were the fortunate one.

"Ah, that Vesuvius! I hope he will be spitting forth
his smoke and fire and lava while I am there. That Bay
of Naples! I wonder if it is really so beautiful. But
no, there's nothing so beautiful there as our Giotto's
Tower in Florence! I will tell my Uncle Tony and my
Aunt Vanna about that, how lovely it is, rising up beside the Cathedral like a finger pointing heavenward."

## VI

When at last in August the cocoons had been carefully
loosened from the delicate threads that held them tied
to the twigs, and when each girl had neatly rolled and
wrapped up her straw braid, they all went again to
Florence.   Annina said not a word in all the four lovely
miles, ripe with the ripeness of the late summer, but
listened to the gay and excited talk of Mario and Fioretta, both so anxious for the trip to Naples. But was
not she herself just as eager to go? Yes, but......

When they sat down, in view of the lovely Giotto's
Tower, to rest a moment, with their bundles on the
ground beside them, Annina had made up her mind to
something. Very carefully, she exchanged her bundle
for Fioretta's, and Fioretta, so gay and lively, never knew
it. So it happened that when grumpy old Nello examined the two bundles of braid, he gave Fioretta the larger
sum of money, saying that her braid was better than her

sister's. And, since Mario had fewer cocoons to show for his summer's work than he had hoped to have, why, there you were! It was Fioretta who was to go!

By this time, of course, Grandmother knew what the children were doing for her, and her little brown face was once more a happy one. When she heard that old Nello had thought Fioretta's braid better than Annina's, she was surprised. She had watched those pieces of braid growing. She knew which was the better piece. She spoke to Margaretta about it, but neither of them mentioned it to the girls.

The day came at last when Ugo brought the oxen and cart to the door to take Grandmother and Fioretta to the station at Florence. Annina looked a little pale, but she cheerfully helped Grandmother and Fioretta into the cart and handed Fioretta the bundle, wrapped in an old shawl, which held her rather skimpy wardrobe. Then, with a laugh, Fioretta jumped out!

"Me," she cried, "I'm not going at all! Do not think it. I have packed Annina's clothes into the bundle. It is Annina that is going. Me, why should I leave the Giotto's Tower? Naples would look shabby to me. Annina may go and see that Vesuvius and that . . . . ."

For just a moment Annina could not speak. Then she said, "But our Mario, he is the oldest; he could take the best care of Grandmother. Me, I shall not go. I shall kneel in the Cathedral on Sunday and pray for a safe journey for Grandmother and Mario."

Then there followed those shouts and gestures that always accompany an argument in Italy, in which all are talking at the same time. And in the end it was Mario, shy and gloriously happy, who went with Grandmother to Naples.

### Notes and Questions

1. Tell in one sentence just what this story is about. You might begin this way: "This is a story about four Italian children who . . ."

2. The parts of this story have numbers but not titles. Write the numbers I to VI on your paper, and after each number write a title for that part. Your first title might be: *1. The Bernados and Their Home.*

3. Make up a title for each of the three pictures in the story.

4. Make a list of all the people in the story, and in a word or two tell who each one was, like this: *1. Ugo Bernado, the father.*

5. What name belongs where each letter is?

....(*a*).... was thoughtful and unselfish.

....(*b*).... was a happy but careless worker.

....(*c*).... was faithful in doing his share even though he could not go.

6. If you went to Florence, what three things might you see that are told about in this story?

7. On a map of Italy find Florence, Naples, Sicily, Mount Vesuvius, Mount Aetna. Be ready to show them on the wall map.

Some other stories about Italian children are: "Marda's Masterpiece," Crew (in *Saturday's Children*); "The Italian Drummer-boy," de Amicis (in *Child-Library Readers, Book Five*); and *Dino of the Golden Boxes,* Olcott.

# ESTEBAN, PAGE TO A CARNIVAL QUEEN
### Caroline Mabry

American boys and girls are not the only ones who have holidays to celebrate. But the boys and girls of other nations have many different holidays from ours, and they celebrate them in different ways. This story tells how Three Kings' Day and Ash Wednesday are celebrated on the island of Porto Rico.

Esteban was proud of his school garden. In the Porto Rican school of San Juan each child had been awarded a garden plot, and Esteban had tended his with such care that it was trimmer and finer than any of the others. He wanted it to be like the gardens in the United States, for to her Porto Rican children the United States is a wonderland. Today Esteban was especially happy because a friend of his teacher's from the United States had come to visit the school.

She sat smiling at the scholars in history class, and when Esteban was called upon to tell how Columbus had landed on this island, the boy's heart beat with pride. He told the story in glowing words, while he looked at the visitor out of the corner of his eye to see whether she was watching him. It was here in Porto Rico that Columbus had found his new world. It was here that he had set the Spanish flag. Esteban was almost sorry for the visitor to think that his little island had been so honored, and that Columbus had never seen New York, where the visitor lived.

When she came out later to look at the school gardens, Esteban tried to think of some way to make her forget that the great Columbus had not set foot on her native soil. She stood praising the gardens. Now the prize object in Esteban's garden was a large red tomato that had grown bigger than any of the others. It was fine and smooth, and it hung from its vine as round and red as the morning sun. When the visitor spoke of it, Esteban was so proud that he plucked it for her and pressed it into her hands.

"Like the United States?" he asked, looking up shyly.

"It's the finest tomato I ever saw," she said. "It will make three salads."

Esteban stood beaming even after she had gone. And then his joy was suddenly turned to dismay. He had been so busy caring for his garden that he had not heard the other boys planning the part each would take when they sang carols the night before Three Kings' Day. The Porto Rican children do not have gifts on Christmas, but their gifts come on Three Kings' Day, which is January the sixth. The kings are said to ride on camels, and every child gathers grass for the camels and puts a little box of it under his bed so that they will find it when they bring the kings with their gifts.

On the night before the kings come, bands of children throng the streets, singing carols. They stop before

many houses, and the night rings with their music.   The
part each child wants is that of a king.   There are two
white kings and one black one, as the Bible teaches, and
now it was that Esteban learned how the other boys had
been chosen for the part of the white kings, and the part
left for him was that of the black king.   He would have
to blacken his face and his hands with burnt cork.

When the night came, Esteban made himself black,
and wrapped around him the Spanish cloak that had been
his grandfather's.   It swept the ground, but Esteban,
small as he was, wore it gracefully, for many of his fore-
bears had worn such cloaks not only for warmth, but for
adornment.   The little band of singers went first to the

governor's palace. It was a beautiful palace of more than thirty rooms, and for many years it had been the pride of Porto Rico. And yet the children sang for its household one of the simple, kindly songs which they also sang at humble doorways:

> The house we stand before,
> Has kindly doors of wood,
> And those who live within
> Are generous and good.

As they sang, the palace door opened, and the children were invited to come into the courtyard, where they were given sweet cakes, as was the custom in Porto Rico. They had their cakes and trooped out happily to sing before the next house. This house had an iron balcony facing the street, and there stepped out on the balcony the loveliest girl Esteban had ever seen. Her black hair shone above big dark eyes, which smiled on the children in welcome. Esteban had heard it whispered that she was to be chosen queen of the next carnival which would take place the day before Ash Wednesday, as it did every year. He hoped she would be the queen, for he was sure no carnival ever had a queen more beautiful. When she invited the children into the house for more cakes, Esteban's heart beat proudly. As she put the cakes into his hands, she stopped to talk with him, and he was very happy.

"I could hear your voice above the others," she whispered. "It is clear and sweet."

The singers trooped on to other houses. The Three Kings came with their gifts. Esteban was not forgotten. The day to which all the children had looked forward passed, as happy days will.

February came, and now they were enjoying the merry whirl of the carnival. Gay crowds thronged the streets, hurling confetti and paper ribbons. There were mischievous boys spraying a powder into the air that made everyone sneeze. It was all part of the fun.

Esteban was very busy, for he needed to earn some money. He had hired himself as a messenger boy to a jeweler in San Juan. And there were so many balls at carnival time that Esteban was very busy delivering bright trinkets to the grand houses. But he performed his duty faithfully, and because he had proved himself trustworthy, he was given the queen's crown to deliver. As he took the box, he noticed the name on the cover. It was *her* name—that of the beautiful girl he had hoped would be queen. And so proud was he of his errand that he stopped to wash his face and smooth his hair. He couldn't carry the crown, looking like a ragamuffin.

As he hurried through the streets with his precious package, there were many sights to take his mind from it. A parade was passing. There were strange figures with big plaster heads and gay costumes. They danced through the streets. But Esteban held his treasure fast and did not stop to see all of them. He must take the queen her crown.

As he passed the capitol with its high white pillars of marble, which had been brought all the way from Georgia, he saw a group of boys playing about the long seat built in the sea wall that faces the capitol. Marble lions guarded the seat, and almond trees shaded it. The boys called to Esteban, and he was tempted to join them. He paused; then holding the package close, he shook his head and went on. The queen must have her crown.

A servant opened her door for him, and he asked to see the queen, for the crown must be delivered into her own hands. When she came, Esteban was sorry to see a troubled look on her face. He had expected to find it happy and shining. Perhaps the crown would bring the glad light into her eyes. He wanted to wait and see.

"My master would know if the crown pleases," Esteban said, for his master had put his finest work on it.

The queen untied the box and lifted out the sparkling crown. For a moment her eyes shone like the jewels, and then the same troubled look came again into her face. Esteban could not leave until he knew what caused this look in the queen's eyes.

"You like it?" he asked, pointing to the crown.

"Yes—yes," she answered quickly. "It is the most beautiful crown I've ever seen."

"Then—why doesn't it make you glad?" Esteban burst forth.

"It does," she said, "but I haven't any page to carry my train when I walk up to the throne. The train is three yards long and very heavy, for it has golden palm leaves embroidered on it. My nephew was to carry it, and today he's all broken out with measles. He looks like a little boiled lobster. Can you imagine? Measles! At carnival time, too."

Esteban's heart was beating fast. He had played he was a king. He could carry her train with princely grace. He knew it. And his longing was so great that his heart grew bolder. "Let me be your page," he cried.

She looked into his eager eyes. He was so glad he had washed his face. It was shining as he stood before her, his heart trembling with hope.

She hesitated. "You are just his size," she murmured, and then she beckoned Esteban to follow her. "Come, and we'll see if the page's costume fits you."

She led him into a room hung with silken curtains. She showed him the satin suit that had been intended for her nephew. It had short white trousers and a blue velvet coat with crystal buttons. Its blue hat had a long feather trailing from it.

"Try it," she said, leaving the room.

Esteban slipped into the gleaming satin trousers. He put on the blue velvet coat, and when he stood before the mirror, he looked so grand that he had to sing to make sure that it was himself he saw. His burst of song recalled the queen.

"You're the boy who played the black king, aren't you? I remember your voice."

"Yes," he gasped, "but I didn't think you'd know me."

"But I do know you," she said. "And the costume fits you beautifully. You wear it like a real prince—and indeed I don't imagine any other carnival queen has had a king to carry her train for her."

"I will be your Majesty's slave," said Esteban, bowing before her.

That night was the happiest of Esteban's life. In the gay ballroom, the beauty of San Juan had gathered. The queen had twenty ladies-in-waiting, and as her court gathered about her, it had no more loyal subject than her page, Esteban. The aisle up which she was to walk toward the throne was lined with eager faces. The band played to announce her coming. She started up the aisle, and stepping proudly behind her, Esteban walked in glory.

### Notes and Questions

1. What word or words belong where the letters are?

In Porto Rico the people give presents on ......(a)...... This comes in the month of ......(b)...... The ......(c)...... take the place of our Santa Claus, and ......(d)...... take the place of Santa's reindeers. Instead of hanging up stockings, the children put a box of ......(e)...... for the ......(f)...... On the night before, the children go through the streets ......(g)...... A great carnival is held to celebrate ......(h)......

2. From this story, what do you learn about the difference in weather between Porto Rico and the United States?

3. What is the capital city of Porto Rico?

4. Which two of the following reasons were most important in helping Esteban to be page?

(a) The American lady's visit.

(b) Being messenger for the jeweler.

(c) Being the black king.

(d) Being a good singer.

(e) The nephew's illness.

5. Which reason tells why Esteban wanted to be page?

(a) To have a pretty costume.

(b) To have a part in the grand celebration.

(c) To serve the beautiful queen.

If you enjoyed this story, you will want to read "Easter Monday in Washington," Fox (in *Uncle Sam's Animals*) and *The Boy with the Parrot*, Coatsworth.

# ABDUL AZIZ, A BOY OF THE DESERT

## Eunice Tietjens

In northern Africa, along the Mediterranean coast, is a country called Tunis. It is ruled over by France, but most of its people are Arabs. Here in the little village of Hammamet lived Abdul Aziz. Eunice Tietjens visited Abdul's country and wrote this story about him and his people. His life, as you shall learn, was different from ours in many ways.

### ABDUL AZIZ GROWS UP

Abdul Aziz continued to grow up. Somehow the mysterious spirits in which the Arabs believe protected him, so that he grew strong and plump.

He learned to do all the proper things. He could ride a donkey in his sleep. He sat very far back and sidewise without any saddle. When he wanted the donkey to go faster, he kicked both feet very fast in the air and made a loud, whirring sound, "Errrrrr—hey!" Also he had many strange names for the donkey, of which "Son of Satan" was the most polite.

He could play the darbouka, the pottery drum, in many strange ways, so that it throbbed and beat like an imprisoned spirit for hours together. He could keep his father's shop for him, and never be cheated at all. He could argue and bargain and sputter with the best of them over a few cents, looking as though he were about to burst with rage; and then, when the bargain was settled, he could be in an instant calm and polite.

He knew two dozen polite things to say when someone of importance came to the house, or when he went
to weddings.  He also knew how to talk French, how to
beat the French boys at marbles, and how to spin a car-
rot on its pointed end as though it were a top.   In fact,
he was quite an accomplished young person.

Once in a while he used to think.  Being an Arab, he
was never in a hurry.  He did not in the least mind
sitting still for an hour or two at a time, doing nothing
at all but soaking in the sun, or watching the wind toss
the olive branches about, or listening to the sleepy hum
of the flies.  And at these times thoughts flowed through
his brain, as water flows in a river bed.

He thought of everything under the sun, but most
often, perhaps, he thought of what his friend the artist
had said to him.  The artist himself had stayed only a
few months and then gone elsewhere, but what he had
told the boy of the greatness of the Arabs remained.
Other things which his father, Sadoc, said fitted in with
the picture, too.  And he made fine dreams about what
he would do, when he grew up, to help his people.

In the meanwhile he managed to get on in school
without too many thumpings from the master's ruler,
and Sadoc was proud of him, though of course he never
admitted as much to the boy. When the father met one
of his friends, the conversation was apt to go like this:

"Good evening, Sadoc."

"Good evening, Achmed."

"May Allah protect you."

"May he grant you long life."

"May your goods increase."

"May your day be blessed."

"May Allah grant you health."

"May he give you salvation."

"May you lack for nothing."

"How is your son, who is a good lad?"

"Praise to Allah, he kisses your hand."

All this was just the polite way to begin a conversation—all except the words, "who is a good lad," which his friends need not say unless they wanted to.   So Sadoc was pleased.   Nobody ever asked him how Kadijah, his wife, was, for that would have been as impolite as the other was proper.   The Arabs never speak to each other of their women folks if they can possibly avoid it.

Abdul Aziz, being only a boy, was allowed to go into the neighbors' houses.   So he knew most of the women. Sometimes even, at the season of the olive crop, he worked with them.   For in the village of Hammamet it is the women and the children who harvest the olives in the orchards outside the town.

### IN THE OLIVE ORCHARDS

Olive-picking is great fun, and the poor women, who otherwise never see the fields or the trees, look forward to it all the year.   When the time comes in the late autumn, there is great hurrying and scurrying, preparing of food, and packing up. For often, if the orchard is rather far away, the women sleep there for days together, without going home. It is understood at this season that the men shall not go near the orchards.

The year that Abdul Aziz was nine Sadoc came home one evening in early December and said to Kadijah: "The olives in the far orchard are ripe. On Saturday you will go with my two sisters to pick them. You will take Abdul Aziz with you, and the little M'na." M'na was Abdul Aziz's cousin, and he was very fond of her.

Kadijah answered, as a proper Arab wife should answer, "As you command, my husband." But she smiled as she spoke, and they all knew that she was very happy.

So one morning, quite early, when the sun was just slipping, all pink and gold, out of the sea, a little caravan marched out of the village gate and up the white road. There were three brown bundles with plump bare feet, two donkeys loaded with bedding and cooking pans and food, and in the rear two excited children.

Sadoc's orchard lay well off the road in a secluded place in a sort of little valley. He had dug a well there and put up a little one-room house of mud and stones, where the women slept. The olive trees were old and gnarled and gray, and their branches sighed softly in the wind. Under them the ground was quite bare and a deep red in color. Nothing would grow in this dry place except the olive trees, which sent their thirsty roots far

down into the earth where the water lay hidden under the hard, dry surface.

After the brown bundles had unwrapped themselves and become women, they unloaded the donkeys and hobbled them.  Then they brought out from the little house a ladder and some large squares of old canvas. The ladders were for the women.  Abdul Aziz and his cousin had no trouble in scrambling up without them into the gray rustling world of the olive branches, where the little leaves stirred and whispered, and the round black olives shone like bits of polished onyx.  When Abdul Aziz could reach the olives, he picked them by hand, and threw them down on the squares of canvas which had been spread on the ground under the trees. When the branches were too high, he shook them till the fruit fell like dark hailstones, with a little pattering noise.

In the evenings, when the work was done, the women cooked wonderful dishes, with lots of pimentos in them, on the pottery fire-pots.  After dinner Abdul Aziz beat his darbouka, and they sang songs. Sometimes, too, the women danced.

His mother, Kadijah, was like another person out here under the sky, in the freedom of the orchard.  She laughed and sang, and she was in a good humor from morning till night.  This year Abdul Aziz noticed it, and one afternoon when they were resting a little, standing looking out across the red earth, under the rustling trees, to the sea which lay like a deep blue carpet in the distance, he asked her about it.

At first his mother would not answer, saying only: "Your father does not like me to talk of it."  But Abdul Aziz begged, and presently she told him.

"I was not born in the village, like the other women here.  I am a Bedouin, and I was born in a tent, far away on the great desert to the south.  The Bedouins my people, live a free, roving life, under the stars, and under the hot sun of the desert.  I was free, too.  My face was not veiled.  I was free to come and go as I liked in the hills and the wide air.

"Then came a great drought in the South.  For three

years not a drop of rain fell, and everything dried up.
The desert wells were dry. There was no pasture for
our animals. So we came north, searching for food.
One day we camped in the fields outside Hammamet, and
there we gave a festival in honor of a marriage in the
tribe. Many people from the village came, among them
your father. He saw me and spoke to me—I have told
you that I was free then—and from that moment he
loved me. And I loved him." Her voice grew gentle
as the breeze in the olive leaves. "I loved him, too.

"So we were married, and I came to live in the village.
Your father shut me up as the village women are shut
up. I am no longer free, but I am content. I would
not leave him even for the stars and the desert. But
sometimes I smother a little in the house. So you can
see, my little son, why I love the olive-picking, and why
I am gay, here under the sky."

After this Abdul Aziz had something new to think of
when he lay on his back in the sun. But he never spoke
to his father about it.

### ABDUL AZIZ PLEASES HIS FATHER

When the olives had all been gathered, Sadoc came
with his brother, bringing more donkeys, each with two
baskets hanging on its flanks. In these baskets the
olives were loaded and carried to the mill to be pressed.
So the little caravan of women, now turned again into
brown bundles, set out once more for the village with

the children and the loaded donkeys. But they were
not so gay as when they went.

After the olives had been pressed, the oil was stored
in big pottery jars. They were red-brown in color, with
handles at each side of the top, and they were just such
jars as those in which the forty thieves were hidden in
the old story of "Ali Baba and the Forty Thieves"; for
in many ways the life of the Arabs has not changed
since the days of the "Arabian Nights." Only Sadoc's
jars were a little smaller. He put these in a small
room, a sort of storehouse, next door to his house, to keep
until he should be able to go to the city of Tunis to sell
them at the oil market. For the harvest from his olive
orchard was the chief source of Sadoc's income.

This storehouse was not connected with the house itself, but was a separate building, with a door of its own
which opened on to the street. This door was always
kept locked with a strong padlock, for fear of thieves.
And, lest someone might break in, Sadoc kept a watch-
dog on the flat roof of the storehouse, which was lower
than the roofs beside it.

Abdul Aziz's bed was below a window which looked
out over the roof of the storehouse, and when he looked
out on moonlit nights, he could see the dog moving rest-
lessly about, or hear it howling to the moon. Sometimes
he felt sorry for it.

One night, while the oil was stored next door, Abdul
Aziz waked up suddenly, hearing the dog growl in its

throat.   It was not a loud growl, but it sounded surprised.   Abdul Aziz looked out, but the night was dark,
and there were no street lights in the village.   He could
see nothing.   But he listened intently.

Sure now that something was wrong, the boy sprang
to his father's bed, for Sadoc was still sleeping soundly,
and called him.

"Father, father, wake up!" he cried.   "Someone is
trying to steal the oil!"

Sadoc leaped to his feet, seized a heavy stick, and
made for the door of the house with the boy at his heels.
He opened it cautiously and peered out.   He could see
little, but the sound he made had frightened the robbers,
and he heard them running off up the street.   Sadoc ran
after them.   In the distance the boy heard the sound of
wheels and knew that the robbers were making off in the
cart they had brought to carry away the oil.

After a while Sadoc came back.

"They got away," he said, "but I think I know who
they are, and I shall bring them to justice."

Then, very quietly, he took out ten francs and gave
them to Abdul Aziz.   It was more money than the boy
had ever had of his own in his life before, and he looked
at it in a daze as he heard his father saying solemnly:

"Abdul Aziz, by your quick-wittedness you have saved
me five thousand francs.   Take this, and spend it as you
like.   You are a son of whom I am proud."

## Notes and Questions

1.  Make a list of six things that are strange to you about life in Hammamet. Perhaps you can find more. You can begin like this: (*a*) *Donkeys are used to carry loads.*

2.  Why might you guess from this story that France rules Tunis? Think hard. There are two reasons.

3.  What three things does this story tell you about olives?

4.  For each word in the first column, choose a word or group of words in the second column that means about the same thing. Write the pairs of words together.

| | |
|---|---|
| (*a*) secluded | black stone |
| (*b*) onyx | hurrying here and there |
| (*c*) roving | seriously |
| (*d*) gnarled | lack of rain |
| (*e*) hobbled | place from which something comes |
| (*f*) drought | hidden |
| (*g*) source | feet tied together loosely |
| (*h*) solemnly | roaming |
| (*i*) scurrying | twisted and knotty. |

5.  Be ready to tell in your own words the story of Abdul Aziz's mother.

You will like to read *Boy of the Desert,* by Eunice Tietjens, from which this story came. Other good stories of North Africa are "The Brass Bowl" and "The Farm," Palmer (in *Abdul, the Story of an Egyptian Boy*).

# JOHN GOES DOWN TO TOY VALLEY

## Margaret Warner Morley

High up among the Alps Mountains in Austria lies Toy Valley. Here for many years men, women, and children have been carving wooden blocks into toys which are sold for boys and girls in many parts of the world.

Up on the side of a high mountain overlooking the valley, lived the Hofer family. In the thick forests Father Hofer chopped trees to be made into blocks for the wood-carvers down in the valley.

### THE SLED RIDE TO THE VALLEY

Early one morning Father Hofer got out a sled, put on his wooden shoes with the long spikes in the heels, wrapped up well, and wound a scarf many times around his head and neck. John knew his father was going down to the village and almost fell over with surprise and delight when asked if he would like to go too. He was ready in a moment, and they trudged, all three, for Mother Hofer must see them start, through the snow to where the gully led down far toward the bottom of the valley.

Father Hofer placed the sled carefully and firmly on the platform of snow at the top. Then he seated himself and John got on behind, his arms around his father's waist and his legs drawn well up out of the way. He had often taken short sled trips with his father down the mountain-side near home, but he had never yet gone down the long slide to the village in the valley. He had often come there to see his father start and had held his breath as he saw him flash down and out of sight under the great rock. Then he and his mother would wait patiently for the father to return, for they did not know until he got back whether or not he had reached the bottom alive. Now they were both going down, and the poor mother stood alone with clasped hands and murmured a prayer as she watched them.

John was eleven now and very proud to be allowed to go down into the Toy Valley in the winter time. "Are you quite ready, my son?" his father asked in a serious voice, and John knew the great moment had come. He gripped his father very tight, shut his eyes, and bowed his head against his father's back as he felt the sled move; faster and faster it went until John felt as though they had left the earth entirely and were flying through the air. Then came a strange, swaying motion that gave him a sudden sick sensation. He felt his father's body sway far out, and he, clutching fast, swayed too; then the sled shot ahead again faster than before, and John knew the dangerous curve had been passed and that they were flying down the mountain in safety.

It is no wonder John almost lost his senses clinging there, for the sled shot down through the icy air with the rapidity of a railway train. In what seemed to John ages, though it was only a few minutes, the speed slackened; finally the sled stopped, and John raised his

head to look about. They were in the midst of a forest
of fir trees whose branches dipped to the ground, burdened with snow. The sun was shining brightly, and
Father Hofer was looking at John in a kindly manner.

"Well done, my son," he said, while John, who was
yet so dazed he could hardly stand, smiled broadly.

They dragged the sled after them a little way and then
flew down another steep gully, but not so long nor so
steep as the first one. Again the sled came to a stand-
still, but this time only wide, white slopes lay about them.
They were quite below the black fir forest, and now they
slid easily enough down over the steep open meadows to
the very bottom of the valley.

They went at once to the store, where Father Hofer left a package of lace to be sent away and sold. There was nobody in the store but the man behind the counter, for in the winter all the people were busy carving and stayed all day long in their own houses. But Father Hofer and the shopkeeper had a long talk, while John looked about the store at the many things it contained, until he discovered a wooden frame filled with carver's tools of many shapes and sizes. Before these tools he planted himself until his father was ready to go.

John followed through the crooked street, so narrow now with banks of tumbled snow piled high above his head that he could not walk at his father's side, but had to trot on behind. His father went so fast that he had no time to look at the gay paper toys pinned up in some of the windows, although he knew the children who had put them there. And the broad window sills!—how well they were filled with green moss and bright berries— though none were prettier than their own at home. Still, he would have liked to stop and look at them and at the bright flowers growing in pots in the window where Dono and Peter lived.

But his father went too fast, straight on to the large wide-roofed, latticed house where the Herders lived. They pushed open the outside door and went into a smoke-stained room like the entrance to their own house. Beyond this was another room, larger than theirs, with

a big brick stove in one corner.   Here Mr. and Mrs.
Herder and three of their children were sitting at a long
wooden table at work.

They all got up when John and his father entered.
They were glad to see them and had many questions to
ask about the health of the family and how the winter
was going up on the mountain.   Then they sat down,
and the Herders took up their work again, while the visitors looked on, and the talk continued.   Mr. and Mrs.
Herder sat opposite each other, each with a stick of
wood clamped to the table in front, against which they
held the bit of wood they were cutting, and into which
the tool struck when it glanced off.

They were carving little wooden horses and doing it
very quickly.   The oldest boy made the first cuts in the
rude block.   Father Herder finished hewing out the form
and then passed it along to Mother Herder, who, with her
small, sharp tools, quickly and neatly separated the hind
legs, smoothed and shaped them, cut down the front legs
until they were slender and shapely, modeled the ears,
the nose, the neck, until the little horse, no larger than
your hand, looked quite alive.   Then she passed it to her
boy Henrico, who, with a little tool, made some long, fine
lines to represent the mane.

John went and stood behind Henrico.   He longed to
take the little tool and try, but he only said, "It looks
easy to do."

"Yes," said Henrico, proudly, "I learned it all this

winter. When I first tried, the lines went crosswise and looked not at all like a horse's mane. But now, see," and he moved the tool very quickly; the shavings rolled out, and the mane grew under his skillful touch in quite a wonderful way.

"It looks so easy," said John, "I wish I could try."

"No, no," said Mother Herder, anxiously, "you would spoil the wood and maybe break the tool. It takes practice."

"John wants to carve," said Father Hofer, "but I tell him it is folly, for none of our family has ever carved." He said this a little sadly, for it was a great honor in the Toy Valley to be able to carve.

"I am going to carve," came a piping voice, apparently from the roof. John looked around and saw little Hans peeping down at him from the bed made on the platform above the stove. He had gone up there to take a nap because it was so warm. All the children laughed, for little Hans was a great pet.

### A VISIT WITH THE WAGON AND DOLL CARVERS

In a few minutes John's father got up. They said good-by, and again went out into the sparkling, white world, along a lane that led them out of the village, down across a bridge over a little stream that made a pleasant sound as it rushed along between its ice-bound banks.

They followed a path across some meadows, quite across the valley to a little stone house under the shadow of the opposite mountain. In this house lived Father Hofer's old friend Ampezzang.

Ampezzang and his wife and son were at work in the inner room. Herr Ampezzang sat alone at a little table on which was a lathe turned swiftly by the rushing brook outside, and by means of which Herr Ampezzang was cutting out toy wagon wheels at a great rate.

The wife and son were fitting little spokes into the wheels, a task that looked very easy, indeed. But when Frau Ampezzang put a wheel rim and some spokes into John's hand and told him to try, he could not do it at all. First the rim flew across the room; then he broke the spoke that he was trying to force into place. Young Ampezzang laughed, but Frau Ampezzang, seeing how red John's face became, looked kindly at him and said it didn't matter, as they had plenty of the little spokes, and some of them often were broken.

"He thinks he wants to carve," said Father Hofer, shaking his head, "but I know he never could learn."

"Bless the child!" cried Frau Ampezzang. "Of course he could learn. *It is just wanting to hard enough and keeping at it long enough,*" and she smiled so kindly that John had a sudden warm feeling at his heart, and his blue eyes shone with pleasure.

When they were leaving, Frau Ampezzang looked at John and said again, very slowly and in a tone he never forgot, "It is just wanting to hard enough and keeping at it long enough."

John would have liked to stay there close to kind Frau Ampezzang all day, but his father soon took leave, and they went next to see the Wolferlos, who lived at the foot of the steep bluff on top of which stood a tiny, close village and a church with a tall spire.

Here the whole family were painting wooden horses. Two lads painted them white and set them aside to dry. The others took the white horses that had already dried and painted black spots on them and a black stripe down their backs; though, why they did this I cannot tell you, and I doubt if they could have told themselves. Certainly no living white horse ever had such spots on it or such a line down its spine. But horses were scarce in the Toy Valley, and probably no one in it had ever seen a white horse; so they had to do the best they could, and once, away back, no doubt, some carver with a bright imagination had so painted his horses, and ever after, all his descendants, who knew no more about white horses than he did, had painted them that way, too.

John and his father did not stay here long, but visited at another stone house with deep overhanging porches and broad lattices. This family was also at work, even to the old grandfather, making wooden dolls—not those sticks of wood with a doll's head on top that the babies of the Toy Valley love to hug (somebody else made *them*), but real dolls with jointed legs and arms.

"See," said the grandfather, holding out a handful of dolls no more than an inch long, "these are the smallest jointed dolls in the world." And sure enough, those mites were jointed and could bend their knees and elbows and sit down!

"It takes skill," he cried, chuckling, "and the mother does it all. Hers are the only fingers fine enough for such work as that," and he looked with pride at the tiny things lying in the palm of his great hand.

Dolls were everywhere in this room, hanging and standing about, so that the paint on them might dry, and John came near sitting down in a basketful of dolls' arms, while another one full of leg-joints stood ready on the table. The children were all busy fitting the joints together and fastening them with little wooden pegs, while the father, who had a jolly red face, was boring holes for the pegs to go into.

They were a merry set, these doll-makers, and the children had round faces and round eyes and little pug noses and bright red cheeks and looked very much like their own dolls come to life—and grown bigger, of course. Only they were not a bit wooden, but laughed and chattered and showed John everything they had.

He had seen all this toy-making many times before, but today it was different; it seemed as though he were looking at it for the first time. The desire to become a carver had come to him the summer before, and now everything connected with it had a new meaning.

### THE RETURN TO THE MOUNTAIN HOME

They did not stay long with the doll-makers, but went next to his father's relative, he whom they called Uncle Francesco. He had been a hunter in his young days, but now that he was old, he stayed at home and worked the piece of land he owned on the slope above the village.

They had dinner there, and as soon as it was over, John was sent to the store to get the sled his father had left there and which he meant to leave in Uncle Francesco's shed until summer time, when he would bring Franz, the horse, down and let him carry it home on his back. He had three or four of these sleds which he used for sliding down to the Toy Valley in the winter time. When John got back with the sled, his father said, "Now we must be starting up the mountain." He got up and began to wind his scarf about his neck. It was early yet, but it would take a long time to climb up through the snow, and the days were short.

They had no trouble going up the open slopes, for there were paths everywhere made by the people to go from farm to farm, and from their houses down to the village. But when they had climbed above the open slopes into the woods, there was no path. Still, Father Hofer knew the way very well and how to find the least snowy trails under the cliffs, while the long spikes in their shoes kept them from slipping.

It was very cold and very still in the woods, and every little while they heard a loud report which Father Hofer said was the cold splitting the trees. John's breath froze in a thick fringe on the scarf wound about his neck and ears, but inside his warm wrappings his blood tingled, and he did not feel the cold at all.

If you had been there, you would have thought you were climbing up through a forest of Christmas trees, for each evergreen was hung with snow wreaths and glittering ice jewels.

It was very beautiful, and yet it was a long, hard climb for John, and as night came early, they had to hurry. When finally they reached the top and Mother Hofer opened the door and let out a flood of warmth and the fragrant odor of the cooking supper, John rushed in— never so glad in all his life to be at home.

He was almost too tired to eat, but he felt very proud to think he had really been down to the valley in the winter time. He felt as though he were quite grown up and not at all the little boy who that morning had hugged his father so closely. "Soon I shall be able to slide down by myself," he thought sleepily, as he climbed to his warm bed above the great stove, and all night long he seemed to be speeding through the air after wonderful toy horses that galloped swiftly ahead of him.

## Notes and Questions

1. What two reasons did Father Hofer give why John could never be a wood-carver?

2. What was the first thing John did in this story that let you know he was interested in wood-carving?

3. What two things did Frau Ampezzang tell John he had to do to become a wood-carver?

4. Why would you not expect to find many horses or automobiles in John's country?

5. Do you think life was harder or easier in John's country than in Abdul's? Why?

Are you wondering whether John ever became a wood-carver? You can find out by reading *Donkey John of Toy Valley*, from which this story was taken.

# A BACKWARD LOOK

Now turn back to page 225 and read again the poem that you find there. Do you feel that you know a little more about the boys and girls of other lands and understand them a little better? Do you see that they work and play and think and feel in many ways just as you do, even though they speak languages that you cannot understand and live in countries that are in many ways different from yours? Can you tell some of the ways in which people in other countries are like us and ways in which they differ from us? It would certainly be interesting to visit them.

Which of these lands, about which you have read, seemed most like our own land? Which country seemed most different from ours? Which would you most like to visit? You have probably seen many pictures of the countries told about in these stories. It would be fun to gather pictures of Italy, Austria, North Africa, and Porto Rico for a bulletin board or a scrap-book.

One of the stories told you about toy-makers. Did you ever look on the bottom of a toy to see whether it had a little label telling where it was made? You might be surprised to find that it came from a far-away land. Perhaps there are other things in your home that came from far away. One fifth-grade girl found in her home articles from Italy, England, India, Japan, and France.

You have read stories about four countries. Of course, there are more stories of the boys and girls of these lands, and of other lands. On page 432 you will find a list of books that will give you many a pleasant hour of travel.

# PART SIX
## ·WORKERS AND THEIR WORK·

## THE CLOCK CALLS TO WORK

### HELEN COALE CREW

I am the master workman, and my work
Is never done—I count the hours that fly,
And from the top shelf, lifted up on high
That all may see me, call to those that shirk
And bid them hasten, since the world's good work
Cannot be done by those who sit and sigh
While precious minutes haste forever by.
"Come then," I call. "Come work, and work,
   and work!"

# MACHINES ARE OUR SERVANTS

HAVE you ever watched in wonder some great, throbbing steam locomotive or a roaring printing press? Surely you have ridden a bicycle, and perhaps you have run a sewing machine. Maybe you have a toy motor or an electric train. These are all machines—machines to give us pleasure or to do our work.

You will be surprised if you count the number of machines you see and use every day. And if these machines were suddenly taken away, you would be very much upset. You turn a faucet to get water, and it is a machine that pumps the water to your faucet. Machines make the electricity that lights your home. The milk that you drink is probably put into the bottle by a bottling-machine. Even an egg beater is a machine.

So, you see, machines are really our servants. They help us to do things in easier ways, and they make it possible to do things faster. Machines, we say, do the work of the world.

But we must never forget that all these machines we enjoy came from the careful, patient work of men. Even though you and I cannot possibly understand how some powerful or delicate machine works; even though no person could possibly do what the machine does, yet some man or group of men made that great or delicate machine that means so much to us all.

Some of the most interesting stories to read are those that tell how machines work and how men have thought, and planned and studied to invent machines which make life easier for us all.

# CYRUS HALL McCORMICK INVENTS
# THE REAPING MACHINE

## ELIZABETH WATSON

Cyrus Hall McCormick had spent many a weary day swinging a scythe back and forth across the fields of golden grain. Then he began to think and work. When he finished, he had made a machine. Most people laughed at it, but the kind of machine he made will cut more wheat in one day than Cyrus could cut in twenty days with his scythe.

This is the true story of a man named Cyrus Hall McCormick, who as a boy lived on a farm in the Shenandoah Valley in the beautiful Blue Ridge Mountains of Virginia.

At that time almost everyone in the United States lived on a farm, and a great many of those farms were in the valleys along the rivers and streams that flowed to the sea. In those days there were only a few roads in the entire country, and those roads were so narrow, so rough and so full of tree stumps and deep mud-holes that people would not use them if they could possibly travel by water. Everyone tried to live near a river or stream, on which boats could be used to carry the corn, wheat, flax, and wool down to the market towns on the coast, where they could be traded for the salt, iron, tea, tools, and other things that were needed.

Great-grandfather McCormick had lived on a farm in Pennsylvania. On this farm he plowed and harvested the grain with the farm tools he had brought with him from his home in Europe. In those early days there were no machines such as we have today to help with the farm work; in fact, farmers were just beginning to discover new ways of making hand tools which could do more work than the old tools their forefathers had used.

These farm tools were as old as Time. The plow with which Great-grandfather McCormick broke his ground, and the sickles with which he cut his grain, were like the plows and sickles the farmers of Egypt over a thousand years before had used on their farms along the banks of the Nile River. The short scythes used on the McCormick place were almost exactly like the scythes used on the old farms of Rome.

When Great-grandfather McCormick's son grew up and wanted a farm of his own, there was little good land left on any of the rivers or streams near his father's home. So Son McCormick took his tools and went off across the Indian trails running through the forest and over the hills and came out on the banks of the Shenandoah River in Virginia. Here there was still plenty of land to be had for nothing. He cut down trees, built himself a log house, then plowed and planted his newly cleared land with corn and wheat. The land was rich, and it grew splendid crops. Everything went well with the young McCormick family. As time went on, the family grew

bigger and bigger. As the McCormick family grew, the
farm spread out over more and more land.

This Virginia farm had great fields of oats, corn,
wheat, and other grains; beautiful pastures with strong,
fine horses, good cows, and fleecy sheep; and large barn-
yards of hens, ducks, and geese. There were two grist-
mills for grinding McCormicks' and their neighbors' grain
into flour and meal. Two sawmills quickly turned logs
into broad planks and stout boards. A smelting furnace
turned iron ore from the near-by mountain into lumps of
pure iron all ready for the farm's blacksmith to hammer
and beat into horseshoes, pincers, tongs, crowbars,
hammers, and other tools needed on the farm. They

spun and wove their own cloth and made it into clothing; they made their own soap and candles, dyes, hogsheads, barrels, tubs, and vats.   In fact, that old McCormick family, like all other farmers of the time, did everything for themselves.

Every year they plowed and planted great fields of corn, wheat, and oats.   And every year when the grain was ripe, every man, woman, and child of the McCormick family went out into the grain fields to help bring in their winter's food.

How everyone did work!   The harvest season was so short that there was not a single minute to waste if the precious grain was to be put under cover before the fall storms came.   Rain, wind, and sunshine were good for grain all through the long months of the growing season, but rain, wind, and too much sunshine were anything but good for grain that was tall and ripe. And so the moment the grain was ripe enough to be cut, the whole family went into the fields and worked from daylight until dark. They hastened to get their harvest in before the storms overtook them, or before the warm sun over-ripened the seeds, so that they fell to the ground to be blown away by the slightest breezes.

The men with sickles went ahead.   They held a bunch of grain with one hand, swung the sickle with the other, and let the stalks fall to the ground as they cut their way across the field.   Each man with a sickle was followed by another worker who gathered up the fallen stalks, tied them into bundles, and tossed them back to the ground. The men who had the scythes with the long handles and blades did not need to hold the grain as they cut it. They used both hands to swing the scythe, and they cut a wider path through the grain as they worked their way across the fields.

The tools that Son McCormick and his neighbors used in harvesting their crops were the same as those used by Great-grandfather McCormick on his farm back in Pennsylvania. After using such tools for many years, Son McCormick bought a scythe he had seen the farmers along the coast using to harvest their grain. They called the new kind of scythe a cradle scythe because it had long wooden fingers on the handle just above the knife. These fingers cradled, or held the grain until the knife had finished its work, then laid it in neat rows at one side. The picture on page 279 shows men using cradle scythes.

Fifty years went by, and the sons and grandsons of the first McCormick who had settled in the Shenandoah Valley were still harvesting their grain with the cradle scythe. One of the McCormick sons spent every spare moment of his time in his workshop. There he had discovered several new ways of making many of the old farm tools into new tools which did a great deal more work than any of the old ones had ever been able to do. But try as he would, he could *not* find any better or quicker way of cutting the ripe grain.

As he went about the country and saw field after field

of ripe grain that could not possibly be cut and gathered in time to save it, he began to see that men with *hand tools* alone could not keep up with the huge crops the rich farmlands were producing. Some kind of harvesting *machine* was needed. So he began to study and plan and work. When his machine was finally finished, he and his son Cyrus Hall McCormick tried it out in one of their fields. Something went wrong; it trampled down the grain instead of cutting it.

Then Cyrus Hall McCormick began experimenting with his father's machine. After many trials he sent out word one day to the farmers that he had made a reaping machine. He invited them to come and see it work. More than a hundred neighbors gathered at Farmer Ruff's field, where the machine was to be tried out. The reaping machine rattled and clattered as Cyrus Hall McCormick drove it out of the barn and into the field. Dogs barked and boys yelled and whistled through their fingers as the machine rattled clumsily along. The negro slaves chuckled and laughed; farmers grinned and shook their heads in disbelief. They did not believe that such an awkward-looking machine could ever cut grain, and they did not hesitate to say what they thought.

The field was rough and hilly. Jolting and jerking from side to side, the reaping machine cut the grain in such irregular fashion that Farmer Ruff ordered Cyrus Hall McCormick to stop the horses and cease ruining his field of wheat. A bystander shouted to McCormick,

"Pull down that fence; drive over into my field and try your machine there." In that field, which was smooth and level, Cyrus Hall McCormick's machine cut six acres of oats easily before the sun went down!

The new machine could do all the work of cutting grain. It had a divider that separated the grain to be cut from the grain left standing. It had fingers that caught and held the stalks while the knife blade moved back and forth, cutting with each stroke. In fact, it had all the main parts of the reaping machines we use on our farms today. The McCormick farm of the Shenandoah Valley had made history.

Our present-day harvester cuts off the heads of wheat,

threshes it, weighs it, and dumps it into sacks which are thrown off as fast as two expert workmen can sew them up. It is pulled by a tractor engine or by teams of horses. This great machine will reap seventy-five acres and more a day. It owes its beginning to Cyrus Hall McCormick's clumsy old reaping machine.

## NOTES AND QUESTIONS

1. In the early days of our country, why did most of the settlers live near rivers?

2. (a) In what state did the McCormicks live? (b) In what famous valley?

3. Name six things that the McCormicks made for themselves that we would buy rather than make at home.

4. What two reasons made it necessary to harvest the grain quickly?

5. Below are three possible reasons why the reaper was such a great invention. Which of the three is the best reason?

(a) Farmers did not have to work so hard.

(b) Farmers could get the harvesting done more quickly.

(c) Farmers could grow more wheat.

6. What were the three main parts of the reaper?

7. What things does the modern reaper do that McCormick's reaper did not do?

8. What is the greatest use that is made of wheat?

Other interesting stories of the world of machines are: "Invention of the Reaper," Tappan (in *Heroes of Progress*); "The Magic of Iron," Paine, and "What the Clock Told Dolly," Clarke (in *Child-Library Readers, Book Five*); "New Machines for Workers," Bourne and Benton (in *Story of America and Great Americans*).

# THE STORY OF BREAD

ALICE THOMPSON PAINE

All over the world people are eating bread—rye bread, corn bread, wheat bread, rice bread, even oat bread. We may call bread the most important food in the world. Thousands of people are busy every day making it for us, and wonderful machines have been invented to help them make enough for the great hungry mouth of the world.

When the Swiss Family Robinson were cast away on a desert island, do you remember how they made bread? They dug roots and ground them to a pulp. Then, after squeezing out the juice, they made the pulp into little flat cakes, which they baked. When they did this, they were making bread in the very same way that it was made away back in the beginning of things. Nobody knows when people first began to make bread, but it was probably the first thing that primitive men and women cooked for themselves after they passed the first rude stages of eating raw meat and fish, or berries and roots.

The women began it, of course, just as they began all the industries of the home. When the men were away on the war path or the hunting trail, the women stayed at home to take care of their children. They probably grew very hungry while they waited in their caves or huts for the hunters to come home, and doubtless they remembered the starving days when the hunters found no game. Therefore it was natural for them to dig in the earth for

something to eat to keep themselves and their children alive. And these primitive women with their "digging sticks" marked the beginning of all agriculture.

In time they learned not only to find roots and grains that were good to eat but also to plant seeds and to cultivate corn, wheat, rice, oats, and barley. Then it was natural to crush the hard grains between stones just as today a boy walking in the woods, who finds a nut too hard to crack with his fingers or teeth, hunts up two stones and with them does the trick.

We know that the people of the Stone Age had learned how to grow grain and grind it into meal, because among the remains of Stone-Age dwelling-places wooden plows have been found, and stone hand-mills (a hollowed stone and a round stone for crushing, such as you see in the picture on page 286), together with the burnt remains of cakes made of coarsely ground grains of wheat and barley. This Stone-Age bread was probably baked in thin cakes on flat stones. The stone was heated, the paste or dough made of crushed grain and water was spread upon it, and the whole was covered with hot ashes.

We know, too, from studying ancient monuments on which pictures of bread and bread-making are carved, that the Egyptians knew how to make the finest of white bread. An early writer tells us that Egyptian bread-makers kneaded the dough with their feet. Pictures of their bread show that the loaves were small and round, somewhat like our biscuit. You have probably heard, too, of the grains of wheat found with Egyptian mummies.

In England bread was so important that it helped to make the English language. The word "lady" comes from two old words that mean "loaf-maker," and the word "lord" comes from two words meaning "loaf-keeper." That is, the loaf of bread represented the food and the home. The lady made it, and the lord protected it.

When Captain John Smith landed on the shores of Virginia in 1607, he found the Indians growing corn and grinding it into meal, from which they made bread. All the work was done by the squaws, for the Indian braves, like the early cave men, had to attend to the hunting and fighting. Sometimes when their crops failed, they used roots for bread. It was, in fact, Indian corn that kept the colonists from starving, and one of the most important things that Captain John Smith did was to persuade the Indians to give the colonists enough corn to live on until supplies could come by ship from England.

When an Indian squaw made bread, she had to do all the work herself. She had to dig up the ground, plant the seed, cultivate the growing corn, harvest it, shell it, grind it, mix it into dough, and bake it. Today all this work has been divided among many different groups of people scattered all over the country.

Take first the planting, cultivating, and harvesting. Where and how is that done today? It is done in hundreds of little plots and in thousand-acre wheat farms, north, south, east, and west; but what we think of chiefly are the wide prairies of the West, with waving grain as far as eye can see—green in summer and golden in the autumn. Then we see the huge harvesting machines driven by powerful tractors or pulled by four or five horses abreast. Then all over the prairies the threshing machines wave their plumes of flying chaff, and presently high piles of straw gleam in the sun, and along the roads lines of "grain tanks" are hauled to the nearest elevator, which is always beside a railroad track leading to some great city.

How is the grain made into flour? Instead of the little stone hand mortar used in early days, there are now great flour mills, like those that line the river front in Minneapolis. The grain comes from the prairies to these mills in hundreds of freight cars. There, in a world of humming machinery, it is cleaned, ground between rollers, and separated from all the husk. Then it is sifted through fine cloth until it is the soft, white substance that reaches our kitchens. And in order that it may always be the same, always fine and pure and nourishing, it is examined and tested at every stage.

The Indian squaw did one thing that these great mills cannot do. She mixed and baked the bread. How is that done today? In many homes bread is still baked in the home kitchen, but more and more it is being taken out of the kitchen into the factory. However much we like the odor of freshly baked bread at home, we must admit that it saves our mothers a great deal of time and work if the bread can be bought all wrapped up in waxed paper to keep it fresh and clean. Not so many years ago it was a sad thing to have to eat "baker's bread," but this is no longer true. In fact, there are very few cooks who can make bread as fine and light as the baker's bread of today, and this is not because they are poor cooks, but because the modern baker has machinery and ways of testing and measuring that no home cook can have.

The modern bakery is almost as clean as a hospital room and as bright and sunny as the home kitchen. The men and women who make the bread are dressed in white clothing and wear white caps, and they are required to keep themselves and their surroundings spotlessly clean. An army of experts work constantly testing, weighing,

yes, even tasting, to see that every loaf of bread comes
up to standard. So today we may have almost perfect
bread—white bread, rye bread, whole-wheat bread, which
many people consider more healthful, and Graham bread
(named for the man who believed in leaving all the bran
in the flour). We have also a great variety of rolls and
buns, to say nothing of all the cakes made in bakeries
today.

But there is still baking to be done in the home,
and each country has its favorite kind of home-made
bread. Scotland has its oatcakes, and its bannocks made
of barley meal. Central America has its tortillas, made of
crushed corn. Our Southern states have beaten biscuit,

corn pone, and all the delicious hot breads that go with fried chicken, Virginia ham, and candied yams.

Someone has said, "Tell me what you eat and I'll tell you what you are." This may or may not be possible, but it is certainly true that the bread a nation eats tells us a great many things about that nation. When only the rich eat fine white bread, while the poor eat coarse black bread, we know that something is wrong with that nation and trouble is ahead. When fleets of bakery wagons speed through the streets and over the highways carrying millions of loaves of carefully tested, carefully wrapped, fine white bread, we know that the nation is prosperous, because there is food for everyone.

## NOTES AND QUESTIONS

1. How did Cyrus Hall McCormick help the world to have more bread?
2. What was the first "flour mill" like?
3. In what kind of "stove" was bread first baked?
4. What grain did the Indians make into meal?
5. Name the grain used for most of our bread flour.
6. Name five grains that are used to make bread.
7. Tell in one sentence what we mean by "bread." You might begin this way: *Bread is a food made . . . .*

Other stories of how we get our food are "Wheat," "Milk," and "Corn," Wells (in *An American Farm*); "Our Daily Bread," "King Corn," and "The Man Who Feeds the World," Baker (in *The Wonderful Story of Industry*).

# DONALD'S VISIT TO THE WOOLEN MILLS

### Sara Ware Bassett

Donald had worn woolen clothes all his life, but he did not know how the wool got from the sheep's back to his back. Perhaps he had not even thought about it until he visited the ranch and saw the sheep having their coats taken off by the clippers. Do you know how a sheep's coat is made into cloth for your coat? This story will tell you.

## IN THE WAREHOUSE

Donald Clark had spent several months with his father on the Crescent Ranch in Idaho. This sheep ranch was owned by Clark and Sons, of Boston. It supplied wool to that company's large warehouse, of which Donald's father was manager. When Mr. Clark returned with Donald from the ranch, he brought Thornton, a young ranchman, with them to work in the Boston warehouse. The warehouse was not new to Donald, for he had often been there with his father; but to Thornton this part of the wool business was entirely new.

Mr. Clark assigned the young ranchman to work on the upper floors of the warehouse, where the wool was stored. Here were great piles of loose wool, reaching from floor to ceiling. Some piles contained only the finest wool; other piles held that which was next best in quality; still others were made up of coarser varieties of fleece. There were piles of scoured wool, piles of wool from South America and from Australia—wool everywhere!

With keen interest Thornton wandered from one vast pyramid of fleeces to another, catching up handfuls of the different varieties and examining them. Then he walked to the place where the men were busy opening the first spring shipments of wool from the Crescent Ranch. This wool was emptied from the sacks on to the floor in great heaps. The crews of men—skilled in judging the fiber— set to work to sort it, separating the different qualities into piles. The young ranchman rolled up his sleeves, and with the other men began to grade the wool.

Mr. Clark, who had watched Thornton closely for several weeks, said to Donald, "Thornton is proving himself a thoroughly useful man. Because his knowledge of the ranch and of the wool itself is so excellent, I shall make him foreman of the shipping department. In the meantime, before you start in with your studies, and before Thornton gets so rushed that he cannot be spared, I want to take you both to visit the Monitor Woolen Mills at Lawrence. Thornton has never seen the manufacture of woolen goods and will be the more intelligent for doing so. As for you, I am anxious to have you complete the story of wool-growing which you began at the Crescent Ranch."

"I do want to know the rest of the story very much, father," Donald replied.

"It happens that some matters have come up which

require me to go to the Monitor Mills tomorrow. I shall take Thornton with me, and if you wish, you may go also."

"Of course I'd like to go!" exclaimed Donald eagerly.

### AT THE WOOLEN MILLS

Within the mills, next day, Donald and Thornton found the vast buildings throbbing with the beat of engines, the click and whir of bobbins, and the clash of machinery.

When they entered, Mr. Munger, the manager, came forward cordially.

"We were glad to hear by telephone that you were coming out today, Mr. Clark," he said. "Mr. Bailey, the president, is waiting to see you in his private office."

"Very well," answered Mr. Clark. "While I am talking with Mr. Bailey, I should be glad to have my son Donald and my foreman, Mr. Thornton, go over the works. They have never visited a woolen mill."

"We shall be delighted to show them around," answered Mr. Munger. "The bookkeeper will go with them."

Donald and Thornton followed their guide into a building just across the yard. Here wool was being sorted by workmen called staplers, who were expert in judging its quality. As they handled the wool and tossed it into piles, they picked out straws, burs, and other waste matter caught in it.

"The work of sorting must be carefully done," explained the bookkeeper, "or the wool will not take the dye well. Much depends on having the fleeces clear of waste matter. We are also very particular about the sorting. The finest wool, as you know, comes from the sides of the sheep; that which is clipped from the head and legs is coarse and stiff. These two kinds of wool we put in separate piles before we send the fleeces on to be scoured. In this next room you will see how the wool is washed."

Donald and Thornton were next shown how steam was blown through the wool, which not only removed the dirt but softened the fibers. Then the fleeces were thoroughly washed by being put through a series of great tubs of soap and water.

"Here again great care must be taken to have the water clean and the soap pure, else the wool will not dye perfectly. We use the best potash soap in washing the wool. We must take great care also not to curl or snarl the wool while we are washing it."

"I don't see how you can help it," Donald said.

"We can if we take proper care," replied the guide.

"What is that machine for?" inquired Thornton, pointing to one at the end of the room.

"That machine is picking the wool apart, so that the air can get through it to dry it. After it is picked up light and fluffy, we pass it through these heavy rollers; they are like wringers and are used to squeeze out the remaining moisture. During all these processes we must always be careful not to snarl the wool. See, here is where it comes out white and clean, ready to go to the dyeing room."

Donald looked at the snowy fleeces with wonder.

"Isn't it beautiful? It is not much the way it looks when it leaves the ranch, is it, Thornton?"

"I should say not," agreed the ranchman. "The sheep ought to see how handsome their coats are."

"In the next room you will see how the dyeing is done," the guide continued. "We use revolving machines which scatter the wool as they whirl rapidly around. Besides these machines, we use others to keep the wool spread and turned. In spite of all our care, the wool often becomes matted and must therefore be picked apart again. So we pass it through these revolving drums which, you see, have sets of spikes on them. As the spikes on the different drums turn, they catch in the wool and pick it all apart; so it is again light and fluffy as it was before."

"Doesn't so much washing and dyeing make the wool very dry?" inquired Thornton.

"Yes, it does! That is just the trouble. Therefore we are forced to put some oil back into it; otherwise it would be so harsh and stiff that we could do nothing with it. We put the thin layers of wool into these machines which carry them along to an apparatus that sprays them evenly with oil. We use olive oil, but some manufacturers prefer lard oil or vegetable oil."

"It seems funny to have to put oil back into the wool after you have just washed it out!" remarked Donald.

"It is funny, isn't it?" nodded the bookkeeper. "Now on this other side of the room they are blending fleeces. Sometimes we blend different qualities of wool to get a desired effect; sometimes we mix the wool with cotton or with another kind of fiber. We take a thin layer of wool and put another layer of a different kind over it. Then it is all picked until a uniform mixture is secured."

"It is a surprise to me to learn that the wool has to go through so much before it comes to the spinning," Thornton said.

"It is a long process," responded their guide. "When I first saw it, it seemed endless; now I think little of it."

Just then a hearty laugh came from behind them; turning, they saw Mr. Clark and Mr. Munger.

"I came to hunt you up," said Mr. Clark. "It seemed to me that by this time you must have finished spinning your next-winter's overcoat, Donald."

"But I haven't, father," retorted the boy, smiling into his father's face. "I have not even begun to make the cloth at all."

"The yarn is not spun yet, sir," said the bookkeeper.

"You are a slow guide, I fear," said Mr. Munger with a laugh, laying a kindly hand on his bookkeeper's shoulder. "Now let us hurry along. These men must get back to Boston today, you know." Mr. Munger bustled ahead, conducting his visitors across a bridge and into the next mill.

Here was the carding room. Layers of wool entered the carding machine and were combed by a multitude of wire teeth until all the fibers lay parallel. The thin film of wool then passed into a cone-like opening and came out later in a thick, heavy rope of untwisted fibers.

"It is now ready to go to the drawing-frames," Mr. Munger explained. "You will notice how these drawing-frames pull the wool into shape for twisting and spinning, drawing it out to uniform size and finally winding it on bobbins. The machine is a complicated one to explain, but you can watch and see what it does."

"How wonderful it is that machinery can do all this work," Mr. Clark remarked thoughtfully.

"Yes, it is," Mr. Munger agreed. "Years ago every part of the work was done by hand. But little by little, machines have been made so perfect that they seem almost human. Shall we go now and see the yarn spun?"

When they reached the spinning room with its clatter of shifting bobbins, Mr. Munger turned to Donald:

"I wonder if you know that wool is worked into two different kinds of yarn—worsted and woolen yarn. The fibers for worsted yarn are long and lie nearly parallel, and when woven, have a smooth surface. Broadcloth is made from worsted yarn. Woolen yarn, on the other hand, has its fibers lying in every direction, and all these loose ends, when woven, give a rough surface. Of course when this cloth is finished, it is smooth, but not so smooth and fine as a worsted cloth."

"I think I understand," Donald said. "Are we to see the cloth woven next?"

"Yes. This mill weaves nothing but woolens; you must go to a worsted mill to see the other kinds of cloth made. The processes, though, are much alike."

Mr. Munger then hurried the party to the weaving mills, where, amid an uproar of thousands of moving wheels, bobbins, and shuttles, the threads of yarn traveled back and forth, back and forth, and came out of the looms as cloth. The cloth was then steamed, pressed, and rolled or folded.

"And now, young man," said Mr. Munger to Donald, "you know the whole story of wool."

## NOTES AND QUESTIONS

1. In the four sentences below, which word or words are the right ones to finish the sentence?

(*a*) Sheep are raised mostly in the *New England States Southern States Western States.*

(*b*) The woolen mills are mostly in *New England the Southern States the Central States.*

(*c*) The wool is cut from the sheep in the *fall late summer spring.*

(*d*) The best wool comes from the *legs head sides* of the sheep.

2.    Below are ten words and nine sentences with letters in them.  Choose the word that belongs where each letter is.

blending      carding      spinning      weaving      fleece
dyeing        worsted      woolen        yarn         fibers

The wool of a sheep is called ....(a)....
The separate hairs are called ....(b)....
Changing the color is called ....(c)....
Wool thread is called ....(d)....
Mixing wool with some other fiber is called ....(e)....
The wool is combed out by a ....(f).... machine.
....(g).... the wool means twisting it into thread.
The threads are made into cloth by ....(h)....
....(i).... yarn makes a smoother cloth than ....(j)....

3.    Here is a list of the things which happen to wool that is to be made into cloth.  But they are not in the right order.  Put them in the right order.

(a)  Twisted into thread.
(b)  Colored with dyes.
(c)  Combed out by the carding machine.
(d)  Washed and dried.
(e)  Sometimes mixed with other fibers.
(f)  Picked apart to keep it from matting.
(g)  Sprayed with oil.
(h)  Sorted into different kinds.
(i)  Woven into cloth.

You will like also to read "Cloth Making in Pioneer Days," Watson (in *The Story of Textiles*); "Our Woolen Clothes," Baker (in *The Wonderful Story of Industry*); "A Visit to a Cotton Mill" and "Bob's Overcoat," Carpenter (in *The Clothes We Wear*).

# HOW CANDY MINTS ARE MADE

Milton Wright

Do you know that when you open a package of candy mints, your hands are the first that have ever touched them? You say, "Somebody must have made them." But you are wrong. Fingers and hands and arms of iron and steel and leather did the work, as this story will tell you.

To learn how candy mints are made, we journeyed to the biggest factory of the kind in the country. The materials they contain are sugar and mint flavor—nothing else. Granulated sugar, received in barrels, is emptied into a conveyor near the receiving platform on the first floor. A continuous bucket elevator carries it to the roof, where it is stored in hoppers until used. Up to the roof of the building go the raw materials. Down, down they come, rolling, sliding, tumbling, falling, passing through this piece of machinery and that, until they come out on the second floor, wrapped and in cartons ready for delivery. In all the work no hands have touched them.

The first manufacturing step is powdering or pulverizing the sugar. Pulverizers located on the fifth floor do this job. As soon as the sugar is powdered, it drops into mixers on the fourth floor. From the mixers it is put through a machine which drops the mass of sugar in the shape of small kernels on to moving belts that lead to elevators. Here the kernels are placed in drying units,

and the whole mass is dried before being passed into other units called blenders, where flavoring oils are added.

The plant has a completely equipped laboratory, where the flavor is prepared and measured out into containers, so that for each batch of 200 pounds of sugar mixture a uniform amount of flavoring oil is added in order that each batch may be exactly like every other one.

From the blenders the mass is fed into tablet-forming machines on the third floor.  To each tablet a pressure of 14,000 pounds is applied, giving it a china-like hardness.

After the mints are formed, they are passed on to wrapping and packaging machines, also on the third floor.  It took eight years to develop these machines, but now, it is believed, they are as nearly perfect as human skill can make them. Each machine wraps and labels an average of 1000 boxes a day, running at a speed of thirty-five to forty rolls a minute. These machines receive into their hoppers mints in bulk direct from the tablet-forming machines. A device turns them on edge and assembles them in rows of fourteen each. Then each group of fourteen is gripped by steel fingers which carry them on to a piece of tin foil which has been cut to the desired length from a big spool of foil beneath the machine. The tin foil is then spun around the candy, and the ends are twisted.

Now comes the pasting on of the label. This is applied in the same manner as the tin foil, except that to make it secure, instead of twisting, a small strip of vegetable glue is applied along one side. Assembled and wrapped, the packages are dropped on to a moving belt which delivers them to packers.

At this point on our trip through the factory, we asked a question: "Why not have machines pack the rolls in cartons?"

"Machines have been perfected for such a task," was the reply, "but as yet no machine has been made which will make sure that each package is laid in the carton so that the trade-mark and flavor name on the label are uniform in appearance and can be seen when the carton is opened. That is a problem yet to be solved by some invention. It means a lot to have a perfect and uniform display of the cartons and their contents on the store counters."

With the placing of the rolls in the cartons, the trip of the sugar down from the roof is not completed. For the cartons, after being packed, are carried on a belt conveyor to a wax machine. Here a paper, waxed only on the outside, is wrapped around the carton, and the end is folded in a peculiar manner. The carton now passes through an electric heating unit, which melts the wax just enough to cause a tightly sealed package when the wax hardens again.

Through spiral chutes the finished cartons drop to the second floor, where they are packed in boxes.

## Notes and Questions

1. In what ways are the candy-mint materials moved from one place to another?

2. Which of these machines do you think is the most wonderful: the pulverizer, the blender, the tablet-forming machine, or the wrapping and packaging machines?

3. How are the cartons sealed tight?

4. Make a list of eight steps in the manufacture of candy mints, including their wrapping. You might begin this way: (1) *The materials are carried to the roof.*

Other stories about the work-a-day world are: "Maple Sugar and Sorghum Molasses," Wells (in *An American Farm*); "A Sweet Story," Baker (in *The Wonderful Story of Industry*); "Three Lumps of Sugar," Carpenter (in *The Foods We Eat*).

# A BACKWARD LOOK

CYRUS Hall McCormick saw that there was great need of a machine to harvest wheat. Before men could get the golden grain into the barns, much of it was wasted or spoiled. So the young man thought and worked and tried things until he made a successful reaper. Someone watched the slow weaving of yarn into cloth by hand. He said, "I believe we can make a machine to do that work. Then we shall be able to do it faster and make more cloth in less time."

When men have needed a machine badly enough, they have put their brains and their hands to work at the job of making one. So today we live in a world of machines. There is hardly a thing we eat or wear that has not at some stage been put through a machine. And that machine has come from the long and careful work of some person.

Can you make a list of all the machines you have yourself used? Can you tell how they make life easier? It would be fun to imagine what you would have to do if all machines were taken away for twenty-four hours. You would surely have to carry water. What other things would you have to do?

Do you know of any other great inventions besides the reaper? In your history and geography books you have surely read of some. Could you name at least one great inventor today? What things has he invented?

To read stories of machines—how men have made them and how they use them—is fascinating. There are only four such stories in this book, but many books have been written that tell how machines make life easier for us. You will find some of these books in the list on page 434.

306

# PART SEVEN
# ·FAMOUS HEROES OF LONG AGO·

## ARABIAN NIGHTS

### ANNA BIRD STEWART

Oh, Ali Baba's forty thieves,
    Aladdin's lamp, the Singing Tree,
Are stories everyone believes,
    And things I'd dearly love to see.

# SOME STORIES NEVER GROW OLD

THERE are some stories that never grow old. Year after year, century after century, men and women and boys and girls read them and love them. The people in the stories become almost as real as people who have actually lived. They come to be known all over the world. Cinderella, Robinson Crusoe, Alice in Wonderland, Beowulf, Siegfried, Guinevere, and Roland—almost anywhere you go, you will find someone who knows these story-book people.

You are now going to read three very famous stories. The first two of these are so old that no one has ever been able to find out when they were first told. It is thought that they were first put down in writing about a thousand years ago in Persia. But they were probably told by the story-tellers long before that. It is thought that perhaps story-tellers in India first made them up— how long ago nobody knows. These two stories are "Aladdin, or the Wonderful Lamp," and "Ali Baba and the Forty Thieves." They are part of a great group of stories called *The Arabian Nights*. So much have people liked these stories that they are known all over the world. Except for the Bible, nothing else has ever been translated into so many different languages.

The third story is that of the famous Robinson Crusoe, the shipwrecked sailor who spent twenty-seven years on a lonesome island. It, too, has been a great favorite.

Are there other heroes from famous stories that you would like to know?

# ALADDIN, OR THE WONDERFUL LAMP

Perhaps after you have read this story, you will be able to tell why men and women and boys and girls for hundreds of years have liked to read it.

### ALADDIN MEETS HIS UNCLE

Aladdin was the son of Mustapha, a poor Chinese tailor. When the boy was old enough to learn a trade, his father took him into his own workshop. But Aladdin, being an idle fellow, loved play more than work and spent his days in the public streets with other boys as idle as himself.

His father died while Aladdin was yet very young, but the boy still continued his foolish ways. His mother was forced to spin cotton night and day in order to keep herself and her boy.

When Aladdin was about fifteen years old, he was one day playing in the streets with some of his companions. A stranger who was going by stopped and looked at him. This stranger was a famous magician, and it happened that he was in need of the help of some ignorant person. No sooner did he see Aladdin than he knew by the boy's manner and appearance that he was fit to be made a tool of. The magician inquired of some persons standing near, the name and character of Aladdin, and the answers proved to him that he had judged rightly of the boy.

The stranger, pressing in among the crowd of lads, clapped his hand on Aladdin's shoulder and said, "My good boy, are you not the son of Mustapha, the tailor?"

"Yes, sir," said Aladdin, "but my father is dead."

"Alas!" cried he. "What unhappy news! I am your father's brother. I have been many years abroad; and now that I have come home in the hope of seeing him, you tell me he is dead!" And all the while tears ran down the stranger's cheeks, and his bosom heaved with sighs. Then, pulling out a purse, he gave Aladdin two pieces of gold, saying, "Take this, my boy, to your mother. Tell her that I will come and see her tonight and sup with her."

Pleased with the money, Aladdin ran home to his mother. "Mother," said he, "have I an uncle?" His mother told him he had not; then Aladdin pulled out his gold and told her that a man who said he was his father's brother was coming to sup with her that very evening. Full of wonder, the good woman set out for the market, where she bought provisions, and was busy preparing the supper when the magician knocked at the door. He entered, followed by a porter who brought all kinds of delicious fruits and sweetmeats for their dessert.

As soon as they sat down to supper, he gave Aladdin's mother an account of his travels, saying that for forty years he had been away from home, in order to see the wonders of distant countries. Then, turning toward Aladdin, he asked his name. "I am called Aladdin," said he. "Well, Aladdin," said the magician, "what business do you follow?"

At this question Aladdin hung down his head and was not a little ashamed when his mother made answer: "Aladdin is an idle fellow; his father did all he could to teach him his trade, but could not succeed; and since his death, in spite of all I can say to him, he does nothing but idle away his time in the streets, so that I despair of his ever coming to any good." With these words the poor woman burst into tears, and the magician, turning to Aladdin, said: "This is not well, nephew; you must think of making a living. I will help you as far as I may. What think you—shall I take a shop and furnish it for you?" Aladdin was overjoyed at the idea, for he thought there was little labor in keeping a shop, and he told his uncle this would suit him better than anything else.

"I will take you with me tomorrow," said the magician, "clothe you as handsomely as the best merchants in the city, and then we will open a shop."

Aladdin's mother then thanked him very heartily, and begged Aladdin to behave so as to prove himself worthy of the good fortune promised by his kind uncle.

Next day the stranger called for Aladdin, as he had promised, and led him to a merchant's where clothes for all sorts of people were sold. Then he told Aladdin to try on the handsomest suits; and choosing the one Aladdin preferred, he paid the merchant for it at once. The pretended uncle then took Aladdin to visit the bazaars and the inns where the foreign merchants were, and in the evening he gave the boy a merry feast.

The next morning Aladdin got up and dressed himself very early, so eager was he to see his uncle. Presently he saw the man coming and ran out to meet him. The magician greeted him very kindly. "Come, my good boy," he said; "I will show you some very fine things."

He then led Aladdin through beautiful gardens with great houses standing in the midst of them. The boy was amazed at their beauty, and so his uncle led him on farther and farther into the country.

"We shall now go no farther," said he to Aladdin, "for I shall here show you some wonders that no one besides yourself will ever have seen. I am now going to strike a light, and you collect all the dry sticks and leaves that you can find, in order to make a fire."

There were so many pieces of dry sticks scattered about this place that Aladdin collected more than enough by the time his uncle had struck a light. The magician then set them on fire, and as soon as they were in a blaze he threw a certain perfume, that he had ready in his hand, upon them. A dense smoke arose, while the magician spoke some mysterious words. At the same instant the ground shook slightly, and, opening in the spot where they stood, showed a square stone about a foot and a half across, with a brass ring in the center.

Aladdin was frightened out of his wits and was about to run away, when the magician suddenly gave him a box on the ear so violent as to beat him down and very nearly to knock some of his teeth out. Poor Aladdin, with tears in his eyes and trembling in every limb, got up. "My dear uncle," he cried, "what have I done to deserve so severe a blow?" "I have good reasons for it," replied the magician. "Obey me, and you will not repent of it. Underneath that stone is a great hidden treasure, which will make you richer than many kings if you will pay attention to what I tell you."

Aladdin had now got the better of his fright. "Well," said he, "what must I do? Tell me; I am ready to obey you fully!" "Well said!" replied the magician. "Come to me, then; take hold of this ring and lift up the stone."

To Aladdin's surprise the stone was raised without
any trouble, and then he could see a small opening three
or four feet deep, at the bottom of which was a little
door, with steps to go down still lower. "You must
now," said the magician, "go down into this cavern, and
when you have come to the bottom of the steps, you
will see an open door which leads into three great halls.
In each of these you will see, on either side of you, four
bronze vases as large as tubs, full of gold and silver, but
you must not touch any of it.

"When you get to the first hall, bind your robe around
you. Then go to the second without stopping, and
thence in the same manner to the third. Above all, be

very particular not to go near the walls or even to touch them with your robe; for if any part of your dress should touch them, you will die instantly.  At the far end of the third hall there is a door which leads into a garden planted with beautiful trees, all of which are full of fruit. Go straight forward, and follow a path which you will see.  This will bring you to the bottom of a flight of fifty steps, at the top of which there is a terrace.

"There you will see a niche and in it a lighted lamp. Take the lamp and blow it out.  Then throw out the wick and the liquid that is within and put the lamp in your bosom.  If you should wish very much to gather any of the fruit in the garden, you may do so; and there is nothing to prevent your taking as much as you please."

When the magician had given these directions to Aladdin, he took off a ring which he had on one of his fingers and put it on his pretended nephew, telling him at the same time that it was to save him from every evil that might otherwise happen to him.  "Go, my child," he said; "descend boldly.  Now both of us shall become immensely rich for the rest of our lives."

### ALADDIN FINDS THE WONDERFUL LAMP

Aladdin jumped willingly into the opening and went down to the bottom of the steps.  He found the three halls exactly as the magician had said.  These he passed through with the greatest care, keeping in mind his uncle's warning.  He went on to the garden and mounted to the terrace without stopping. There in a niche was the lamp, which he seized, and after he had thrown out the oil which it contained, he put it in his bosom.

This done, he returned to the garden. The trees here were full of the most wonderful fruit. Never before had he seen fruits of so many different colors. The white were pearls; the sparkling and transparent were diamonds; the deep red were rubies; the green, emeralds; the blue, turquoises; the violet, amethysts; those tinged with yellow, sapphires. All were of the largest size, and finer than had ever been seen in the whole world. Aladdin was not yet old enough to know their value and thought they were only pieces of colored glass.

However, the unusual color and size of each sort tempted him to gather some of every color; and he took so many that he filled both his pockets, as well as the two new purses the magician had bought for him at the time he made him a present of his new suit. Since his pockets were already full, he fastened one of the purses on each side of his girdle and also wrapped some of the gems in its folds, as it was of silk and made very full. In this manner he carried his treasures so that they could not fall out. He did not forget to fill even his bosom quite full, between his robe and his shirt.

Laden in this manner with the great treasure, though ignorant of its value, Aladdin made haste through the three halls, in order that he might not make his uncle wait too long. Having passed through them, he began to climb the steps he had come down, and reached the entrance of the cave, where the magician was waiting.

When Aladdin saw his uncle, he called to him, "Help me up!" "My dear boy," replied the magician, "you had better first give me the lamp, as that will only hinder you." "It is not at all in my way," said Aladdin, "and I will give it to you when I am out." The magician still wished to get the lamp before he helped Aladdin out of the cave, but the boy had so covered it with the fruit of the trees that he refused to give it. The wicked magician was in the greatest despair at the refusal the boy made, and fell into the most violent rage.

He then threw some perfume on the fire, and had hardly spoken two magic words, before the stone at the entrance to the cavern returned of its own accord to the place, with all the earth over it, where it was when the magician and Aladdin first arrived there.

When Aladdin found himself buried alive, he called aloud a thousand times to his uncle, telling him he was ready to give him the lamp. But all his cries were useless, and, having no other means of making himself heard, he remained in perfect darkness.

Finally he went down to the bottom of the stairs, intending to go toward the light in the garden, where he had been before. But the walls, which had been opened by magic, were now shut by the same means. The poor boy felt all around him several times, but could not discover the least opening. He then cried aloud and sat down upon the step of his dungeon, without the least hope of ever seeing the light of day again.

For two days Aladdin remained in this state, without either eating or drinking. On the third day, feeling that his death was near, he clasped his hands in prayer and said in a loud voice, "There is no strength or power but in the great and high Heavens." In this act of joining his hands he happened, without thinking, to rub the ring which the magician had put upon his finger.

Instantly a horrid-looking genie rose out of the earth. This genie, who was so extremely tall that his head touched the roof, addressed these words to Aladdin: "What do you wish? I am ready to obey you as your slave, both I and the other slaves of the ring." Weak and terrified, and scarcely daring to hope, Aladdin cried, "Whoever you are, take me out of this place, if you are able!" No sooner had his lips formed the words than he found himself on the outside of the cave, at the very spot where the magician had left him. Almost unable to believe his good fortune, he arose trembling, and seeing the city in the distance, made his way back by the same road over which he had come. Such a long weary road he found it to his mother's door that when he reached it, he was fainting from hunger and fatigue.

His mother, whose heart had been almost broken by his long absence, received him joyfully and refreshed him with food. When he had regained his strength, he told her all and showed her the lamp and the colored fruits

and the wonderful ring on his finger. His mother thought little of the jewels, as she was quite ignorant of their value; so Aladdin put them all behind one of the cushions of the sofa on which they were sitting.

Next morning when Aladdin awoke, his first thought was that he was very hungry and would like some breakfast. "Alas, my child," said his mother, "I have not a morsel of bread to give you. Last night you ate all the food in the house. However, I have a little cotton of my own spinning. I will go and sell it and buy something for our dinner."

"Keep your cotton, Mother, for another time," said Aladdin, "and give me the lamp which I brought with me. I will go and sell it, and the money will serve us for breakfast and dinner, too; perhaps also for supper."

Aladdin's mother took the lamp from the place where she had put it. "Here it is," she said to her son; "but it is very dirty; if I were to clean it a little, perhaps it might sell for something more." She then took some water and a little fine sand with which to clean it. But she had scarcely begun to rub the lamp, when a gigantic genie rose out of the ground before her and cried with a voice as loud as thunder, "What do you wish? I am ready to obey you as your slave, both I and the other slaves of the lamp."

Aladdin's mother was much terrified; but Aladdin, who had seen the genie in the cavern, had no fear. Seizing the lamp, he answered in a firm voice, "I am hungry;

bring me something to eat." The genie disappeared and returned a moment later with a large silver basin, which he carried on his head. In it were twelve covered dishes, filled with the most delicious meats, and six loaves as white as snow, and in his hand he carried two silver cups. These he placed upon the table, and vanished.

When Aladdin's mother had recovered from her fright, they both sat down to their meal, in the greatest delight, for never before had they eaten such delicate meats or seen such splendid dishes.

The remains of this feast provided them with food for some days, and when it was all gone, Aladdin sold the silver dishes one by one for their needs. In this way they lived happily for several years, for Aladdin now behaved with great wisdom. He took care to visit the principal shops and public places, speaking only with wise persons; and in this way he gathered much wisdom and grew to be a courteous youth.

### ALADDIN WEDS THE PRINCESS

One day Aladdin told his mother that he intended to ask the Sultan to give him his daughter in marriage.

"Truly, my son," said his mother, "you seem to have forgotten that your father was only a poor tailor; and indeed I do not know who will dare go and speak to the Sultan about it." "You yourself must," said Aladdin decidedly. "I!" cried his mother, in great surprise, "I go to the Sultan! Not I, indeed! You know very well that no one can make any demand of the Sultan without bringing a rich present, and where shall such poor folk as we find a present?"

Thereupon Aladdin told his mother that while talking with the merchants in the bazaar, he had learned to know the value of gems. And for a long time he had known that nothing which the merchants had in their shops was half so fine as those jewels he had brought home from the enchanted cave. So his mother took them from the drawer where they had been hidden and put them in a dish of fine porcelain.

Aladdin's mother, now sure that such a gift was one that could not fail to please the Sultan, at last agreed to do everything her son wished. She took the porcelain dish with its precious contents and folded it up in a very fine linen cloth. She then took another, less fine, and tied the four corners of it together, that she might carry it without trouble. This done, she took the road toward the palace of the Sultan.

Trembling, she told the Sultan of her son's boldness, and begged his mercy for Aladdin and for herself. The Sultan heard her kindly; then before giving any answer to her request, he asked her what she had with her so carefully tied up in a linen cloth. Aladdin's mother unfolded the cloths and laid the jewels before him.

It is impossible to express the surprise which this ruler felt when he saw before him so many brilliant jewels, the size of which was greater than any he had ever seen

before.  For some moments he gazed at them speechless.
Then he took the present from the hand of Aladdin's
mother, and exclaimed, joyfully, "Ah!  How very beautiful, how very wonderful they are!"

Then turning to his grand vizier, he showed him the
gems and talked privately to him for some minutes.  At
last he said to Aladdin's mother:  "My good woman, I
will indeed make your son happy by marrying him to the
Princess, my daughter, as soon as he shall send me forty
large basins of gold.  These vessels must be filled with
the same varieties of precious stones which you have
already given me.  They must be brought by an equal
number of black slaves, each of whom shall be led by a
white slave, young, handsome, and richly dressed.  These
are the conditions upon which I am ready to give him the
Princess, my daughter.  Go, my good woman, and I will
wait till you bring me his answer."

Full of disappointment, Aladdin's mother made her
way home, and told her son the Sultan's strange wish.
But Aladdin only smiled, and when his mother had gone
out, he took the lamp and rubbed it.  Instantly the genie
appeared, and Aladdin commanded him to lose no time
in bringing the presents for which the Sultan had wished.

In a very short time the genie returned with forty
black slaves, each carrying upon his head a large golden
basin of great weight, full of pearls, diamonds, rubies,
and emeralds, quite as fine as the jewels that Aladdin's
mother had given the Sultan.  Each basin was covered

with a cloth of silver, embroidered with flowers of gold. There were also the forty white slaves. All these slaves with their golden basins entirely filled the small house, as well as the court in front and the garden behind it.

Aladdin's mother now came back and almost fainted when she saw this great crowd and all its magnificence. Aladdin told her at once to follow the procession of slaves to the palace and present his gifts to the Sultan.

The astonishment of the Sultan at the sight of all these riches is hardly to be imagined. After gazing upon the slaves with their shining heaps of jewels, he said to Aladdin's mother, "Go, my good woman, and tell your son that I am waiting with open arms to embrace him!"

Aladdin was so delighted with this news that he could hardly answer his mother, and, hastening to his chamber, he shut the door. Once more he summoned the genie, who brought to him garments that shone like the sun. The genie also brought him a splendid horse and twenty slaves to march on either side of him on the way to the Sultan's palace, all holding purses of gold to scatter among the people.

If there had been a crowd before, there was ten times as great a one now to watch Aladdin as he rode to the Sultan's palace, and to pick up the gold pieces which were showered by his slaves as he went. The Sultan came down from his throne to greet him, and all was feasting and joy in the palace.

After the feast the judge drew up a marriage contract between Aladdin and the beautiful Princess. As soon as this was done, the Sultan asked Aladdin if he wished to remain in the palace and have the marriage take place that day. "Sire," he replied, "however impatient I may be to have entire possession of all your majesty's bounties, I beg you to permit me to wait until I shall have built a palace worthy to receive the Princess in; and for this purpose I request that you will have the goodness to point out a place for it near your own."

"My son," answered the Sultan, "take the open space before my palace; but remember that, to have my happiness complete, thou canst not too soon be united to my daughter." Having said this, he again embraced Aladdin, who now took leave of the Sultan as if he had spent all his life at court.

As soon as Aladdin reached home, he again summoned the genie and commanded him to build instantly the most gorgeous palace ever seen, on the spot of ground given by the Sultan. Early the next morning the genie appeared. "Sir," said he, "your palace is finished; see if it is as you wish."

Words cannot tell how astonished the Sultan and all his household were at seeing this gorgeous palace shining in the place which only the day before had been empty and bare. The Princess, too, rejoiced much at the sight. Her marriage with Aladdin was held the same day, and their happiness was the greatest that heart could wish.

For some months they lived thus, Aladdin showing great kindness to the poor, and pleasing all by his generosity.

### ALADDIN LOSES AND REGAINS THE LAMP

About this time his old enemy, the magician, found out by some of his magic arts that Aladdin was alive and very rich, instead of being, as he had supposed, dead in the enchanted cave. He was filled with rage, and, vowing to destroy Aladdin, he immediately set out for China. There he learned that Aladdin had gone hunting, and was not expected home for three or four days.

The magician bought a dozen shining new lamps, put them in a basket, and set out for Aladdin's palace. As he came near it, he cried, "Who will change old lamps for new?"

When he came under the windows of the Princess, one of her slaves said, "Come, let us see if the old fool means what he says; there is an ugly old lamp hanging in the hall of four-and-twenty windows; we will put a new one in its place if the old fellow is really in earnest." The Princess having given permission, one of the slaves took the lamp to the magician, who willingly gave her the best he had among his new ones.

As soon as night arrived, the magician summoned the genie of the lamp and commanded him to whisk the Princess, the palace, and the magician himself to the farthest corner of Africa.

The grief of the Sultan was terrible when he found the palace gone and his daughter lost. The people ran in fear through the streets, and the soldiers were sent in search of Aladdin, who had not yet returned.

Soon Aladdin was found and dragged before the Sultan like a criminal. He would have been beheaded had not the Sultan been afraid to make the people angry. "Go, wretch!" cried the Sultan. "I grant thee thy life; but if ever thou appearest before me again, death shall come to thee, unless in forty days thou bringest me tidings of my daughter."

Aladdin, wretched and downfallen, left the palace, not knowing where to go or what to do. At length he stopped at a brook to bathe his eyes, which smarted with the tears he had shed.  As he stooped, his foot slipped, and, catching hold of a piece of rock to save himself from falling, he pressed the magician's ring, which he still wore on his finger.  Instantly the genie of the ring appeared before him.  He bowed low, and said, "What would you have?" "Oh, Genie," cried Aladdin, "bring my palace back without delay."

"What you command," replied the genie, "is not in my power; you must call the genie of the lamp."

"Then I command you," said Aladdin, "to bear me to the place where now it stands."  Instantly Aladdin found himself beside his own palace, which stood in a meadow not far from a strange city; and the Princess was then walking in her own chamber, weeping for her loss.  Happening to come near to the window, she saw Aladdin under it, and making a sign to him to keep silent, she sent a slave to bring him in.  When the Princess and her husband had kissed each other and shed many tears, Aladdin said, "Tell me, my Princess, what has become of an old lamp which I left in the hall of four-and-twenty windows?"

The Princess then told how her slave had exchanged the old lamp for a new one, and said that the tyrant who had her in his power always carried that very lamp in his bosom.  Aladdin was then sure that this person was no other than his old enemy, the magician.

After talking a long while, they hit upon a plan for getting back the lamp.  Aladdin went into the city in the disguise of a slave and bought a powder. Then the Princess invited the magician to sup with her. As she had never before shown him the least kindness, he was delighted and came. While they were at table, she ordered a slave to bring two cups of wine, one of which she had prepared by mixing in the powder. After pretending to taste the one she held in her hand, she asked the magician to change cups, as was the custom in China. He joyfully seized the goblet, and drinking all of it at once, fell senseless on the floor.

Aladdin was at hand to snatch the lamp from his bosom. Hastily rubbing it, he summoned the genie, who instantly transported the palace and all it contained back to the place whence they had come.

Some hours after, the Sultan, who had risen at break of day to mourn for his daughter, went to the window to look upon the spot which had been empty and vacant for so many days. There to his unspeakable joy he saw Aladdin's palace shining in its place! He summoned his guards and hastened to embrace his daughter; and during a whole week nothing was heard but the sound of drums, trumpets, and cymbals, and there were all kinds of music and feasting, in honor of Aladdin's return with the Princess.

Some time after this, the Sultan died, and Aladdin and the Princess became rulers of the country. They reigned together many years and left many noble sons and daughters at their death.

NOTES AND QUESTIONS

1. Which two of these reasons best tell why for so many years people have liked this story?

  (a) It is so exciting.

  (b) It tells so many funny things.

  (c) It tells us interesting things about strange countries.

  (d) It tells about a magic lamp such as we all wish we could have.

2. Make a list of the main points of this story so that you could use it to tell the story. You can begin this way: *(1) The magician meets Aladdin.*

3. Was the magician really Aladdin's uncle? Find lines to prove your answer.

4. Did the sultan really want to make Aladdin happy, or did he have some other reason for letting Aladdin marry his daughter? Be ready to read lines that prove your answer.

5. Find and be ready to read the lines that tell about each of the pictures.

6. Were there words in this story whose meanings you did not know—such as *niche, transparent, bazaar, bounties,* and *account?* Don't forget to use your Glossary.

On page 434 you will find the names of two books of Arabian Nights stories that were made especially for boys and girls. You will like to read them and to look at the beautiful pictures in them.

# ALI BABA AND THE FORTY THIEVES

In this story Ali Baba, a poor man, finds a treasure cave and learns the magic word that opens it. But if Morgiana, the slave girl, had not been so clever and so brave, it would have been an unlucky day indeed for Ali Baba when he heard the magic words, "Open Sesame!"

## ALI BABA FINDS THE CAVE

In an old town of Persia there lived two brothers, Cassim and Ali Baba. Cassim married a wife who owned a fine shop, a warehouse, and some land; he soon became one of the richest men in the town. Ali Baba, on the other hand, who had a wife no better off than himself, lived in a very poor house. He supported his family by cutting wood in the forest and carrying it on his donkeys to sell about the town.

One day Ali Baba went to the forest, and when he had almost finished cutting as much wood as his donkeys could carry, he saw high in the air a thick cloud of dust which seemed to be coming toward him. He gazed at the cloud for a long time, until he saw a company of men on horseback, riding so fast that they were almost hidden by the dust.

Although that part of the country was not often troubled by robbers, Ali Baba thought that these horsemen looked like evil men. Therefore, without thinking at all what might become of his donkeys, his first and only care was to save himself. So he climbed up quickly into a large tree, the branches of which spread out so thick that from the midst of them he could see everything that passed, without himself being seen.

The robbers rode swiftly up to this very tree and there alighted. Ali Baba counted forty of them and saw that each horseman took the bridle off his horse and hung over its head a bag filled with barley. Then they took their traveling bags, which were so heavy that Ali Baba thought they must be filled with gold and silver.

With his bag on his shoulder, the Captain of the thieves came close to the rock at the very spot where the tree grew in which Ali Baba had hidden himself. After the rascal had made his way through the shrubs that grew there, he cried out, "Open Sesame!" so that Ali Baba distinctly heard the words. No sooner were they spoken than a door opened in the rock. The Captain and all his men passed quickly in; then the door closed again.

There they stayed for a long time. Ali Baba was compelled to wait in the tree with patience, for he was afraid some of them might come out if he left his hiding-place.

At length the door opened, and the forty thieves came out. After he had seen all the troop pass out before him, the Captain exclaimed, "Shut Sesame!" Each man then bridled his horse and mounted it. When the Captain saw that all were ready, he put himself at their head, and they rode off as they had come.

Ali Baba watched them as long as he could; nor did he leave the tree for a long time after he had lost sight of them. Then, remembering the words the Captain had used to open and shut the door, he made his way through the bushes and called out to it, "Open Sesame!" Instantly the door flew wide open!

Ali Baba expected to find only a dark cave; he was very much astonished at seeing a fine large chamber, dug out of the rock, and higher than a man could reach. The cave received its light from a hole in the top of the rock. In it were piled all sorts of rare fruits, bales of rich merchandise, silk stuffs and brocades, and great heaps of money, both silver and gold, some loose, some in large leather bags. The sight of all these things almost took Ali Baba's breath away.

But he did not hesitate long as to what he should do. He went boldly into the cave, and as soon as he was there, the door shut; but since he knew the secret by which to open it, this gave him no fear. Leaving the silver, he turned to the gold which was in the bags, and when he had gathered enough of the treasure, he brought his three donkeys to the rock, loaded them, and covered the sacks of gold with wood so that no one could suspect anything. This done, he went to the door, and had no sooner said the words, "Shut Sesame," than it closed.

Now Ali Baba took the road to the town, and when he got home, he drove his donkeys into the yard and shut the gate with great care. He threw off the wood that hid the gold and carried the bags into the house. There he laid them down in a row before his wife, who was sitting upon a couch.

When he had told the whole story of the cave and the forty thieves, he emptied the sacks, making one great heap of gold that quite dazzled his wife's eyes.

His wife rejoiced in this good fortune, and began to count over, piece by piece, the money that lay before her. "What are you going to do?" said he. "Why, you would never finish counting them. I will dig a pit for the treasure; we have no time to lose."

"We should know about how much there may be," replied the wife. "I will go and borrow a small grain measure, and while you are digging the pit, I will find how much there is."

So the wife of Ali Baba set off and went to her brother-in-law, Cassim, who lived a short way from her house. Cassim was away from home, so she begged his wife to lend her a measuring vessel for a few minutes. "That I will," said Cassim's wife. She went to seek a measure, but knowing how poor Ali Baba was, she was curious to know what sort of grain his wife wanted to measure; so she put some tallow on the bottom of the measure in such a way that no one would notice it.

The wife of Ali Baba returned home, and placing the measure on the heap of gold, filled it over and over again, till she had measured the whole. Ali Baba by this time had dug the pit for it, and while he was burying the gold, his wife went back with the measure to her sister-in-law. But she did not notice that a piece of gold had stuck to the bottom of the vessel.

The wife of Ali Baba had scarcely turned her back, when Cassim's wife, looking at the bottom of the measure, was astonished to see a piece of gold sticking to it. "What!" said she. "Ali Baba measures his gold! Where can the wretch have got it?" When her husband, Cassim, came home, she said to him, "Cassim, you think you are rich, but Ali Baba must have far more wealth than you; he does not count his gold as you do; he measures it." Then she showed him the piece of money she had found sticking to the bottom of the measure.

Far from feeling glad at the good fortune which had come to his brother, Cassim grew so jealous of Ali Baba that he passed almost the whole night without closing his eyes. The next morning before sunrise he went to his brother. "Ali Baba," said he, harshly, "you pretend to be poor and miserable and a beggar, and yet you measure your money. How many pieces," added he, "have you like this piece of gold my wife found sticking to the bottom of the measure yesterday?"

### CASSIM VISITS THE CAVE

From this speech Ali Baba knew that Cassim, and his wife also, must suspect what had happened. So, without showing the least sign of surprise, he told Cassim how he had found the cave of the thieves, and where it was; he offered, if he would keep the secret, to share the treasure with him.

"This I certainly expect," replied Cassim in a haughty tone; "otherwise I will inform the police of it."

Ali Baba, led rather by his good nature than by fear, told him all, even to the words he must pronounce, both on entering the cave and on quitting it. Cassim made no further inquiries of Ali Baba; he left his brother and set off the next morning before break of day with ten mules laden with large baskets which he proposed to fill with treasure from the cave. He took the road which Ali Baba had pointed out and arrived at the rock and the tree; on looking for the door, he soon discovered it. When he cried, "Open Sesame!" the door obeyed; he entered, and it closed again.

Greedy as Cassim was, he could have passed the whole day in feasting his eyes with the sight of so much gold; but he remembered that he had come to take away as much as he could; he therefore filled his sacks, and coming to the door, he found that he had forgotten the secret words, and instead of saying, "Open Sesame" he said, "Open Barley." So the door, instead of flying open, remained closed. He named various other kinds of grain; all but the right one were called upon, and still the door did not move.

Toward noon, the thieves returned to their cave. When they were within a short distance of it and saw Cassim's mules laden with baskets, standing about the

rock, they were a good deal surprised. They drove away the ten mules, which took to flight in the forest. Then the Captain and his men, with their swords in their hands, went toward the door and said, "Open Sesame!" At once it flew open.

Cassim, who from the inside of the cave heard the horses trampling on the ground, did not doubt that the thieves had come and that his death was near. Determined, however, on one effort to escape, he placed himself near the door ready to run out as soon as it should open. The word "Sesame" was scarcely pronounced when it opened, and he rushed out with such force that he threw the Captain to the ground. He could not, however, escape from the other thieves, who slew him on the spot.

On entering the cave the thieves found, near the door, the sacks which Cassim had filled, but they could not imagine how he had been able to get in.

The wife of Cassim, in the meantime, was in the greatest uneasiness when night came and her husband did not return.   After waiting as long as she could, she went in great alarm to Ali Baba and said to him, "Brother, I believe you know that Cassim has gone to the forest; he has not yet come back, although it is almost morning.   I fear some accident may have befallen him."

Ali Baba immediately set off with his three donkeys and went to the forest to seek Cassim.   As he drew near the rock, he was astonished to see that blood had been shed near the cave.   When he reached the door, he said, "Open Sesame!" and it opened.

He was shocked to see his brother's body in the cave. He decided to carry it home and placed it on one of his donkeys, covering it with sticks to conceal it.   The other two donkeys he quickly loaded with sacks of gold, putting wood over them as before.   Then, commanding the door to close, he took the road to the city, waiting in the forest till nightfall, that he might return without being seen. When he got home, he left the two donkeys that were laden with gold for his wife to unload; and having told her what had happened, he led the other donkey to the home of his sister-in-law.

Ali Baba knocked at the door, which was opened to

him by Morgiana, who was a very clever slave-girl. "Morgiana," said he, "the first thing I have to ask you is to keep a deep secret! This packet contains the body of your master, and we must bury him as if he had died a natural death. Let me speak to your mistress, and listen to what I say to her."

Morgiana called her mistress, and Ali Baba then told her all that had happened before his arrival with the body of Cassim. "Sister," added he, "here is a great sorrow for you, but we must bury my brother as if he had died a natural death. And then my wife and I shall be glad to offer you and your slave a shelter under our own roof."

Cassim's widow decided that she could not do better than consent. She therefore wiped away her tears and thereby showed Ali Baba that she accepted his offer of a home.

Ali Baba left her in this frame of mind, and Morgiana went out with him to a shop where drugs were sold. She knocked at the door, and when it was opened, asked for a certain kind of tablet often used in dangerous illness. The drug-seller gave her the medicine, asking who was ill in her master's family. "Ah!" exclaimed she with a deep sigh, "it is my worthy master, Cassim himself. He can neither speak nor eat!"

Meanwhile, as Ali Baba and his wife were seen going backward and forward to the house of Cassim in the course of the day, no one was surprised on hearing in the

evening the cries of his widow and Morgiana, announcing
his death.

And so the body of Cassim was prepared for its burial,
which took place the next day, attended by Ali Baba and
Morgiana.  As for his widow, she remained at Ali Baba's
home to weep with her neighbors, who, according to the
usual custom, called at the house during the burial, and
joining their cries to hers, filled the air with sounds of
woe.  Thus the manner of Cassim's death was so well
hidden that no one in the city knew anything about it.

### THE ROBBERS SEEK REVENGE ON ALI BABA

But let us now leave Ali Baba and Morgiana, and
return to the forty thieves.  When they came back to
their cave, they found the body of Cassim gone, and with
it much of their treasure.  "We are discovered," said the
Captain, "and we shall be lost if we are not very careful.
All that we can at present tell is that the man whom we
killed in the cave knew the secret of opening the door.
But he was not the only one; another must have found
it out, too.  Having slain one, we must not let the other
escape.  Well, the first thing to be done is that one of
you should go to the city in the dress of a traveler and
try to learn who the man we killed was."  The thief who
agreed to carry out this plan, having disguised himself
so that no one could have told who he was, set off at
night and entered the city just at dawn.

By asking questions in the town he discovered that a

body had been prepared for burial at a certain house. Having found the house, the thief marked the door with chalk and returned to the forest.

Very soon after this, Morgiana happened to go out, and she saw the mark which the thief had made on the door of Ali Baba's house. "What can this mark mean?" thought she. "Has anyone a spite against my master, or has it been done only for fun? In any case, it will be well to guard against the worst that may happen." She therefore took some chalk, and as several of the doors, both above and below her master's, were alike, she marked them in the same manner, and then went in without saying anything of what she had done either to her master or mistress.

The thief in the meantime arrived at the forest and related the success of his journey. They all listened to him with great delight, and the Captain, after praising him, said, "Comrades, we have no time to lose; let us arm ourselves and depart. When we have entered the city, which we had best do separately, let us all meet in the great square, and I will go and find out the house with the chalk mark."

Thus the thieves went in small parties of two or three to the city without causing any suspicion. The thief who had been there in the morning then led the Captain to the street in which he had marked the house of Ali Baba. When they reached the first house that had been marked by Morgiana, he pointed it out, saying that was the one.

But as they continued walking on, the Captain saw that the next door was marked in the same manner. At this the thief was quite confused and knew not what to say, for they found four or five doors more with the same mark.

The Captain, in great anger, returned to the square. When he met the first of his men, he commanded them to tell the rest that there was nothing left to do but to return to the forest; that all their work had been for nothing. When they had reached the forest, the Captain declared the mistaken thief deserving of death, and he was at once killed by his companions.

Next day another thief, in spite of this, determined to succeed where the other had failed. He went to the city, found the house, and marked the door of it with red. But, a short time after, Morgiana went out and saw the red mark and did not fail to make a similar red mark on the neighboring doors.

This thief, when he returned to the forest, boasted of his success, and the Captain and the rest took themselves into the city with as much care as before. The Captain and his guide went immediately to the street where Ali Baba lived, but the same thing occurred as before.

Thus they were obliged to return again to the forest disappointed. The second thief was put to death as a punishment for deceiving them.

Next time, the Captain himself went to the city and found the house of Ali Baba. But not choosing to amuse

himself by making marks on it, he examined it carefully. Not only did he look at it in passing; he passed before it several times, until at last he was certain he could not mistake it.

Thereupon he returned to the forest and told the thieves he had made sure of the house and had made a plan such that at last he was certain he could not mistake it. And first he ordered them to divide into small parties, and to go into the neighboring towns and villages and buy nineteen mules and thirty-eight large leather jars to carry oil, one of which must be full, and all the others empty.

In the course of two or three days the thieves returned,

and the Captain made one of his men enter each jar, armed as he thought necessary. Then he closed the jars as if each were full of oil, leaving, however, a small slit open to admit air. The mules were then laden with the thirty-seven thieves, each concealed in a jar, and the jar that was filled with oil. The Captain took the road to the city at the hour that had been agreed, and arrived about an hour after sunset. He went straight to the house of Ali Baba, where he found Ali Baba at the door, enjoying the fresh air after supper. "Sir," said he, "I have brought oil from a great distance to sell tomorrow at the market, and I do not know where to go to pass the night; if it would not give you much trouble, do me the favor to take me in."

Although Ali Baba had seen, in the forest, the man who now spoke to him and had even heard his voice, yet he had no idea that this was the Captain of the forty robbers, disguised as an oil merchant. "You are welcome," said he, and took him into the house, and his mules into the stable. The jars were left in the court.

### THE OIL MERCHANT IN THE HOME OF ALI BABA

Ali Baba, having told Morgiana to see that his guest was supplied with everything he wanted, added, "Tomorrow before daybreak I shall go to the bath. Make me some good broth to take when I return." After giving these orders, he went to bed.

In the meantime the Captain of the thieves, on leaving

the stable, went to give his people orders what to do. Beginning with the first jar, and going through the whole number, he said to each, "When I shall throw some pebbles from my chamber, do not fail to rip open the jar from top to bottom with the knife you have and to come out; I shall be with you soon after." The knives he spoke of were sharpened for the purpose. This done, he returned, and Morgiana took a light and led him to his chamber. Not to cause any suspicion, he put out the light and lay down in his clothes, to be ready to rise as soon as he had taken his first sleep.

Morgiana did not forget Ali Baba's orders; she prepared his linen for the bath and gave it to Abdalla, Ali Baba's slave, who had not yet gone to bed. Then she put the pot on the fire to make the broth, but while she was skimming it, the lamp went out. There was no more oil in the house, and she had no candle. She did not know what to do. She wanted a light to see to skim the pot, and mentioned it to Abdalla. "Take some oil," said he, "out of one of the jars in the court."

So Morgiana took the oil jug and went into the court. As she drew near the first jar, the thief who was concealed within said in a low voice, "Is it time?"

Any other slave except Morgiana, in the first moment of surprise at finding a man in the jar instead of some oil, would have made a great uproar. But Morgiana collected her thoughts, and imitating the voice of the Captain, answered, "Not yet, but presently." She went on to the next jar, and the others in turn, making the same answer to the same question, till she came to the last, which was full of oil.

Morgiana by this means discovered that her master, who supposed he was giving a night's lodging to an oil-merchant only, had provided shelter to thirty-eight robbers, including the pretended merchant, their Captain. She quickly filled her oil jug from the last jar and returned to the kitchen. After having put some oil in her lamp and lighted it, she took a large kettle and went again into the court to fill it with oil from the jar. This done, she brought it back again, put it over the fire, and made a great blaze under it with wood; for the sooner the oil boiled, the sooner her plan would be carried out. At length the oil boiled. She then took the kettle, and poured into each jar, from the first to the last, enough boiling oil to kill the robbers.

This being done without any noise, she returned to the kitchen with the empty kettle and shut the door. She put out the large fire she had made up for this purpose, and left only enough to finish boiling the broth for Ali Baba. She then blew out the lamp and remained perfectly silent, determined not to go to bed until she had watched what would happen, from a window which overlooked the courtyard.

Morgiana had waited scarcely a quarter of an hour, when the Captain of the robbers awoke. He got up, and opening the window, looked out. All was dark and silent.

He gave the signal by throwing the pebbles, many of which fell on the jars, as the sound plainly proved. He listened, but could hear nothing that would lead him to think his men obeyed the signal. He became uneasy at this delay, and threw some pebbles down a second time, and even a third. They all struck the jars, yet when nothing moved, he became frightened.

He went down into the court in great alarm. Going up to the first jar, he was about to ask if the robber inside was asleep. But as soon as he drew near, he caught a strong scent of burning oil coming out of the jar. From this he feared that his wicked plan had failed. He went to the next jar, and to each jar in turn. Then he realized that all his men were dead.  Terrified at this, he jumped over the garden gate and made his escape.

Before daybreak Ali Baba, followed by his slave, went to the bath, entirely ignorant of what had taken place in his house during his sleep.

When he returned from the bath, the sun being risen, Ali Baba was surprised to see the jars of oil still in their places; so he inquired the reason of Morgiana.

"My good master," said Morgiana to Ali Baba's question, "may God preserve you and all your family.  You will soon know the reason, if you will take the trouble to come with me."  Ali Baba followed Morgiana, and when she had shut the door, she took him to the first jar and bade him look in and see if it contained oil.  He did as she desired; and seeing a man in the jar, he hastily drew back with a cry of surprise.  "Do not be afraid," said she.  "The man you see there will not do you any harm, for he is now dead."

"Morgiana!" exclaimed Ali Baba, "what does all this mean?  Do explain this mystery."  "I will explain it," replied Morgiana, "but pray do not awaken the curiosity of your neighbors to learn what you should keep secret.  Look first at all the other jars."

Ali Baba examined all the rest of the jars, one after the other.  This done, he stood, sometimes casting his eyes on Morgiana, then looking at the jars, yet without speaking a word, so great was his surprise.  At length he said, "And what has become of the merchant?"

"The merchant," replied Morgiana, "is just as much a merchant as I am. I can tell you who he is."

She then described the marks made upon the door, and the way in which she had copied them, adding: "You see this is a plot formed by the forty thieves of the forest, whose troop is now reduced to three at most. The events of last night prove that they are determined to take your life, and you will do right to be on your guard against them, so long as even one of the robbers remains."

Ali Baba, full of gratitude for all he owed her, replied, "I will reward you as you deserve, before I die. I owe my life to you, and from this moment I give you your liberty, and will soon do still more for you."

## MORGIANA'S GREAT COURAGE AND REWARD

Meanwhile the Captain of the forty thieves had returned to the forest full of rage, and determined to revenge himself on Ali Baba.

Next morning he awoke at an early hour, put on a merchant's dress and returned to the city, where he took a lodging at an inn. Then he bought a horse, which he made use of to carry to his lodging several kinds of rich stuffs and fine linens, bringing them from the forest at various times. In order to dispose of these wares, he rented a shop and established himself in it. This shop was exactly opposite to that which had been Cassim's, and was now occupied by the son of Ali Baba.

The Captain of the thieves, who had taken the name

of Houssam, soon succeeded in making friends with the son of Ali Baba, who was young and good-natured. He often invited the youth to sup with him, and made him rich gifts.

When Ali Baba heard of it, he resolved to make a return for this kindness to Houssam, little thinking that the pretended merchant was really the Captain of the thieves. So one day he asked Houssam to do him the honor of supping and spending the evening at his house. "Sir," replied the merchant, "I am grateful for your kindness, but I must beg you to excuse me, and for a reason which I am sure you will think sufficient. It is this: I never eat of any dish that has salt in it. Judge, then, how uncomfortable I should be at your table."

"If this be your only reason," replied Ali Baba, "it need not prevent your coming to supper with me. The bread which is eaten in my house does not contain salt; and as for the meat and other dishes, I promise you there shall be none in those which are served to you."

So Ali Baba went into the kitchen, and desired Morgiana not to put any salt in the meat she was going to serve for supper, and also to prepare two or three dishes of those that he had ordered, without any salt.

Morgiana obeyed, though much against her will; and she felt some curiosity to see this man who did not eat salt. When she had finished, and Abdalla had prepared the table, she helped him in carrying the dishes. On looking at Houssam, she instantly recognized the Captain of the robbers, in spite of his disguise. Looking at him more closely, she saw that he had a dagger hidden under his dress. "I am no longer surprised," said she to herself, "that this villain will not eat salt with my master; he is his enemy, and means to murder him!  But I will prevent the villain!"

When the supper was ended, the Captain of the thieves thought that the time for revenging himself on Ali Baba had come.  "I will make them both drink much wine," thought he, "and then the son, against whom I bear no malice, will not prevent my plunging my dagger into the heart of his father, and I shall escape by way of the garden, as I did before, while the cook and the slave are at their supper in the kitchen."

Instead, however, of going to supper, Morgiana did not allow him time to carry out his wicked plans.  She dressed herself as a dancer, put on a suitable headdress, and wore round her waist a fancy girdle of gold, to which she fastened a dagger, made of the same metal.  Her face was hidden by a very handsome mask.  When she had so disguised herself, she said to Abdalla, "Take your tabor, and let us go and entertain our master's guest, who is the friend of his son, as we do sometimes by our performances."

Abdalla took his tabor and began to play, as he walked before Morgiana, and entered the room.  Morgiana followed him, making a low curtsy, and performed several dances.  At length she drew out the dagger, and dancing

with it in her hand, she surpassed all she had yet done,
by her light movements and high leaps; sometimes thrust-
ing the dagger as if to strike, and at others holding it to
her own bosom, as if to stab herself.

At length, as if out of breath, she took the tabor from
Abdalla with her left hand, and holding the dagger in her
right, she held out the tabor to Ali Baba, who threw a
piece of gold into it. Morgiana then held the tabor out
to his son, who did the same. Houssam, who saw that
she was coming to him next, had already taken his purse
from his bosom, and was putting his hand into it, when
Morgiana, with great courage, suddenly plunged the
dagger into his heart.

Ali Baba and his son, terrified at this action, uttered a loud cry: "Wretch!" exclaimed Ali Baba, "what have you done? You have ruined me and my family forever!"

"What I have done," replied Morgiana, "is not for your ruin, but for your safety." Then opening Houssam's robe to show Ali Baba the dagger which was concealed under it, "See," continued she, "the cruel enemy you had to deal with; examine him, and you will recognize the pretended oil-merchant and the Captain of the forty thieves! Do you now see why he refused to eat salt with you?"

Ali Baba, who now saw all that he owed to Morgiana for having thus saved his life a second time, cried, "Morgiana, I gave you your liberty, and at the same time I promised that I would do more for you at some future time. This time has come, and I present you to my son as his wife."

A few days after, Ali Baba had the marriage of his son and Morgiana celebrated with great feasting.

After the marriage, Ali Baba decided to visit again the cave of the forty thieves. On reaching it, he repeated the words, "Open Sesame." At once the door opened, and entering the cave, he found that no one had been in it from the time that Houssam had opened his shop in the city. He therefore knew that the whole troop of thieves had been killed, and that he was the only person in the world who knew the secret of the cave.

From that time Ali Baba and his son, whom he took

to the cave and taught the secret of how to enter it, enjoyed its riches and lived in great happiness and comfort to the end of their long lives.

## NOTES AND QUESTIONS

1.   Name the five most important characters in this story. Put the most important one first.

2.   What names belong where the letters are in the sentences below?

....(a).... was clever, brave, and faithful.

....(b).... was greedy, deceitful, and envious.

....(c).... was revengeful, bold, and clever.

....(d).... was kind-hearted, good-natured, and generous.

3.   In what three ways did Morgiana show that she was a quick-witted girl?

4.   Why did Ali Baba pretend that his brother had died of illness?

5.   What were the four most exciting moments in this story?

6.   Write about eight sentences that will give the main points of this story, so that you could use them for an outline in telling it.   You might begin this way:   *(1) Ali Baba finds the treasure cave.*

7.   Make up a name for each of the five pictures in this story.

If you liked these two Arabian Nights stories, you will want to read some of the others.   You might start with "Sinbad the Sailor" and "The Fisherman and the Genie" (in *Legends of the Seven Seas*, Price).

# ROBINSON CRUSOE

## DANIEL DEFOE

Daniel Defoe, an Englishman, wrote this story about two hundred years ago. He got the idea for the story from the adventures of a sailor named Alexander Selkirk, who spent four years on a lonesome island about four hundred miles off the western coast of South America. Even boys and girls of other lands have enjoyed this story, for it has been translated into many other languages.

### HOW I WENT TO SEA AND WAS SHIPWRECKED

I was born at York, in England, on the first of March, 1632. From the time that I was quite a young child I had felt a great wish to spend my life at sea, and as I grew, so did this taste grow more and more strong; till at last on September 1, 1651, I ran away from my school and home and found my way on foot to Hull, where I soon got a place on board a ship.

Never did any young adventurer's misfortunes begin sooner or continue longer than mine, for when we were far out at sea, some Turks in a small ship came on our track in full chase. After a long pursuit our vessel was captured, and all on board were taken as slaves.

The chief of the Turks took me as his prize to a port which was held by the Moors. There I remained in slavery for several years, and bitterly did I repent having left my good parents in England.

At length I found an opportunity to escape to a vessel that was passing by, and was kindly received by the captain, an Englishman, bound on a voyage of trade.

I had not been aboard more than twelve days when a high wind took us off, we knew not where. All at once there was a cry of "Land!" and the ship struck on a bank of sand, in which she sank so deep that we could not get her off. At last we found that we must make up our minds to leave her and get to shore as well as we could. There had been a boat at her stern, but we found it had been torn off by the force of the waves. One small boat was still left on the ship's side, so we got into it.

There we were, all of us, on the wild sea. The heart of each now grew faint, and our cheeks were pale, for there was but one hope, and that was to find some bay, and so get in the lee of the land. But the sea grew more and more rough, and its white foam curled and boiled till at last the waves in their wild sport burst on the boat's side, and we were all thrown out.

I could swim well, but the force of the waves made me lose my breath too much to do so. At length one large wave took me to the shore and left me high and dry, though half dead with fear. I got on my feet and made the best of my way for the land, but just then the curve of a huge wave rose up as high as a hill, and this I had no strength to keep from; so it took me back to the sea. I did my best to float on the top and held my breath to do so. The next wave was quite as high and shut me up

in its bulk. I held my hands down tight to my sides, and then my head shot out at the top of the waves. This gave me breath, and soon my feet felt the ground.

I stood quite still for a short time, to let the sea run back from me, and then I set off with all my might to the shore; but yet the waves caught me, and twice more did they take me back, and twice more land me on the shore. I thought the last wave would have been the death of me, for it drove me on a piece of rock with such force as to leave me in a kind of swoon. I soon regained my senses and got up to the cliffs close to the shore, where I found some grass out of the reach of the sea. There I sat down, safe on land at last.

I felt so wrapped in joy that all I could do was to walk up and down the coast, and thank God for all that he had done for me, when the rest of the men were lost. I now cast my eyes round me, to find out what kind of place it was that I had been thus thrown in, like a bird in a storm. Then all the glee I felt at first left me; for I was wet and cold, and had no dry clothes to put on, no food to eat, and not a friend to help me.

I feared that there might be wild beasts here, and I had no gun to shoot them with, or to keep me from their jaws. I had but a knife and a pipe.

It now grew dark; and where was I to go for the night? I thought the top of some high tree would be a good place to keep me out of harm's way; and that there I might sit and think of death, for, as yct, I had no hope of life. Well, I went to my tree and made a kind of nest to sleep in. Then I cut a stick to keep off beasts of prey, in case any should come, and fell asleep just as if the branch I lay on had been a bed of down.

When I woke up, it was broad day; the sky, too, was clear, and the sea calm. But I saw from the top of the tree that in the night the ship had left the bank of sand and lay but a mile from me. I soon threw off my clothes, took to the sea, and swam up to the wreck. But how was I to get on deck? I had gone twice around the ship, when a piece of rope caught my eye, which hung down from her side so low that at first the waves hid it. By the help of this rope I got on board.

## HOW I MADE AND USED A RAFT

I found that there was a bulge in the ship, and that she had sprung a leak. You may be sure that my first thought was to look around for some food, and I soon made my way to the bin where the bread was kept, and ate some of it as I went to and fro, for there was no time to lose. What I stood most in need of was a boat to take the goods to shore. But it was vain to wish for that which could not be had; and as there were some spare yards in the ship, two or three large planks, and a mast or two, I fell to work with these to make a raft.

I put four spars side by side, and laid short bits of plank on them, crossways, to make my raft strong. Though these planks would bear my own weight, they were too slight to bear much of my freight. So I took a saw which was on board and cut a mast in three lengths, and these gave great strength to the raft. I found some bread, rice, a Dutch cheese, and some dry goat's flesh.

My next task was to screen my goods from the spray of the sea; and this did not take long, for there were three large chests on board which held all, and these I put on the raft.

"See, here is a prize!" said I, out loud (though there was none to hear me); "now I shall not starve." For I found four large guns. But how was my raft to be got to land? I had no sail, no oars; and a gust of wind would make all my store slide off. Yet there were three things which I was glad of—a calm sea, a tide which set in to

the shore, and a slight breeze to blow me there. I had
the good luck to find some oars in a part of the ship in
which I had made no search till now. With these I put
to sea, and for half a mile my raft went well; but soon
I found it driven to one side. At length I saw a creek,
up which, with some toil, I took my raft.

I saw that there were birds on the isle, and I shot one
of them. Mine must have been the first gun that had
been heard there since the world was made, for, at the
sound of it, whole flocks of birds flew up, with loud cries,
from all parts of the wood. The beak of the one I shot
was like that of a hawk, but the claws were not so large.

I now went back to my raft to land my stores, and this
took up the rest of the day. What to do at night I knew
not, nor where to find a safe place for my stores. I did
not like to lie down on the ground, for fear of beasts of
prey, as well as snakes; but there was no cause for these
fears, as I later found. I put the chests and boards round
me, and thus made a kind of hut for the night.

As there were still a great many things left in the ship
which would be of use to me, I thought that I ought to
bring them to land at once; for I knew that the first
storm would break up the ship. So next day I early went
on board, and took good care this time not to load my raft
too much.

The first thing I sought for was the tool chest. In it
were bags of nails, some spikes, saws, knives, and such
things, but best of all, I found a stone to grind my tools

on. There were two or three flasks, some large bags of shot, and a roll of lead, but this last I had not the strength to hoist up to the ship's side. There were some spare sails, too, which I brought to shore.

Now that I had two loads of goods on hand, I made a tent with the ship's sails to stow them in and cut the poles for it from the wood. I now took all the things out of the casks and chests and put the casks in piles round the tent to give it strength; and when this was done, I shut up the door with the boards, spread on the ground one of the beds which I had brought from the ship, laid two guns close to my head, and went to bed. I slept all night, for I was much in need of rest.

The next day I was sad and sick at heart, for I felt how dull it was to be thus cut off from all the rest of the world! I had no great wish for work, but there was too much to be done for me to dwell long on my sad lot. Each day I went off to the wreck to fetch more things, and I brought back as much as the raft would hold.

The last time I went to the wreck the wind blew so hard that I made up my mind to go on board next time at low tide. I found some tea and some gold coin; but as to the gold, it made me laugh to look at it. Said I, "Thou art of no use to me! I care not to save thee. Stay where thou art till the ship goes down; then go thou with it!"

Still, I thought I might just as well take it; so I put it in a piece of the sail and threw it on deck, that I

might place it on the raft.   By and by the wind blew
from the shore; so I had to hurry back with all speed,
for I knew that at the turn of the tide, I should find it
hard work to get to land.   But in spite of the high wind
I came to my home all safe.   At dawn I put my head out
and looked out to sea, when lo! no ship was there!

This loss of such a friend quite struck me down.   Yet
I was glad to think that I had brought to shore all that
could be of use to me.   I had now to look out for some
spot where I could make my home.   Halfway up the hill
there was a small plain, four or five score feet long and
twice as broad; and as it had a full view of the sea, I
thought that it would be a good place for my house.

### HOW I MADE MYSELF A HOME ON THE ISLAND

I first dug a trench round a space which took in twelve
yards; and in this I drove two rows of stakes till they
stood firm like piles, five and a half feet from the ground.
I made the stakes close and tight with bits of rope and
put small sticks on the top of them in the shape of spikes.
This made so strong a fence that no man or beast could
get in.

The door of my house was on top, and I had to climb
up to it by steps, which I took in with me, so that no one
else might come up by the same way.   Close to the back
of the house stood a sand rock, in which I made a cave,
and laid all the earth that I had dug out of it round my
house, to the height of a foot and a half.   I had to go

out once a day in search of food. The first time, I saw some goats, but they were too shy to let me get near.

At first I thought that for the lack of pen and ink I should lose all note of time; so I made a large post, in the shape of a cross, on which I cut these words: "I came on shore here on the thirtieth of September, 1659." On the side of this post I made a notch each day, and this I kept up till the last.

I have not yet said a word of my four pets, which were two cats, a dog, and a parrot. You may guess how fond I was of them, for they were all the friends left to me. I brought the dog and two cats from the ship. The dog would fetch things for me, and by his bark, his whine, his growl, and his tricks, he would almost talk to me. If I could but have had someone near me to find fault with, or to find fault with me, what a treat it would have been! I was a long way out of the course of ships; and oh, how dull it was to be cast on this lone spot with no one to love, no one to make me laugh, no one to make me weep, no one to make me think! It was dull to roam day by day from the wood to the shore, and from the shore back again, alone with my thoughts all the while.

So much for the sad view of my case; but like most things, it had a bright side as well as a dark one. For here was I safe on land, while all the rest of the ship's crew were lost. True, I was cast on a rough and rude part of the globe, but there were no beasts of prey on it to kill or hurt me. God had sent the ship so near to me that I had got from it all things to meet my wants for the rest of my days. Let life be what it might, there was surely much to thank God for. And I soon gave up all dull thoughts and did not so much as look for a sail.

My goods from the wreck remained in the cave for more than ten months; I decided then that it was time to put them right, as they took up all the space and left me no room to turn in; so I made my small cave a large one and dug it out a long way back in the sand rock.

Then I brought the mouth of the cave up to my fence, and so made a back way to my house. This done, I put shelves on each side to hold my goods, which made the cave look like a shop full of stores. To make these shelves was a very difficult task and took a long time, for to make a board I was forced to cut down a whole tree, chop away with my ax till one side was flat, and then cut at the other side till the board was thin enough, when I smoothed it with my adz. But, in this way, out of each tree I would get only one plank. I also made for myself a table and a chair, and finally got my castle, as I called it, in good order.

I usually rose early and worked till noon, when I ate my meal; then I went out with my gun, after which I worked once more till the sun had set; and then to bed. It took me more than a week to change the shape and size of my cave. Unfortunately, I made it far too large, for, later on, the earth fell in from the roof; and had I been in it when this took place, I should have lost my life.

I had now to set up posts in my cave, with planks on the top of them, so as to make a roof of wood.

## HOW I SUPPLIED MY NEEDS

*Alan*

I had to go to bed at dusk, till I made a lamp of goat's fat, which I put in a clay dish; and this, with a piece of hemp for a wick, made a good light. As I had found a use for the bag which had held the fowls' food on board ship, I shook out from it the husks of grain. This was just at the time when the great rains fell, and in the course of a month, blades of rice and barley sprang up. As time went by, and the grain was ripe, I kept it, and took care to sow it each year; but I could not boast of a crop of grain for three years.

*Louise*

I knew that tools would be my first want and that I should have to grind mine on the stone, as they were blunt and worn with use. But as it took both hands to hold the tool, I could not turn the stone; so I made a wheel by which I could move it with my foot. This was no small task, but I took great pains with it, and at length it was done.

*Alice?*

I had now been in the isle twelve months, and I thought it was time to go all round it in search of its woods, springs, and creeks. So I set off, and brought back with me limes and grapes of the finest kind, large and ripe. The little valley on the banks of which they grew was fresh and green, and a clear, bright stream ran through it, which gave so great charm to the spot as to make me wish to live there. But there was no view of the sea from this vale, while from my house no ships could come on my side of the isle and not be seen by me. Yet the cool, soft banks were so sweet and new to me that much of my time was spent there.

In the first of the three years in which I had grown barley, I had sown it too late; in the next it was spoiled by the drought; but the third year's crop had sprung up well. Few of us think of the cost at which a loaf of bread is made. Of course, there was no plow here to turn up the earth, and no spade to dig it with; so I made one with wood, but this was soon worn out, and for want of a rake I made use of the bough of a tree. When I had got the grain home, I had to thresh it, part the grain from the chaff, and store it up. Then came the want of sieves to clean it, of a mill to grind it, and of yeast to make bread of it.

If I could have found a làrge stone, slightly hollow on top, I might, by pounding the grain on it with another round stone, have made very good meal. But all the stones I could find were too soft; and in the end I had to make a sort of mill of hard wood, in which I burned a hollow place, and in that pounded the grain into meal with a heavy stick.

Baking I did by building a big fire, raking away the ashes, and putting the dough on the hot place, covered with a kind of basin made of clay, over which I had heaped the red ashes. Thus my bread was made, though

I had no tools; and no one could say that I did not earn it by the sweat of my brow.

My chief wants now were jars, pots, cups, and plates, but I knew not how I could make them. At last I went in search of clay and found a bank of it a mile from my house, but it was quite a joke to see the queer shapes and forms that I made out of it. For some of my pots and jars were too weak to bear their own weight, and they would fall out here, and in there, in all sorts of ways; while some, when they were put in the sun to bake, would crack with the heat of its rays. You may guess what my joy was when at last a pot was made which would stand the fire, so that I could boil the meat for broth.

When the rain kept me indoors, it was fun to teach my pet bird Poll to talk; but so mute were all things round me that the sound of my own voice made me start. My dog sat at meals with me, and one cat on each side of me, on stools, and we had Poll to talk to us.

The next thing to turn my thoughts to was the ship's boat, which lay on the high ridge of sand, where it had been thrust by the storm which had cast me on these shores. But it lay with the keel to the sky; so I had to dig the sand from it and turn it up with the help of a pole. When I had done this, I found it was all in vain, for I had not the strength to launch it. So all I could do now was to make a smaller boat out of a tree. I found one just fit for it, which grew not far from shore, but I could no more stir this than I could the ship's boat.

"Well," thought I, "I must give up the boat, and with
it all my hopes of leaving the isle.  But I have this to
think of: I am lord of the whole isle; in fact, a king. I
have wood with which I might build a fleet, and grapes, if
not grain, to load it with, though all my wealth is but
a few gold coins."  For these I had no sort of use, and
could have found it in my heart to give them all for a
peck of peas and some ink, which last I stood much in
need of.  But it was best to dwell more on what I had
than on what I had not.

I now felt that I must try once more to build a boat,
but this time it was to have a mast, for which the ship's
sails would be of great use.  I made a deck at each end to

keep out the spray of the sea, a bin for my food, and a rest for my gun, with a flap to screen it from the wet. More than all, the boat was one of such a size that I could launch it.

My first cruise was up and down the creek, but soon I got bold and made the whole round of my isle. I took with me bread, cakes, a pot of rice, half a goat, and two greatcoats, one of which was to lie on, and one to put on at night. I set sail in the sixth year of my reign. On the east side of the isle there was a large ridge of rocks which lay two miles from the shore, and a shoal of sand lay for half a mile from the rocks to the beach. To get round this point I had to sail a great way out to sea; and here I all but lost my life.

But I got back to my home at last. On my way there, quite worn out with the toils of the boat, I lay down in the shade to rest my limbs, and slept. But judge, if you can, what a start I gave when a voice woke me out of my sleep and spoke my name three times! A voice in this wild place! To call me by name, too! Then the voice said, "Robin! Robin Crusoe! Where are you? Where have you been? How came you here?" But now I saw it all, for at the top of the hedge sat Poll, who did but say the words she had been taught by me.

I now went in search of some goats and laid snares for them, with rice for a bait. I had set the traps in the night and found they had stood, though the bait was all gone. So I thought of a new way to take them, which was to make a pit and lay sticks and grass on it, so as to hide it; and in this way I caught an old goat and some kids. But the old goat was much too fierce for me, so I let him go.

I brought all the young ones home and let them fast a long time, till at last they fed from my hand and were quite tame. I kept them in a kind of park, in which there were trees to screen them from the sun. At first my park was half a mile round; but it struck me that, in so great a space, the kids would soon get as wild as if they had the range of the whole vale, and that it would be as well to give them less room; so I had to make a hedge, which took me three months to plant. My park held a flock of twelve goats, and in two years time there were more than two score.

Now for a word as to the dress in which I made a tour round the isle. I could not but think how strange it would look in the streets of the town in which I was born.

I usually wore a high cap of goatskin, with a long flap that hung down to keep the sun and rain from my neck, a coat made from the skin of a goat, too, the skirts of which came down to my hips. On my legs were trousers of the same skin. I wore no shoes, but had flaps of the fur round my shins. I had a broad belt of the same around my waist, which fastened on with two thongs; and from it hung a saw, an ax, and a pouch for the shot. My beard had not been cut since I came here. But no more need be said of my looks, for there were few to see me.

HOW I DISCOVERED FOOTPRINTS AND SAVED FRIDAY

A strange sight was now in store for me, which was to change the whole course of my life in the isle.

One day at noon, while on a stroll down to a part of the shore that was new to me, what should I see on the sand but the print of a man's foot! I felt as if I could not stir from the spot. By and by I stole a look around me, but no one was in sight. What could this mean? I went three or four times to look at it. There it was—the print of a man's foot: toes, heel, and all the parts of a foot. How could it have come there?

My head swam with fear; and as I left the spot, I made two or three steps, and then took a look around me; then two steps more, and did the same thing. I took fright at the stump of an old tree, and ran to my house, as if for my life. How could anything in the shape of a man come to that shore, and I not know it? Where was the ship that brought him? Then a vague dread took hold of my mind, that some man, or set of men, had found me out; and it might be that they meant to kill me, or rob me of all I had.

Fear kept me indoors for three days, till the want of food drove me out. At last I was so bold as to go down to the coast to look once more at the print of the foot, to see if it was the same shape as my own. I found it was not so large by a great deal; so it was clear that it was not one of my own footprints, and that there were men in the isle.

One day as I went from the hill to the coast, a scene lay in front of me which made me sick at heart. The spot was spread with the bones of men. There was a round place dug in the earth, where a fire had been made, and here some men had come to feast. Now that I had seen this sight, I knew not how to act; I kept close to my home and would scarce stir from it save to milk my flock of goats.

A few days later I was struck by the sight of some smoke, which came from a fire no more than two miles off. From this time I lost all my peace of mind. Day and night a dread would haunt me that the men who had made this fire would find me out. I went home and drew up my steps, but first I made all things round me look wild and rude. To load my gun was the next thing to do, and I thought it would be best to stay at home and hide. But this was not to be borne long. I had no spy to send out, and all I could do was to get to the top of the hill and keep a good lookout. At last, through my glass I could see a group of wild men join in a dance round their fire. As soon as they stopped, I took two guns and slung a sword on my side; then with all speed I set off to the top of the hill, once more to have a good view.

This time I made up my mind to go up to the men, but not with a view to kill them, for I felt that it would be wrong to do so. With a heavy load of arms it took me two hours to reach the spot where the fire was; and by the time I got there, the men had all gone, but I saw them in four boats out at sea.

Down on the shore there was a proof of what the work of these men had been. The signs of their feast made me sick at heart, and I shut my eyes. I dared not fire my gun when I went out for food on that side of the isle, lest there should be some of the men left, who might hear it, and so find me out.

From this time all went well with me for two years; but it was not to last. One day as I stood on the hill, I saw six boats on the shore. What could this mean? Where were the men who had brought them? And what had they come for? I saw through my glass that there were a score and a half at least on the east side of the isle. They had meat on the fire, round which I could see them dance. They then took a man from one of the boats, who was bound hand and foot; but when they loosed his bonds, he set off as fast as his feet would take him, and in a straight line to my house.

To tell the truth, when I saw all the rest of the men run to catch him, my hair stood on end with fright. In the creek he swam like a fish, and the plunge which he took brought him through it in a few strokes. All the men now gave up the chase but two, and they swam through the creek. But they were by no means such good swimmers as the slave.

Now, I thought, was the time to help the poor man, and my heart told me it would be right to do so. I ran

down with my two guns, and went with all speed up a hill, and then down by a short cut to meet them.

I gave a sign to the poor slave to come to me, and at the same time went up to meet the two men who were in chase of him. I made a rush at the first of these, struck at him with the stock of my gun, and he fell. I saw the one who was left, stop and aim at me with his bow; so, to save my life, I aimed carefully and shot him dead.

The smoke and noise from my gun gave the poor slave who had been bound such a shock that he stood still on the spot, as if he had been in a trance. I gave a loud shout for him to come to me, and I took care to show him that I was a friend, and made all the signs I could think of to coax him up to me. At length he came, knelt down to kiss the ground, and then took hold of my foot and set it on his head. All this meant that he was my slave; and I bade him rise and made much of him.

I did not like to take my slave to my house, or to my cave; so I threw down some straw from the rice plant for him to sleep on and gave him some bread and a bunch of dry grapes to eat. He was a fine man, with straight, strong limbs, tall and young. His hair was thick, like wool, and black. His head was large and high, and he had bright black eyes. He was of a dark-brown hue; his face was round and his nose small, but not flat. He had a good mouth with thin lips, with which he could give a soft and pleasing smile; and his splendid teeth were as white as snow.

Toward evening I had been out to milk my goats, and when he saw me, he ran to me and lay down on the ground to show me his thanks. He then put his head on the ground and set my foot on his head, as he had done at first. He took all the means he could think of to let me know he would serve me all his life! And I gave a sign to make him understand that I thought well of him.

The next thing was to think of some name to call him by. I chose that of the sixth day of the week, Friday, as he came to me on that day. I took care not to lose sight of him all that night. When the sun rose, we went up to the top of the hill to look out for the men; but as we could not see them or their boats, it was clear that they had left the isle.

*Howard* I now set to work to make my man a cap of hare's skin, and gave him a goat's skin to wear round his waist. It was a great source of pride to him to find that his clothes were as good as my own.

*Lois* At night I kept my guns, swords, and bow close to my side; but there was no need for this, as my slave was indeed most true to me. He did all that he was set to do, with his whole heart in the work; and I knew that he would lay down his life to save mine. What could a man do more than that? And oh, the joy to have him here to cheer me in this lone isle!

## HOW FRIDAY LEARNED MY WAYS

*Gordon* I did my best to teach him, so like a child he was, to do and feel all that was right. I found him apt and full of fun; and he took great pains to understand and learn all that I could tell him.

*Maxine* One day I sent him to beat out and sift some grain. I let him see me make the bread, and he soon did all the work. I felt quite a love for his true, warm heart, and he soon learned to talk to me. One day I said, "Do the men of your tribe win in fight?" He told me, with a smile, that they did. "Well, then," said I, "how came they to let their foes take you?"

"They run one, two, three, and make go in the boat that time."

"Well, and what do the men do with those they take?"

"Eat them all up."

This was not good news for me, but I went on and said, "Where do they take them?"

"Go to next place where they think."

"Do they come here?"

"Yes, yes, they come here, come else place, too."

"Have you been here with them twice?"

"Yes, come there."

He meant the northwest side of the isle; so to this spot I took him the next day. He knew the place and told me he was there once, and with him twelve men. To let me know this, he placed twelve stones all in a row, and made me count them.

He told me that up a great way by the moon—that is, where the moon then came up—there dwelt a tribe of white men like me, with beards. I felt sure they must have come from Spain to work the gold mines; so I asked him: "Could I go from this isle and join those men?"

"Yes, yes, you go in two boats."

It was hard to see how one man could go in two boats, but what he meant was a boat twice as large as my own.

"Then will you go back to your land with me?"

He said he could not swim so far; so I told him he should help me to build a boat to go in. Then he said, "If you go, I go."

"I go? Why, they would eat me!"

"No, me make them much love you."

We then went to look at the old ship's boat, which, as it had been in the sun for years, was not at all in a sound state. Friday was sure that it would do. But how were we to know this? I told him we should build a boat as large as that, and that he should go home in it.

We soon set to work to make a boat that would take us both. The first thing was to look out for some large tree that grew near the shore, so that we could launch our boat when it was made. My slave's plan was to burn the wood to make it the right shape; but as my plan was to hew it, I set him to work with my tools. In two months' time we made a good, strong boat; but it took a long while to get her to the shore and float her.

Friday had the whole charge of her; and, large as she was, he made her move with ease, and said, "Me think she go there well, though great blow wind!" He did not know that I meant to make a mast and sail. I cut down a young fir tree for the mast, and then I set to work at the sail. It made me laugh to see my man stand and stare when he came to watch me sail the boat. But he soon gave a jump, a laugh, and a clap of the hands when for the first time he saw the sail swing back and forth to catch the wind.

The next thing to do was to stow our boat up in the creek, where we dug a small dock; and when the tide was low, we made a dam to keep out the sea. The time of year had now come for us to set sail; so we got out all our stores to put them into the boat.

**THE ENGLISH SHIP AND HOW I SAILED FOR HOME**

I was fast asleep in my hut one morning, when my man Friday came running in to me and called aloud, "Master, master, they are come, they are come!" I jumped up and went out, as soon as I could get my clothes on. I was astounded when, turning my eyes to the sea, I saw a ship at about a league and a half distance, headed in for the shore, and the wind blowing pretty fair to bring it in.

Upon this I hastily called Friday in and bade him lie close, for we did not know yet whether they were friends or enemies. In the next place, I went in to fetch my spyglass to see what I could make of them; and having climbed up to the top of the hill, I saw a ship lying at anchor, at about two leagues from me, but not above a league and a half from the shore. It seemed to be an English ship, and the boat which was putting off looked much like an English longboat.

They ran their boat on shore upon the beach, at about half a mile from me. When they were on shore, I saw they were Englishmen. There were, in all, eleven men; three of them I found were unarmed, and, as I thought, bound. When the first four or five of them had jumped on shore, they took those three out of the boat as prisoners. I was shocked and terrified at the sight of all this and knew not what the meaning of it could be.

I expected every minute to see the three prisoners killed; so I fitted myself up for battle, though with much caution. I ordered Friday also to load himself with arms. I myself took two fowling pieces, and I gave him two muskets. My figure was very fierce; I had my goatskin coat on, with the great cap, a naked sword, two pistols in my belt, and a gun upon each shoulder.

It was my purpose not to make any attempt till it was dark; but about two o'clock, it being the heat of the day, I found they had all gone straggling into the woods, and, as I thought, had all lain down to sleep. The three poor prisoners had, however, sat down under the shelter of a great tree.

I resolved to show myself to them and learn some-

thing of their condition; immediately I marched toward
them, my man Friday at a good distance behind me. I
came as near them undiscovered as I could, and then, before any of the prisoners saw me, I called aloud to them
in Spanish, "Who are ye, sirs?"

They gave a start at my voice and at my strange dress,
and made a move as if they would flee from me. I said,
"Do not fear me, for it may be that you have a friend at
hand, though you do not think it." "He must be sent
from the sky, then," said one of them with a grave look;
and he took off his hat to me at the same time. "All help
is from the sky, sir," I said. "But what can I do to aid
you? Your speech shows me that you come from the
same land as I do. I will do all I can to serve you. Tell
me your case."

"Our case, sir, is too long to tell you while they who
would kill us are so near. My name is Paul. To be
short, sir, my crew have thrust me out of my ship, which
you see out there, and have left me here to die. They
have set me down in this isle with these two men, my
friend here, and the ship's mate."

"Where have they gone?" said I.

"There, in the wood close by. I fear they may have
seen and heard us. If they have, they will be sure to
kill us all."

"Have they firearms?"

"They have four guns, one of which is in the boat."

"Well, then, leave all to me!"

*Alice S.*

"There are two of the men," said he, "who are worse than the rest. All but these I feel sure would go back to work the ship."

I thought it was best to speak out to Paul at once, and I said, "Now, if I save your life, there are two things which you must do."

But he read my thoughts, and said, "If you save my life, you shall do as you like with me and my ship, and take her where you please."

I saw that the two men, in whose charge the boat had been left, had come on shore; so the first thing I did was to send Friday to fetch from it the oars, the sail, and the gun. And now the ship might be said to be in our hands. When the time came for the two men to go back to the ship, they were in a great rage; for, as the boat had now no sail or oars, they knew not how to get out to their ship.

We heard them say that it was a strange sort of isle, for spirits had come to the boat to take off the sails and oars. We could see them run to and fro, with great rage, then go and sit in the boat to rest, and then come on shore once more. When they drew near to us, Paul and Friday would fain have had me fall on them at once. But my wish was to spare them and kill as few as possible. I told two of my men to creep on their hands and knees close to the ground, so that they might not be seen, and when they got up to the men, not to fire till I gave the word.

They had not stood thus long when three of the crew came up to us. Till now we had but heard their voices, but when they came so near as to be seen, Paul and Friday shot at them. Two of the men fell dead—they were the worst of the crew—and the third ran off. At the sound of the guns I came up, but it was so dark that the men could not tell if there were three of us or three score.

It happened just as I wished it, for I heard the men ask: "To whom must we yield, and where are they?" Friday told them that Paul was there with the king of the isle, who had brought with him a crowd of men! At this, one of the crew said: "If Paul will spare our lives, we will yield." "Then," said Friday, "you shall know the king's will." Then Paul said to them: "You know my voice; if you lay down your arms, the king will spare your lives."

They fell on their knees to beg the same of me. I took good care that they did not see me, but I gave them my word that they should all live, that I should take four of them to work the ship, and that the rest would be bound hand and foot for the good faith of the four. This was to show them what a stern king I was.

Of course I soon set them free, and I showed them how they could take my place on the isle. I told them of all my ways, taught them how to mind the goats, how to work the farm, and how to make the bread. I gave them a house to live in, firearms, tools, and my two tame cats —in fact, all that I owned but Poll and my gold.

I made ready to go on board the ship, but told the captain I would stay that night to get my things in shape, and asked him to go on board in the meantime and keep things right on the ship.

I cast my eyes to the ship, which rode half a mile off the shore, at the mouth of the creek, and near the place where I had brought my raft to the land. Yes, there she stood, the ship that was to set me free and to take me where I might choose to go. She set her sails to the wind, and her flags threw out their gay stripes in the breeze. Such a sight was too much for me, and I fell down faint with joy.

Friday and Paul then went on board the ship, and Paul took charge of her once more. We did not start that night, but at noon the next day I left the isle—that lone isle, where I had spent so great a part of my life.

When I took leave of this island, I carried on board a great goatskin cap I had made and my parrot; also the money which had lain by me so long useless that it was grown rusty or tarnished, and could hardly pass for gold till it had been a little rubbed and handled. And thus I left the island, the nineteenth of December, as I found by the ship's account, in the year 1686, after I had been upon it seven-and-twenty years, two months, and nineteen days. In this vessel, after a long voyage, I arrived in England the eleventh of June, in the year 1687.

## Notes and Questions

1. Which of these three was the most important thing about Robinson Crusoe?

(a) He was brave.

(b) He was cheerful in spite of his troubles.

(c) He was clever in finding ways to do things.

2. What did Robinson Crusoe miss more than anything else during the early part of his life on the island? Find lines to prove your answer, and be ready to read them.

3. What were the three most important things Crusoe had to do for himself when he began his life on the island?

4. Name four things that Crusoe made for himself. Perhaps you can name more.

5. What was the most important thing that Friday meant to Crusoe? Find and be ready to read lines that prove your answer.

6. Find lines that tell how Crusoe made something. Be ready to read them.

7. What was the most exciting part of the story?

8. Find the lines that tell how Crusoe felt when he first found that men had visited his island. Be ready to read them.

This story tells only the main things that happened to Robinson Crusoe. You will want some day to read the entire book of his adventures that Daniel Defoe wrote. You might also like to read *Swiss Family Robinson,* by Wyss, the story of a whole family that was shipwrecked on an island.

# A BACKWARD LOOK

Now you have been introduced to Ali Baba, Morgiana, Aladdin, Robinson Crusoe, and Friday. Just think! it is hundreds of years since they were born into the pages of a story-book. Yet they are no older today than they were then. Ali Baba still finds the treasure cave, and Morgiana saves his life; Aladdin rubs the magic lamp and wins his beautiful princess; Robinson Crusoe still builds his raft, saves Friday, and is rescued from the island.

You are now one of the great family of boys and girls all over the world who know these famous people. If you hear someone say, "John has been a real man Friday to me," you will know exactly what is meant. If someone wishes that he had Aladdin's lamp, you will not have to ask "What lamp?" and "Who is Aladdin?" You will probably catch yourself many times wishing that you could find a treasure cave like Ali Baba's.

Which of these three stories did you like best? Why? Which was most exciting? Who was the cleverest person in the stories? Which one do you think might be a good inventor? Why? Which story sounded the most as if it had really happened?

As you go on with your reading in school, you will meet many famous story-book people. But there are so many that your school books cannot tell you about them all— about Sindbad the sailor, Gulliver the famous traveler, Ivanhoe the brave knight, Little Nell, Robin Hood, Rosalind, King Arthur, Eppie, and countless others. All through your life you can have many pleasant hours with interesting, kind, brave, and funny people who live for us all in the world of story-books.

# PART EIGHT
## · HOLIDAYS AND FESTIVALS ·

## EVERY DAY'S A LITTLE YEAR

### ANNETTE WYNNE

Every day's a little year;
Keep it new and full of cheer,
Keep it glad in any weather;
So, by adding days together,
All the whole big year is true,
Full of cheer, and shining new.

# WHAT IS A HOLIDAY?

To all of us—men and women, boys and girls—a holiday is a time when we drop our everyday work. We leave the office, the factory, and the schoolroom, and enjoy ourselves in play. Often we have a fine dinner, or a picnic in the woods. Our grandparents, aunts and uncles, and cousins may come to visit us, or we may go to visit them. Holidays are happy times for us all.

But we really should spend a little time each holiday thinking of what the day means. Why are people all over our land celebrating it? Something must have happened on that day of the year—something that meant a great deal to all of us.

In the life of every nation there have happened events that meant great things to the people. In a time of great danger or need, a wise and strong man may have risen to lead the nation in its time of trouble. His birthday is a day that the people of his country want never to forget. Perhaps on a certain day a nation won its freedom after long years of struggle and suffering. Surely the people want to keep that day fresh in their memories.

So, in order that we may not forget, and in order that we may show our happiness and thankfulness for the things that have been done for us, holidays have been set aside. See if you can find out from these stories the true meaning of each holiday.

# DICK'S THANKSGIVING SNOWSHOES

## BEN AMES WILLIAMS

Dick was very much surprised to learn that everyone did not have a fine turkey dinner on Thanksgiving Day. And when he learned this, the snowshoes for which he had been saving money did not seem so important as making someone else happy on Thanksgiving Day.

### EARNING AND SAVING FOR SNOWSHOES

Dick Hart's older brother had gone away the year before to a college in the New Hampshire hills. When he came home to Forestville in the summer for the long vacation, he brought with him, among his other belongings, a pair of snowshoes. Dick had read of such things, but he had never seen them. Forestville had an occasional snow of a foot or so, but it never stayed long, and there was little use for snowshoes around the village. Nevertheless, when Dick saw them he wanted a pair.

That evening Dick asked his brother what the snowshoes cost. He was told they could be purchased for six dollars—a good pair, long and narrow, built to glide easily through thick brush, where the broader, ordinary shape would knock against every tree.

"I'm going to get them," Dick thought, and said to his brother, "If I send you the money, will you get me a pair?"

"What use have you got for snowshoes?" his brother asked.

"We-ell, I just want some," Dick answered, flushing. "I guess I can hang them on the wall of my room till I go to college, can't I?"

His brother chuckled. "Sure! I'll get you a pair, all right, if you'll send the money. But where are you going to raise it?"

"Oh, I'll get it!" Dick promised.

And straightway he set about the task of earning a fortune—six dollars.

Six dollars seems a small amount, but to a boy of Dick's age it is wealth. What could he do? He could cut lawns and carry coal and empty ashes and work the pump in his mother's kitchen, and that was about all. He found a surprising number of neighbors willing to let him cut their grass "for fifteen cents."

His mother discovered Dick's new desire for money, and, after watching him for a few days, she decided to encourage him.

"Dick," she said one day, "I think you ought to have a chance to earn money regularly, don't you? I believe I will put you on a salary."

"Salary?" he repeated in surprise.

"Yes, salary. I think I'll pay you twenty-five cents a week for your chores around the house, and, say, a cent a hundred strokes for the pumping you do at the kitchen pump to fill the water tank in the attic."

She watched him, and Dick's eyes grew bright; then his face lighted eagerly.

"All right," he said soberly. "I—guess that'd be fine." The tank in the Harts' attic needed to be filled about three times a week so that the family might have enough water for all its needs. That meant about forty-five hundred strokes at the pump in the kitchen—forty-five cents a week besides the quarter for chores. Seventy cents a week! Riches! He would have the six dollars, he decided, by the third week in November—by Thanksgiving!

## THANKSGIVING PLANS

"Gee!" he thought. "And there'll probably come a big snow then, too. There's nearly always snow for Thanksgiving."

Thanksgiving that year came on the twenty-fourth of November. On the seventeenth Dick counted his money. He had five dollars and thirty cents. His goal, those snowshoes, was in sight!

On the Sunday before Thanksgiving, Dick's mother told his father, "I've ordered our turkey again this year from Mr. Aiken out in the country."

"Good!" his father agreed. "He sent us a fine fat one last year."

"And I think," Mrs. Hart added, "that we're going to have the finest pumpkin-pie you ever saw. Mr. Aiken says he has a big yellow pumpkin all picked out for us." Dick's mouth fairly watered.

Next morning Mrs. Attson came to do the washing, as she did nearly every week. She and Dick were the best

of friends. Dick toiled at the pump while the tall, thin woman toiled above the tubs. He watched her over his shoulder. She looked worried, he thought.

By and by he was sure of it, for she began to tell him what it was that was worrying her. One of her daughters was sick; had hardly any appetite at all. Didn't he think even little girls ought to have good appetites for their food?

Dick did. "I don't see how she can enjoy Thanksgiving without a good appetite," he said, chuckling to himself at the thought of the good things his mother was planning for the dinner.

Mrs. Attson smiled also. "I'm planning quite a nice

Thanksgiving dinner for her, too," she declared. "If it doesn't make her hungry, I don't know what will."

Dick worked away at the pump.

"What are you going to have?" he asked.

Mrs. Attson smiled proudly. "Why," she said, "I'm planning a nice dinner, even if we do have to piece out afterwards for a time." She dipped one of Dick's shirts in the soapy water, and scrubbed it up and down, and dipped it again. "I'm going to get a nice piece of meat, not chuck like we have on Sundays sometimes, but a real nice piece—round steak, maybe. And she's going to have the best part of it. And some rice and potatoes— sweet potatoes fried in sugar the way she likes them. And I'm going to make some apple fritters from some apples I have, too."

Dick pumped his hardest, but he couldn't look at Mrs. Attson. Her voice was so proud! And Dick was horrified. He had supposed every one had turkey for Thanksgiving. He didn't know there was such a thing as Thanksgiving without turkey. Why it wouldn't *be* Thanksgiving without turkey, that's all!

He pumped harder than ever; and then Mrs. Attson asked, as proudly as before, "Don't you think that ought to wake up her appetite a lot?"

"I—sure do," Dick choked hurriedly. Then he growled something to himself under his breath. What was he crying for, anyhow? Guess it must be the steam in this kitchen—or something.

He decided not to finish his pumping that day. He turned around without a word and hurried past Mrs. Attson and up to his room. After a little while he heard the pump going steadily. She was filling the tank for him! He got up and started downstairs to stop her—but he could not face her. She was so proud of that Thanksgiving she had planned. Round steak!

"Mother, is—round steak cheap?" he asked that night.

"Why yes, dear," his mother answered. "Why in the world—"

But she did not repeat the question.

Before he went to bed, Dick counted his money again. Somehow he felt guilty at having so much.

Tuesday morning, when he woke up, it was snowing. It snowed all day. There were ten inches of snow on the ground when Dick's father came home that night. Dick looked out of his window before he went to bed. It had stopped snowing. But before the dawn, the flakes were falling again, a thin, driving snow, the kind that keeps coming.

Dick had had an uncomfortable Tuesday; he had done some hard thinking Tuesday night; and Wednesday morning he got out his money—he kept it in a drawer in his bureau—and counted it again. Then he did some more thinking; then put the money away again and thrust the drawer shut with a hard bang. He seemed to see the tall, thin figure of a woman laboring with something, her shoulders rising and falling. She was working the handle of the pump—

Dick could see nothing, for the mistiness of his eyes. But he could hear a cracked, tired voice, filled with great pride, saying, "Round steak, maybe, and some rice and potatoes."

### DICK BUYS A THANKSGIVING DINNER

"What are you buying a turkey for?" Mr. Holman, the fat grocer, asked in surprise when Dick made his purchase later in the day.

"Oh—I'm just getting one—for somebody," Dick explained lamely. "And—I want some cranberries, too—and a pumpkin, a big one."

Mrs. Attson lived in a ramshackle little house, unpainted, with a low, sloping roof, down near the railroad tracks. Dick had hauled the washing down there once or twice when his mother did not wish the work done at their home. He trudged down that way now through the deep snow in the early dusk of that Wednesday afternoon, with a heavily loaded basket on his arm. It had been snowing all day. There must be a foot and a half or two feet of snow on the ground, a record-breaker for Forestville.

Dick didn't mind—so much. "I probably couldn't walk on snowshoes if I had them," he said to himself.

Nobody saw him, he felt sure. It was almost dark. There was a light in the window of Mrs. Attson's house;

so he knew some one was at home. He laid the basket gently in the deep snow by the door, and then slipped out to the street. From behind a telephone pole he threw snowballs at the door till he caught the click of the latch. Some one was going to open it. Then he put down his head and fled.

### AFTER ALL, SNOWSHOES FOR THANKSGIVING

His father had not come home when he arrived, but his mother was reading a letter from the older brother at college. "Jim says they're having snow up there, too," she said. "He's been snowshoeing. And Dick—he says that you said something about buying some snowshoes. Did you?"

Dick flushed painfully. "Why—yes, Mother, I did," he confessed.

She looked at him thoughtfully. "Dickie," she exclaimed suddenly, "was that why you've been working so hard and saving your money? I knew you weren't spending any, and I wondered!"

"Yes, Mother," Dick admitted, gulping hard.

"That's fine, son!" she told him proudly. "How much have you saved? Perhaps I can make up what you need."

Dick hesitated and kicked at a chair and threw his hat out into the hall. "I—I—it's gone!" he said gruffly. And then, quite suddenly, he turned and stumbled at a run up the stairs to his room.

His mother was still staring out into the hall when his father came home. She rose to help Mr. Hart off with his coat.

"Oh, by the way," said her husband, when their greetings were over, "Holman told me Dick bought a turkey and all the fixings there today. Why was that? Didn't Aiken's bird come?"

"Why—yes!" said Mrs. Hart, in a puzzled tone. "I don't know what it was for."

"Is he here?" Mr. Hart asked; then called: "Dick!"

Dick opened his door upstairs. "What is it, Father?" he answered.

"Who was it you were buying a turkey for, Dick?" his father asked.

Mr. and Mrs. Hart looked up to the darkened upper

hall, but Dick did not appear at the banisters. There was a curious pause. No one said anything. And then suddenly the telephone bell rang.

As Mrs. Hart turned to answer, she heard Dick's door close. She spoke softly for a moment before she rejoined her husband in the living-room. There were happy tears in her eyes.

"Mrs. Attson just called up," she said gently. "She wanted to thank us. Some one left a Thanksgiving basket at her door today—tonight. Mrs. Hughes, across the road, saw the boy. It was Dickie. Mrs. Attson thought we had sent him with it."

Mr. Hart's eyes widened in surprise. "Great Scott!" he cried. "But—where did the boy get the money?"

Mrs. Hart told him, then, of the little hoard Dick had said was "gone."

"The—little scamp!" Mr. Hart exclaimed. Thereafter they sat for a little space, staring into the fire. Then Mr. Hart rose suddenly and went to the telephone in the hall. "Telegraph—office," he directed the operator.

When Dick came down to supper, his parents smiled at him knowingly. He looked—and felt—sheepish; and he felt more so when his father said in an offhand manner:

"By the way, Dick—thought you might want to have some fun with this snow. So I telegraphed to Chicago just now. They're to send the best pair of snowshoes in town —by express. They will be here by Saturday."

Dick looked at his father, and then he looked at his

mother. Mr. Hart coughed gruffly. His mother smiled happily through her tears. Dick choked, and grinned; his eyes were glowing—and wet.

"Thanks, Dad!" he said.

## Notes and Questions

1.  Which do you think was the finest thing about Dick?

    (*a*) He worked hard to earn money.

    (*b*) He spent his money for Mrs. Attson.

    (*c*) He felt sorry for Mrs. Attson.

    (*d*) He did not want anyone to know what he had done.

2.  What happened that made it especially hard for Dick to give up the snowshoes?

3.  Which word belongs where each letter is in the sentences below?

    *unselfish     industrious     modest     kind-hearted*

    Dick was ....(*a*).... when he gave up his snowshoe money to buy the dinner for Mrs. Attson.

    The way he earned the money for the snowshoes showed that he was ....(*b*).....

    He tried to hide what he had done for Mrs. Attson because he was ....(*c*).....

    He was so ....(*d*).... that he couldn't help thinking about Mrs. Attson.

Another good Thanksgiving story is "Bert's Thanksgiving," Trowbridge (in *Children's Book of Thanksgiving Stories,* Dickinson).

# CHRISTMAS BELLS

HENRY WADSWORTH LONGFELLOW

I heard the bells on Christmas day
Their old, familiar carols play,
    And wild and sweet
    The words repeat
Of peace on earth, good will to men!

And thought how, as the day had come,
The belfries of all Christendom
    Had rolled along
    The unbroken song
Of peace on earth, good will to men!

Till, ringing, singing on its way,
The world revolved from night to day,
    A voice, a chime,
    A chant sublime
Of peace on earth, good will to men!

# PAT SANTA'S THRILLING RIDE

## Elliott Flower

No Santa Claus ever needed a reindeer more than Pat Hogan needed one on a certain Christmas eve. It was a strange kind of reindeer that he finally found, but it made possible a happy Christmas for the Ballinger family.

He was first known as Pat Hogan, but a certain Christmas deed gave him the name of Pat Santa Claus, which was later abbreviated to "Pat Santa."

Pat lived and worked close to the end of the peninsula that runs for about eighteen miles straight up Grand Traverse Bay, Traverse City being the base of it and Old Mission near the point. How Pat came there no one knew. He simply appeared one summer during the fruit-gathering season, and went to work on the little farm of Mason Ballinger. Then he remained to assist in cutting timber during the winter, and in the course of two years came to be thought of as almost a member of the family. A strong friendship existed between him and his employer, and there was nothing that Pat would not do for the children.

From *Around the Hearth Fire,* by Wilhelmine Harper. Copyright 1931, D. Appleton and Company, N. Y.

A POOR OUTLOOK FOR CHRISTMAS

But a certain Christmas season two years after Pat's arrival found things in bad condition on the Ballinger farm. The fruit crop, which was depended upon to carry them through the year, had been a failure. Some wood had been sold, but the returns from this were small; and as Christmas approached, Ballinger became worried and anxious. His children were not accustomed to any elaborate celebration of the day, but there always had been something for them. Now it looked as if there would be nothing.

Pat fully understood the situation, and was as much disturbed as his employer. So Pat now worried, said mean things about the world in general, and made daily trips to Old Mission to see if the mail had brought Ballinger the check expected for timber he had sold.

In the gathering dusk of Christmas eve he was seen returning through the snow, as if his life depended on his speed. "Here ye are!" he shouted, wildly waving a letter. "Here's the cash for the timber."

Ballinger ran to meet him, his eyes sparkling. Then suddenly he stopped, his arms dropped to his sides, and he became the picture of a man greatly discouraged.

"Too late," he said. "We can make it up to them later, but Christmas won't be Christmas. There's nothing to be had this side of Traverse City."

Pat's face became as long as one of the gaunt pine trees. Old Mission boasted of only one little general

store, that could supply none of the things needed, and
the only communication with Traverse City, aside from
that furnished by the mail carrier, was supplied by a
stage that made the trip twice a week. "I'll cross to Elk
Rapids on the ice," he suggested, "and get the train."

"Too late for any train until tomorrow," said Ballinger.

"I'll go to Traverse on the ice," asserted Pat.

"Impossible!" exclaimed Ballinger. "It's all of sixteen miles from here, and that means thirty-two miles
between now and morning, with bundles to bring back.
You can't do it, Pat."

"I'll try it," said Pat. "The stores'll be open late this

night, and the children'll be lookin' for Santy Claus in the mornin'. I'll play I'm Santy."

## A HARD JOURNEY FOR SANTA CLAUS

Pat insisted, and Ballinger finally let him go. There seemed to be no chance that he would be back by morning, but if he reached Traverse City before the stores closed, he certainly could rest and get back sometime during Christmas day. That would be better than no Christmas at all.

From the house to Traverse City one could travel in almost a straight line on the ice, making only slight detours round Neahtawanta Point and Marion Island. Yet, as Ballinger had said, it was all of sixteen miles, and traveling over the ice, wearing felt boots and overshoes, is not at all like sprinting over a cinder path in the summer time. Pat could not possibly hope to make more than four miles an hour on the average, and he would be fortunate if he did as well as that.

As a matter of fact, he was not fortunate. The wind was strong and was directly in his face, and this held him back not a little. The fishermen, too, who live in tents on the ice for days and weeks at a time, sought to delay him for the sake of his company. But only once did he stop, and that was to help a man in distress. When one sees a tent blown down and a lone man vainly trying to get it up again and anchor it while the wind is blowing a gale, he finds it hard to go on without giving a helping hand. So Pat lost half an hour and made a friend—a thing for which he had cause to be thankful later.

"Of course," he muttered to himself, "I'm Santy Claus this night, but I never knew the old man had such a hard job of it."

When he finally reached Traverse City, he found the stores open and doing a brisk Christmas-eve trade. The shopping took time, and further time was required to get thoroughly warmed and rested. The sixteen-mile trip down, facing the wind, had been hard; the fact that it had come after a day's work had made it harder; the wind had chilled him; and it required all his courage to face the return journey.

But he started as soon as he was in condition to do so. He had bought a big sled; on this he had packed his purchases, including a whole pig that was to provide the holiday luxury of fresh meat. The load was not a particularly heavy one, but any load would seem heavy in such circumstances.

"The sled weighs a ton!" he growled, although he knew his own weariness was largely to blame for the trouble he experienced.

He resolutely pushed on until he came to the tent that he had helped to anchor on his down trip; here he stopped to speak to the fisherman.

"You look bad," remarked the man.

" 'Tis the way I feel," returned Pat.

"Come inside out of the wind and rest," urged the fisherman.

"Got to go on," said Pat.

"Why?" asked the fisherman.

"I'm Santy Claus," was the reply.

"You don't look it," stated the fisherman. "Where's your whiskers?"

"The wind got them," answered Pat. "But I'm Santy all the same," he added. Then he told the story.

### SANTA GETS A HELPING HAND

The fisherman listened closely, and at the conclusion declared: "You're done up, and can't walk it in time."

"I've got to," insisted Pat.

"Why don't you ride?" asked the fisherman.

"Where's the horse?" demanded Pat.

The fisherman laughed.

"A horse is a plodding old thing beside an ice-boat," he asserted. "Give me a little time, and I'll fix you up for the ride of your life. You helped me out when I was in a bad way, you know."

The fisherman brought a pike-pole from the tent and tied a crosspiece to the handle of it. Then he cut a tent-flap into the shape of a triangle, the shorter side of which was just the width of the crosspiece. This he tied tightly to the crosspiece, letting the canvas hang down so that the point of it could be grasped by the hand that held the mast steady.

"Can you sail?" he asked.

"How d'ye think I know when I never tried?" returned Pat.

"Well, you'll mighty soon find out," laughed the fisherman. "Sit on the pig."

Pat did as directed, and the fisherman jammed the point of the pike-pole into the sled in front of him.

"Grab the pole and the point of the sail with both hands and hang on tight," he instructed. "You've got to go pretty much with the wind, but you can change your course slightly by swaying your body. Ready?"

"Let her slide," said Pat.

### A THRILLING RIDE

The preparations had taken place in the lee of the tent, but the fisherman now pushed the sled out into the wind and gave it as good a start as his strength would permit. For a moment it seemed as if the scheme would prove a failure. The sled seemed to lose speed, rather than gain it, although the sail bellied out with a force that almost jerked Pat from his seat on the pig. But slowly the sled responded to the force of the wind, and the strain on Pat's arms gradually lessened.

"Oho!" he cried happily. "Sailin' is a fine sport when ye get goin'. 'Tis restin' to the legs, anyhow."

Presently, however, he became nervous. His speed was steadily increasing, and he found that the slightest move on his part made the sled swerve a little. Once or twice he almost lost his balance, and only by experimenting could he adjust himself properly.

He saw Marion Island looming up ahead of him in the moonlight, and this gave him another fright.

"If I hit it, goin' like this," he exclaimed, "I'll take it along or leave the sled behind and go sailin' over it like a bird! And I can't stop! Oho! I got the flyin'-machine now, and no brake on it!"

His only hope of avoiding the island was to change his course slightly, which was no easy matter. And to which side should he go? It would be easier to take the east passage, but two or three miles beyond, on that side, Neahtawanta jutted out from the peninsula. He would have to swerve to the east for the island and to the west for Neahtawanta. Unquestionably it would be better to go to the west of both—if possible.

So Pat began working his sled to the west, but it was slow and dangerous work. A sudden movement would have wrecked him. Only a gentle swaying of his body, constantly repeated, that turned the sled a mere trifle to the left, was possible. Each passing minute made it clearer that he could not hope to miss the island except by the narrowest margin.

Little by little he worked to the west, but still not far enough. His speed was too great to give him much time. Once he thought of rolling off the sled and taking the chance of breaking his neck; but he could not forget that he was "carryin' Christmas."

His heart almost stopped beating as he came under the shadow of the island. He knew now that he could clear the land, but there were ice-hummocks in the way. Another gentle swerve, still another; his right runner was lifted by the base of a hummock, the sled

balanced for an instant on the left, and—settled back
to level again. He had cleared the island. Now it was
a straight course before the wind.

"All I have to do now is to stop when the time
comes, but 'tis no easy job," exclaimed Pat.

At once his mind began to busy itself with this problem. To roll off the sled would be extremely dangerous, but for the moment there seemed to be no other
way. "If I could only take down the sail," Pat muttered. He looked up at it, and then laughed. "The
fool that ye are, Pat," he said. "All ye have to do is
to pull up the mast and throw it away."

Thereupon he settled himself for the enjoyment of
the rest of the trip. He had to make no further change

from the straight line in which he was going in order to reach his destination.

## "HERE COMES SANTA CLAUS!"

And the children were waiting for him. He had not expected that, although it was the hour when most children get out of bed on Christmas morning. But he saw them piling out into the snow; he saw Mrs. Ballinger waving a handkerchief from the porch, and he saw Ballinger slip and slide down to the shore-line.

He did not know that Ballinger had been up nearly all night, hoping against hope that Christmas would be Christmas for the children; that he had seen the moving speck from an upper window, and followed it with a field-glass; that he had danced and yelled like a delighted boy when he finally made out what it was; that he had roused the children from bed with the cry of "Here comes Santa Claus!" But there was glory and reward for Pat in what he saw as he made the last mile of his journey.

Pike-pole and sail went over on the ice at what he considered the proper moment, but he misjudged the speed. He cautiously put out a foot to use as a brake. It struck an obstruction, and he and the sled and the pig and the bundles went into a confused heap almost at the feet of Ballinger and the children!

"Merry Christmas!" roared Pat.

"Hurrah for Pat Santa Claus!" cried Ballinger, and the children took up the cry with excited happiness.

"I've brought the Christmas with me," said Pat, proudly, as he got up and shook himself, "but I'll own up to ye I couldn't have done it if a fisherman friend of mine hadn't made me a loan of his reindeer."

### NOTES AND QUESTIONS

1. Which one of these sentences best describes this story?
   (a) This is a story of how a kind-hearted man brought happiness to a family on Christmas day.
   (b) This story tells how one man was helped in time of need because he had been kind to another man.
   (c) This is a story of an exciting ride over the ice on Christmas morning.

2. What does this story show most about Pat—that he was strong, brave, kind-hearted, or clever?

3. Choose two other scenes in this story for which you think good pictures could have been drawn.

4. Write the following words in a column, and opposite each word write a word or phrase that means the same thing, thus, (a) *abbreviated—shortened.*   (a) abbreviated, (b) sprinting, (c) distress, (d) resolutely, (e) conclusion, (f) plodding, (g) Ice, (h) scheme, (i) experimenting, (j) adjust, (k) jutted.

5. Find and be ready to read lines that show Pat's sense of humor.

6. If anyone in the class has ever made an ice-boat or sailed on one, have him tell about it.

Other Christmas stories you would like are: "The Fir Tree," Andersen (in *Child-Library Readers, Book Five)*; "Sandy's Christmas," Travis (in *Christmas in Storyland)*; and "Robin Redbreast," Lagerlöf (in *Christ Legends*).

# SOMEBODY'S MOTHER

(AUTHOR UNKNOWN)

The woman was old and ragged and gray
And bent with the chill of the winter's day.
The street was wet with the recent snow,
And the woman's feet were aged and slow.

She stood at the crossing and waited long,
Alone, uncared for, amid the throng
Of human beings who passed her by,
Nor heeded the glance of her anxious eye.

Down the street with laughter and shout,
Glad in the freedom of "school let out,"
Came the boys like a flock of sheep,
Hailing the snow piled white and deep.

Past the woman so old and gray
Hastened the children on their way,
Nor offered a helping hand to her,
So meek, so timid, afraid to stir,
Lest the carriage wheels or the horses' feet
Should crowd her down in the slippery street.

At last came one of the merry troop,
The gayest laddie of all the group;
He paused beside her and whispered low,
"I'll help you across if you wish to go."

Her aged hand on his strong young arm
She placed, and so, without hurt or harm,
He guided her trembling feet along,
Proud that his own were firm and strong.

Then back again to his friends he went,
His young heart happy and well content.
"She's somebody's mother, boys, you know,
For all she's aged and poor and slow;

"And I hope some fellow will lend a hand
To help my mother, you understand,
If ever she's poor and old and gray,
When her own dear boy is far away."

And "somebody's mother" bowed low her head
In her home that night, and the prayer she said
Was, "God be kind to the noble boy
Who is somebody's son and pride and joy."

# THE LITTLE FLAGS

MARY LEE DALTON

Oh, when you see them flying
  Beside the summer way—
The little flags they put in place
  Upon Memorial Day—
Remember each is crying
  A message straight to you—
A message straight to every lad
  Whose heart is clean and true.

They tell the splendid story
  Of those who marched away
In answer to a voice that said,
  "Your country calls! Obey!"
They heard the call to glory,
  As you can, if you try:
"Your flag demands your best today,
  Not sometime  by and by!"

# A MILE AT A TIME

### NANCY BYRD TURNER

Do you remember how the Bernado children worked together to send Grandmother to Naples? Here is another story of some children who worked together to make an old lady happy.

Jerry and Joan knew why their neighbor, Miss Phoebe Tabb, was sad about her lilac bush. The bush was lovely, but Miss Phoebe's face was wistful when she looked at it. Memorial Day was coming, and there was no way to send the flowers down to Ridgefield to be placed on the grave of her soldier nephew. There had not been a way for a great number of years now.

The neighborhood was thinly settled; Jerry and Joan and their widowed mother were Miss Phoebe's only neighbors. Moreover, the rough roads were seldom used; there was small chance of a traveler's passing at the right time.

"She is too old to walk to Ridgefield," Jerry said, "and we are too young."

"And Mother can't leave the baby," added Joan.

After a while Joan said suddenly, "Jerry, let's carry the flowers one mile, anyway; surely we can find some one to carry them the other miles."

Jerry threw his cap into the air. "We'll do it!" he said.

They hurried home and laid the plan before their mother.

"Mrs. Jennifer's is the only house you could walk to," she said. "You might try there."

"Why, bless your hearts!" Miss Phoebe cried, when the children told her.

She got up early on Memorial Day, picking great sprays of fragrant lilacs and wrapping the stems in thick cotton.

"You can take turns at carrying them," she told the children. "Pass the word along that the blossoms are for the grave of Roderick Tabb. And if you should have to bring them back, I shall not cry."

But the children were afraid she might. "We won't bring them back!" they said.

As they neared the Jennifers' house, Joan said, "Look at that little pony grazing in the yard!" A small boy opened the front door. He told them that he was Ricky Jennifer, and that he had come to spend the month with his uncle.

When he had heard their names and their story, he said: "My uncle and the hired man are away. But mother said I might ride a mile from the place; so my pony and I will carry your flowers to the nearest house. Surely there'll be some one there to carry them on."

Oh, what good fortune!

The interesting pony was saddled and bridled; Ricky mounted him and reached for the flowers. "Stay right

here until I come back," he said, "and then we can take turns riding the pony to your home."

The pony seemed to know that he was on an important errand, for he trotted briskly the whole mile to Dr. Ingram's house.

To Ricky's disappointment, the doctor was about to start off in the opposite direction from Ridgefield.

Priscilla, the doctor's little girl, was listening. "Oh, Father, please!" she said. "I can carry the flowers as far as the blacksmith's shop at the crossroads; maybe some one there will take them the next mile."

"Could you ride my pony?" Ricky asked. "He's very gentle." But Priscilla did not know how to ride.

"Rest after you get there," her father said. "It's very warm."

A few minutes later a large umbrella was moving slowly down the road. Under the umbrella was a slim little girl with a bunch of lilac blooms. Priscilla stopped halfway and dipped the stems in a cool brook; then she trudged on again through the heat. To her dismay she found the shop closed. As she turned toward the blacksmith's house, she saw a huge dog lying by the doorstep.

The dog got up, sniffed, and came toward the gate. "Oh, dog," Priscilla said, clutching the flowers, "if you make me run, I'll drop Miss Phoebe's lilacs. Please don't, dog!" The dog wagged his tail. Just then a little boy on crutches came hobbling around the house, and Priscilla told him her story.

"My father's away," the boy said. "And I'm poor at walking. But here's my dog." Priscilla was puzzled. "Your dog?" she asked.

"He can help," the boy answered, "as sure as my name's Robin. You just wait."

Presently Don, the big dog, was harnessed to a little wagon. His master went into the house for a minute. "I have been driving as far as Ridgefield," he told Priscilla when he came out. "It's only a mile. Mother says you are to come into the house and rest."

Priscilla handed him the lilacs. "For the grave of Roderick Tabb," she said. And away went the little cart.

Later in the afternoon she waked from a long nap, and

there stood Robin. He told her about his trip and handed her a note for Miss Phoebe Tabb that the man in charge of the parade had given him, he said. Priscilla went home happy under her umbrella.

That evening while Jerry and Joan were eating supper, Ricky came riding up.

"Here's a note for Miss Phoebe," he said. "Dr. Ingram and his little girl brought it."

Jerry and Joan had told Miss Phoebe that the flowers got at least as far as the crossroads. When they took the note over, they found her sitting on the doorstep; she was wondering what had finally happened to the lilacs. The note was signed "Mary Drew." Miss Phoebe read it aloud—"Dear Miss Phoebe Tabb": it ran. "Your flowers came all right. A lame boy driving a big dog brought them; they were given to him by a little girl with a large umbrella. She got them from a boy on a pony, and he got them from a brother and sister. I am the Mayor's little girl. The man who is in charge of things asked me to walk in the procession and carry your flowers. They will look beautiful in the cemetery."

"Everyone is so kind," said Miss Phoebe.

"A mile at a time!" Joan said. "Isn't that strange!"

"It's all the doings of you two good children and the others," Miss Phoebe said gratefully. "On Midsummer Day I am going to have a little party opposite this lilac bush, and I hope the guests are going to be three girls and three boys and—"

"A dog," said Jerry, with a little hop.

"And a pony," said Joan, with another little hop.

On Midsummer Day that's exactly the sort of party that Miss Phoebe Tabb had.

## NOTES AND QUESTIONS

1. Why was Miss Phoebe sad?

2. Who thought of the plan of "a mile at a time"?

3. What happened that the children had not planned— something that made everything end perfectly?  Find the lines that tell this and be ready to read them.

4. Be ready to tell this story in your own words.

Two good poems about Memorial Day are: "May Has Decked the World," and "Memorial Day," Wynne (in *For Days and Days*).

# A MAY DAY PRINCESS

## MYRTLE JAMISON TRACHSEL

Philip Carey started out to make himself a desk. He had been planning it for a long time. Then suddenly he changed his plans, and he and his chum, David, did a thing that made them very happy because they made someone else happy.

At last Philip Carey had found the box he needed. He delivered groceries all one Saturday afternoon to pay for it. Now the box was safely deposited in his back yard, and he and David, his chum, were admiring it.

"These four strong pieces and the corners will make the legs," Philip said, "and the three sides will furnish enough boards for the rest."

All through the winter as Philip had worked in his manual-training class at school, he had thought of making a desk for his own room. He called up to his little sister, sitting by her window: "Hello, Margot. Isn't this a dandy box?" Margot turned her curly head and smiled down at him; then her eyes strayed to the next yard, where Edgar Stone was painting his sister's doll buggy.

"I'm putting on two coats of flat paint and one of enamel," Edgar had told the boys. "My sister wants to be in the flower parade on May Day. She and Mother are making paper flowers for decorating the buggy."

Philip and David had scarcely heard this explanation when it was offered, but they thought of it as they noticed the wistful look in Margot's eyes.

"Gee!" said David softly. "I know Margot would like to be in the parade. But of course she can't, poor kid."

No, Margot could not push a doll buggy in the parade as many of the smaller children would do, for Margot had never walked. There was to be an operation soon. The doctor promised that her limbs would be made strong as Philip's, but that would not be until long after the parade.

"We might get a wagon and pull her in it," David suggested.

Philip was thinking. "Ben Ames is training his dog to pull his sister's wagon. Now if we only had a dog or a goat," he said.

"I have an idea, David. Will you help me?"

"Sure," David agreed. "Can we fix up something for her to ride in?"

For an answer Philip ran into the house and returned with a book that had in it the picture of a sedan chair in which a lady was being carried by two men, one walking before and one behind. Philip went over and turned the box up on end.

"Why couldn't we make a sedan chair of this box? We can take the open side for the front, windows can be cut in the sides, and Margot can sit on cushions on the bottom."

He studied the picture a moment. "Mother has a couple of poles she uses for clothes-props. We can fasten them to the box with bolts and use them for handles. But how can we decorate it? I wonder—"

He walked quickly to the fence and said to Edgar, "Will you have any paint left over when you finish the doll buggy?"

"Lots of it. Father gave me all that was left when the kitchen was re-painted."

"What will you sell it for?"

"Oh, about fifty cents."

"Make it twenty-five cents, and I'll buy it."

Philip had saved a quarter to buy glass knobs for the drawer of his desk, but he did not hesitate when Edgar agreed to accept that for the paint.

"Margot," Philip called, "you are going to ride in the May Day parade."

"Oh, am I? Am I? Are you *sure?*"

She clapped her hands together in her excitement and leaned far out from her window to watch the boys. At this point Mother became greatly interested.

"With plenty of cushions Margot will be quite comfortable, and ever so happy."

She studied the picture they showed her in the book.

"Why, boys, I can make Margot a wig out of cotton, and she will look exactly like this dark-eyed princess who was carried about in her sedan chair many years ago in France. She can wear my lace scarf over her yellow silk dress and carry my white feather fan."

"Whoopee!" cried David. "It's getting better and better. I'm going home and get another brush, so we can both put the paint on."

Mother took the picture into the house with her, but after a time she returned with it.

"I have been wondering what you boys could wear. That hat is a simple matter. We can make three-cornered hats out of black cardboard, and attach a little cotton at the backs and sides to imitate the white wigs of that day."

The boys studied the picture. "We could wear white stockings with knee pants, and make cardboard buckles for our knees and our dancing pumps," David suggested.

"But look at the funny long coats they wear!" exclaimed Philip.

"That is the difficulty," said Mother. "I have an old suit with a bright blue lining of satin, and Aunty has one lined with wine-colored satin. Turned wrong side out, these coats would be the very thing. But I am afraid they will make you boys too warm."

"Margot's as light as a feather," Philip insisted, "and the parade will be short because of the little children who are marching."

So the preparations continued. At last the chair, brightly shining and softly padded on the inside with cushions, was locked up in the garage.

On the day of the parade the boys went about noon to old Tim, the florist, to get some flowers ordered by Philip's mother for a finishing touch. They were telling old Tim about the sedan chair when a man came in with several pieces of lattice around which a green smilax vine was twined.

"I'll tell you what, boys," said Old Tim; "that smilax was put on only this morning for an early wedding. You may take it off and fasten it over the chair with brads. It will be sure to stay fresh until after the parade."

They hurried home with the flowers and trailing bunches of smilax. There were hammering sounds out in the garage until it was time to dress for the parade.

Margot was taken to the starting place in an automobile and didn't see the shining chair with its flowers and green trailing vines until she was carried to it.

"Oh!" she cried. "Oh, oh, oh!"

The courtiers, who stood so straight by the chair, smiled brightly at her delight. And in Philip's heart was no

regret at the thought of his lost desk.   During the parade
Margot sat very straight, smiling and nodding gayly as
the children cheered.  "See the little May Day Princess!"
they called.

The parade stopped often to rest.  At such times the
boys put down the chair and stood at attention, one on
either side.  They were near the judges' stand when a
man wearing a badge tapped Philip on the shoulder.

"You will bring the little princess to the stand, please."

Not knowing exactly what this meant, the boys obeyed.
A man stood up, saying, "The judges have decided that
the prize of ten dollars goes to the little princess in the
sedan chair."

Philip and David opened their mouths in surprise. They had not known anything about a prize offer. Margot drew back, refusing to take the offered reward. "Oh, no, please. The boys did it all. Please give it to the boys."

The big man smiled and turned to address the crowd. "The gracious princess desires that the reward be divided between her two faithful courtiers. Long live the May Day Princess!"

Philip and David, each with a new five dollar bill in his pocket, carried the little princess away while the crowd cheered.

"Did you ever!" marveled David. "We can make *real* desks now!"

"And Margot was so happy," added Philip, remembering how her face had beamed when she saw the decorated chair.

### NOTES AND QUESTIONS

1. What two things did Philip give up?
2. How did David show that he was a real chum to Philip?
3. How did Margot show that she was just as unselfish as the boys?
4. What do you think made Philip the happiest?
5. Make up a name for each of the two pictures in the story.
6. Why do you suppose Margot would be particularly happy to be in the parade?

Two good May Day poems are "May Is Pretty, May Is Mild," and "May Baskets," Wynne (in *For Days and Days*).

# A BACKWARD LOOK

These stories and poems of holidays will perhaps help you understand better what some of our holidays mean. How did the boys and girls in these stories show that they knew the true meaning of a holiday? Which of them did the most unselfish thing? Which learned the greatest lesson?

It is easy to wish that other people were happy and having a good time. It is not very hard to help someone else when you do not have to give up anything yourself. But to give up something you have dearly wanted for yourself in order to help someone else is a different matter. Yet, strange to say, many people have found their greatest happiness in giving up things to help others.

Which holiday of the year do you like best? Can you tell why? Do you know the true meaning of the holiday you like best? Are you thankful only on Thanksgiving Day, and loyal to your country only on the Fourth of July? Or do you try to spread out the meaning of these days over the whole year? A holiday should really be a day on which we show what we feel all the year through.

On page 434 you will find a list of books that contain more stories about holidays and festivals. Some of these books will tell you how boys and girls of other lands celebrate their holidays. Perhaps you know that some of our holidays are also celebrated by people in many other lands than ours. Three of the stories you read earlier in this book told you about holidays in other lands. Do you remember them?

# GOOD BOOKS TO READ

## PART ONE. SKYWAYS AND HIGHWAYS

*Skyward*, by Richard E. Byrd. Putnam
*Little America*, by Richard E. Byrd. Putnam
*How We Travel*, by James Franklin Chamberlain. Macmillan
*America Travels*, by Alice Dalgliesh. Macmillan
*The Picture Book of Flying*, by Frank Dobias. Macmillan
*'Board the Airliner: A Camera Trip with the Transport Planes*, by John J. Floherty. Doubleday
*Rear Admiral Byrd and the Polar Expeditions*, by Coram Foster. Burt
*The Picture Book of Ships*, by Peter Gimmage. Macmillan
*Dick Byrd—Air Explorer*, by Fitzhugh Green. Putnam
*The Picture Book of Travel*, by Berta & Elmer Hader. Macmillan
*Youngest Rider: A Story of the Pony Express*, by Louise Platt Hauck. Lothrop
*Playing Airplane*, by John McNamara. Macmillan
*Flash, the Lead Dog*, by George F. Marsh. Penn
*Lindbergh Flies On!* by E. Reeves. McBride
*Travelers and Traveling*, by Eva M. Tappan. Houghton
*Silver Wings*, by Raoul Whitfield. Knopf

## PART TWO. THE OUTDOOR WORLD

*Prince and His Ants*, by Luigi Bertelli. Holt
*The Good Friends*, by Marjorie Bianco. Viking Press
*Traveling with the Birds*, by Rudyerd Boulton. Donohue
*Alice in Elephantland*, by Mary Hastings Bradley. Appleton-Century
*The Seashore Book for Children*, by Thornton Waldo Burgess. Little
*The Smaller Beasts*, by Eric Fitch Daglish. Morrow
*Midget and Bridget*, by Berta and Elmer Hader. Macmillan
*Trails to Woods and Waters*, by Clarence Hawkes. Macrae Smith Co.
*Wild Wings*, by Julie Kenly. Appleton-Century

---

* Recommended for the teacher to read aloud. Interest appeals to fifth-grade pupils, but the reading vocabulary is too difficult for most.

*My Friend Toto: The Adventures of a Chimpanzee,* by Cherry Kearton. Dodd
*The Picture Book of Animals,* by Isabel Ely Lord. Macmillan
\*The Children's Life of the Bee, by Maurice Maeterlinck. Dodd
*Back-yard Zoo,* by Daniel Pratt Mannix. Coward-McCann
*Children's Book of Birds,* by Olive T. Miller. Houghton
*Animals in the Sun,* by W. W. Robinson. Harpers
*Bambi,* by Felix Salten. Simon & Schuster
*Wild Animals I Have Known,* by Ernest Thompson Seton. Scribner
*Creatures Great and Small,* by H. R. Snyder. Loring & Mussey
*Magpie Lane* (poems), by Nancy Byrd Turner. Harcourt
*Bird Stories Retold from St. Nicholas.* Appleton-Century

PART THREE.   STORIES WE ALL SHOULD KNOW

*Franconia Stories,* by Jacob Abbott; edited by Margaret Armstrong. Putnam
*Fairy Tales from Hans Christian Andersen,* translated by Mrs. E. Lucas. Dutton
*East of the Sun & West of the Moon,* by Peter Christian Asbjornsen. Macmillan
*Older Children's Bible.* Macmillan
*The Pied Piper of Hamelin,* by Robert Browning. Warne
*Alice's Adventures in Wonderland,* by Lewis Carroll. Macmillan
*Through the Looking Glass, and What Alice Found There,* by Lewis Carroll. Macmillan
*The Adventures of Pinocchio,* by C. Collodi. Macmillan
*Little Braves,* by Theresa Deming. Stokes
*Wigwam Children,* by Theresa Deming. Stokes
*Red People of the Wooded Country,* by Theresa Deming. Whitman, A.
*Indian Boyhood,* by Charles A. Eastman. Little
*Indian Heroes and Great Chieftains,* by Charles A. Eastman. Little
*The Pointed People* (poems), by Rachel Lyman Field. Macmillan
*Tales from Silver Lands,* by Charles J. Finger. Doubleday
\*Uncle Remus, by J. C. Harris. Appleton-Century

---

\* Recommended for the teacher to read aloud. Interest appeals to fifth-grade pupils, but the reading vocabulary is too difficult for most.

*Christmas Every Day, and Other Stories Told for Children*, by W. D. Howells. Harper
*Just So Stories for Little Children*, by Rudyard Kipling. Doubleday
*The Wonderful Adventures of Nils*, by Selma Lagerlöf. Doubleday
*Chi-Weé: The Adventures of a Little Indian Girl*, by Grace Moon. Doubleday
*Tirra Lirra: Rhymes Old and New*, by Laura Elizabeth Richards. Little
*The Home Book of Verse for Young Folks*, by B. E. Stevenson. Holt
*A Child's Garden of Verses*, by Robert Louis Stevenson. Scribner
*Famous Stories of Five Centuries*, by Walpole & Partington. Farrar
*Indian Stories Retold from St. Nicholas*. Appleton-Century

### PART FOUR. YOUNG AMERICAN CITIZENS

*Son of Light Horse Harry*, by James Barnes. Harper
*Hero of Erie: Oliver Hazard Perry*, by James Barnes. Appleton-Century
*The True Story of George Washington*, by E. S. Brooks. Lothrop
*The Hoosier School-Boy*, by Edward Eggleston. Scribner
*Hitty: Her First Hundred Years*, by Rachel L. Field. Macmillan
*The Willow Whistle*, by Cornelia Meigs. Macmillan
*The American Twins of the Revolution*, by Lucy Fitch Perkins. Houghton
*Farm Boy: A Hunt for Indian Treasure*, by Phil Stong. Doubleday

### PART FIVE. BOYS AND GIRLS OF OTHER LANDS

*Totaram: The Story of a Village Boy in India To-day*, by Irene Mott Bose. Macmillan
*Nanette of the Wooden Shoes*, by Esther Brann. Macmillan
*Lupe Goes to School*, by Esther Brann. Macmillan
*Children of the Soil: A Story of Scandinavia*, by Nora Burglon. Doubleday
*Our Little Friends of Eskimo Land, Papik and Natsek*, by Frances Carpenter. Am. Bk.
*The Boy with the Parrot: A Story of Guatemala*, by Elizabeth Coatsworth. Macmillan

*The Adventures of Andris,* by Elizabeth Jacobi. Macmillan
*Taktuk: An Arctic Boy,* by Helen Lomen and Marjorie Flack. Doubleday
*Abdul: The Story of an Egyptian Boy,* by Winthrop B. Palmer. Macmillan
*Heidi,* by Johanna Spyri. McKay
*Stories of Swiss Children,* by Johanna Spyri. Crowell
*Boys of Other Countries,* by Bayard Taylor. Putnam
*Boy of the Desert,* by Eunice Tietjens. Coward-McCann

PART SIX. WORKERS AND THEIR WORK

*Fire Fighters! How They Work,* by John J. Floherty. Doubleday
*The Story of Mining,* by M. Gruening. Harper
*Wide Road Ahead!* by Henry B. Lent. Macmillan
*Industrial Plays for Young People,* by Virginia Olcott. Dodd
*Gabriel and the Hour Book,* by Evaleen Stein. Page
*An American Farm,* by Rhea Wells. Doubleday

PART SEVEN. FAMOUS HEROES OF LONG AGO

*Robinson Crusoe,* by Daniel Defoe. Cosmopolitan Book
*Stories from the Arabian Nights,* by Laurence Housman. Doubleday
*Legends of the Seven Seas,* by Margaret E. Price. Harper
*The Swiss Family Robinson,* by James David Wyss. Harper

PART EIGHT. HOLIDAYS AND FESTIVALS

*Children's Book of Thanksgiving Stories,* by Asa Don Dickinson. Doubleday
*Three Christmas Trees,* by Juliana Horatio Ewing. Macmillan
*This Way to Christmas,* by Ruth Sawyer. Harper
*Christmas Tree in the Woods,* by Susan Cowles Smith. Minton
*Child's Book of Holiday Plays,* by Frances Wickes. Macmillan
*For Days and Days* (poems), by Annette Wynne. Stokes
*Southern Stories Retold from St. Nicholas.* Appleton-Century

# GLOSSARY

## PRONUNCIATION KEY

The pronunciation of each word is shown just after the word, in this way: **a bun dance** (ạ-bun′dạns). The letters and signs used have sounds as in the words shown below. The accented syllable is marked′. Some long words have the main accent (′) and a lesser or "secondary" accent (′). These are shown by two accent marks, the heavier one being the main accent.

| | | | |
|---|---|---|---|
| a at, can | e end, bend | ö to, move | ụ̄ nature |
| ā came, face | ē be, equal | ô off, song | ḍ gradual |
| ä far, father | ė her, certain | ọ actor, second | ṭ picture |
| â all, ball | ẹ towel, prudent | oi oil, point | th thin |
| ȧ ask | i it, pin | ou out, found | ᴛʜ then |
| ã care, dare | ī line, mine | u up, but | ṅ as in French bon |
| ạ alone, company | o on, not | ū use, pure | *o* is half-way between ō and ô |
| ạ̈ beggar, opera | ō more, open | u̇ put, full | |

A single dot under ā, ē, ō, ö, or ū means that the sound is a little shorter and lighter, as in cot′tạ̄ge, rẹ̄-duce′, gas′ọ̄-line, in′tọ̈, ụ̄-ni′ted.

### A

**Ab dal la** (äb-däl′ạ̈)

**Ab dul A ziz** (äb′du̇l ä-zēz′)

**a bun dance** (ạ-bun′dạns), great plenty or numbers

**ac count** (ạ-kount′), story of things that have happened

**ac cu mu la tion** (ạ-ku-mụ̄-lā′shọn), gathering things together; a collection of things

**Ach med** (äk′med)

**ac tion, get into action** (ak′shọn), begin fighting; doing something

**ac tiv i ty** (ak-tiv′i-ti), work; doing something

**Ad ji dau mo** (äd-ji-dâ′mō)

**a do** (ạ-dö′), fuss

**ad o ra tion** (ad-ọ̄-rā′shọn), praise; worship

**a dored com mand ing** (ạ-dōrd′ kọ-mȧn′ding), took delight in making others obey him

**a dorn ment** (ạ-dôrn′mẹnt), thing which adds beauty; ornament

**adz** (adz), a chopping tool for trimming and smoothing wood

**Aet na** (et′nạ̈), a volcano on the island of Sicily

**af fec tion** (ạ-fek′shọn), love; good will

**ag ri cul ture** (ag′ri-kul-ṭụ̄r), farming

**A lad din** (ạ-lad′in)

**a lert** (ạ-lėrt′), watchful

**A li Ba ba** (ä′lē bä′bä)

**Al lah** (al′ạ̈), the All-Powerful One; Arabic name for God

**a maze ment** (ạ-māz′mẹnt), great wonder and surprise

**am bas sa dor** (am-bas′ạ-dọr), a person sent to look after his country's affairs at the capital of a foreign country

**am e thyst** (am′ẹ̄-thist), a precious stone, purple or violet in color

**Am pez zang** (äm-pet′säng)

**an cient** (ān′shẹnt), belonging to times long past

**An ni na** (ä-nē'nạ)

**an ni ver sa ry** (an-i-vėr'sạ-ri), the day celebrating a special happening or event

**Ant arc tic a** (ant-ärk'ti-kạ), lands around the South Pole

**an ti tox in se rum** (an-ti-tok'sin sē'-rum), a liquid used to prevent or cure certain diseases

**a part ment** (ạ-pärt'mẹnt), a room, or a group of rooms

**ap pa ra tus** (ap-ạ-rā'tus), tools or instruments for doing a certain kind of work

**a re a** (ā'rẹ̄-ạ or ār'ẹ̄-ạ), an open space

**Ar gen ti na** (är-jen-tē'nạ)

**Ash Wednes day** (ash wenz'dạ), the first day of Lent, beginning forty week-days before Easter

**as pen** (as'pẹn), a kind of poplar tree whose leaves are easily moved by the wind; **aspen bow er** (bou'ėr), a group of such trees

**as sem bles** (ạ-sem'blz), arranges; gathers together

**a ston ish ment** (ạ-ston'ish-mẹnt), great surprise and wonder

**a stound ed** (ạ-stoun'ded), greatly surprised or astonished

**ath let ic** (ath-let'ik), used for playing games and taking exercise

**Au gus tin** (â-gus'tin)

**Aus tra lia** (âs-trā'liạ)

**a vail a ble** (ạ-vā'lạ-bl), at hand

**a vi a tion run way** (ā-vi-ā'shọn run'-wä), the part of a landing field used by airplanes when taking off

**awe** (â), great wonder

**az ure space** (azh'ụr), blue sky

## B

**ban nocks** (ban'ọks), flat, round cakes made from barley-meal

**ban quet** (bang'kwet), a large dinner, often followed by speeches; a feast

**bar ri er** (bar'i-ėr), something which stands in the way

**ba zaars** (bạ-zärz'), small stores; a market-place

**bea con** (bē'kọn), a powerful light to show the way

**beast of prey** (prā), an animal that kills other animals for food

**Bed ou in** (bed'ö-in)

**beech en tree** (bē'chẹn), the beech tree

**be moan** (bẹ̄-mōn'), express sorrow; complain

**Ber na do** (bėr-nä'dō)

**be wil dered** (bẹ̄-wil'dėrd), lost and confused

**Big-Sea-Water**, Lake Superior

**blight ed** (blī'ted), withered; spoiled

**bliss** (blis), joy; contentment

**bluff**, a steep, high bank

**boar** (bōr), the wild hog

**bob bin** (bob'in), a spool for winding yarn or thread

**boun ties** (boun'tiz), gifts

**braced** (brāst), held firmly

**brad** (brad), a thin, short nail with a small head

**brakes** (brāks), a large fern; a thicket; brushwood

**Bran deis, Mad e line** (bran'dĭs, mad'ẹ̄-lin)

**Bra zil** (brạ-zil')

**bric-a-brac** (brik'ạ-brak), small ornaments, such as little statues, vases, and dishes

**brisk ly** (brisk'li), in a lively manner; quickly

**broad side** (brôd'sĭd), so that his face and one side showed

**bro cades** (brō-kādz'), heavy silk materials woven with raised figures or flowers on them

**browse** (brouz), feed upon grass

**brush**, a short, brisk fight

**buck et el e va tor** (buk'et el'ẹ̄-vā-tọr), a wide, moving belt with bucket-like containers attached to it

# GLOSSARY

**buck skin** (buk′skin), a strong, soft leather, usually yellowish or grayish in color
**bulge** (bulj), an outward bending or swelling
**bunk,** a narrow bed set against a wall like a shelf
**bur i al** (ber′i-al), the act of placing in a grave

## C

**car a van** (kar′a-van), a company of people on a journey
**ca ressed** (ka-rest′), rubbed gently; petted
**car ni val** (kär′ni-val), a time of merrymaking and feasting
**car ton** (kär′ton), a pasteboard box
**cas cades** (kas-kādz′), waterfalls; **cascades of blossoming vines,** a tangled covering of vines
**case ment** (kās′ment), a window that opens on hinges like a door
**cask** (kåsk), a heavy barrel
**cau tion ing** (kâ′shon-ing), warning
**cau tious ly** (kâ′shus-li), slowly and carefully
**cav ern** (kav′ėrn), a large cave
**cer e mo ny** (ser′ē-mō-ni), the celebration of a great happening or event
**chaff** (chåf), little husks or hulls around the kernels of grain
**Cher bourg** (sher-bör), an important French seaport
**chore** (chōr), a light daily task
**chuck** (chuk), meat from the neck and shoulders of a beef animal
**chute** (shöt), a sloping trough or tube down which articles may slide
**cock pit** (kok′pit), the section of an airplane for the pilot's seat and the instruments
**col lect ed her thoughts** (ko-lek′ted), thought quickly

**coming cham pi on** (cham′pi-on), soon strong enough to be leader
**com mu ni ty** (ko-mū′ni-ti), a group of people living together in a town or village
**com pass** (kum′pas), an instrument for showing directions
**com pelled** (kom-peld′), forced to do something
**com pli cat ed** (kom′pli-kā-ted), difficult
**con duct ed** (kon-duk′ted), guided or led
**cone-shaped** (kōn′shāpt), having rounding sides coming together in a point at the top
**con ferred** (kon-fėrd′), given as an honor
**con fet ti** (kon-fet′tē), bits of colored paper used in merrymaking
**con grat u la tion** (kon-grat-ū-lā′shon), telling a person you are pleased over his success or good fortune
**con struc tion** (kon-struk′shon), building.
**con ta gious** (kon-tā′jus), catching; spreading from one to another
**con vey or** (kon-vā′or), machinery used for carrying materials from place to place
**cor ral** (ko-ral′), a pen for horses
**cour tiers** (kōr′tiėrz), persons who attend a princess
**cov et ed** (kuv′e-ted), longed for; much desired
**crave** (krāv), wish for greatly
**creek-bot tom** (krēk′bot′om), low lands along a small stream
**crest** (krest), top of a hill or building
**crest fall en** (krest′fâ′ln), ashamed; discouraged; downhearted
**crev ice** (krev′is), a narrow opening or crack

at, cāme, fär, åll, àsk, cāre, alone; end, bē, hėr, towel; it, līne; on, mōre, tö, ôff, actor; oil, out; up, ūse, pùt, natūre; picture; th, thin; ᴛн, then. See full key on p. 435.

**crim i nal** (krim′i-nạl), a person who has done something that is against the law

**cruise** (krōz), a trip in a boat

**cu ri ous** (kū′ri-us), strange; unusual

**curt** (kėrt), short and sharp

**cyl in der** (sil′in-dėr), an object shaped like a tin can

**cym bals** (sim′bạlz), a pair of round brass plates clashed together to make a ringing sound

**cy press** (sī′pres), an evergreen tree with hard wood and dark leaves

## D

**dar bou ka** (där-bö′kạ), a small pottery drum

**dead li er** (ded′li-ėr), more to be feared

**dear,** costly; expensive

**de cay** (dē-kā′), rot; fall to pieces

**de la Ra mee** (dė là rà-mā)

**de nied** (dē-nīd′), not allowed to have; refused

**De part ment of Ag ri cul ture** (dē-pärt′mẹnt; ag′ri-kul-ṯụr), a branch of the United States Government handling farm problems and affairs

**de scend** (dē-send′), go down

**de scend ants** (dē-sen′dạnts), those of his family who lived after him, such as children, grandchildren, etc.

**de spair** (dē-spār′), loss of hope

**de vel oped** (dē-vel′ọpt), treated the camera film, or plate, so that it would print a picture

**de vice** (dē-vīs′), a part of a machine or a small machine that does a special work

**dig ni fied** (dig′ni-fīd), serious-looking; solemn

**dis ease** (di-zēz′), illness

**dis tin guished** (dis-ting′gwisht), well-known; famous

**Distinguished Flying Cross,** a small bronze cross given to a flier for a very brave or important deed

**down** (doun), soft, fluffy feathers under the outer stiff feathers

**drought** (drout), dryness; lack of rain

**duc at** (duk′ạt), an old gold coin, worth about $2.28

**dun geon** (dun′jọn), an underground prison

## E

**ear nest ness, in earnestness and sin cer i ty** (ėr′nest-nes; sin-ser′i-ti), really wanting to lose the Golden Touch

**earth en** (ėr′thn), made of baked clay

**East Green wich** (grin′ij)

**easy grace,** smoothness; beauty of form or movement

**E gyp tians** (ē-jip′shạnz)

**ei der duck** (ī′dėr), a sea-duck which lines her nest with soft down from her body

**el e va tor** (el′ē-vā-tọr), a building for storing grain, so called because the grain is carried to the top to be poured in

**e nam els** (e-nam′ẹlz), smooth, glossy paints

**en cir cled** (en-sėr′kld), held close; surrounded

**en er get ic** (en-ėr-jet′ik), lively; full of energy

**en gi neer** (en-ji-nēr′), one who understands machinery; a builder

**en large** (en-lärj′), make larger

**en riched** (en-richt′), made more fertile

**en treat ing ly** (en-trē′ting-li), pleadingly; earnestly

**ep i dem ic** (ep-i-dem′ik), rapid spreading of disease so that many people have it at the same time

**e quip ment** (ē-kwip′mẹnt), supplies

**es tate** (es-tāt′), a large piece of land

**Es te ban** (es-tā′vän)

**E wa yea** (ē-wâ-yā′)

**ex pe di tion** (eks-pē-dish′ọn), a group of people making an important journey

**ex pe ri ence** (eks-pē′ri-ẹns), doing things or living through certain happenings

**ex pert** (eks′pèrt), person who knows a great deal about some special thing

**ex tend ed** (eks-ten′ded), offered; stretched out

**ex ult ed** (eg-zul′ted), was very happy

**F**

**fain** (fān), gladly

**Fabre, Jean Hen ri** (fäbr, zhäṅ äṅ-rē)

**fam ine, weath er famine** (weᴛʜ′èr fam′in), a time without weather of any kind

**fare** (fär), food

**fa tigue, grit ty with fatigue** (grit′i; fạ-tēg′), stinging with pain because she was so tired

**feat** (fēt), a great deed; an act requiring great skill, strength, or daring

**fea tures** (fē′tụrz), the parts of the face—eyes, nose, mouth, etc.

**fer ry boat** (fer′i-bōt), a boat for carrying people or goods across a river or narrow stretch of water

**fer tile** (fèr′til), having rich soil that will grow good crops

**fes ti val** (fes′ti-vạl), a time of feasting or celebration

**fetch** (fech), to go and get; bring

**fi ber** (fī′bèr), a thread or thread-like substance

**Fi o ret ta** (fē-ō-rā′tạ)

**fire arms** (fīr′ärmz), guns

**fit ting** (fit′ing), of the right kind

**fit to be made a tool of,** easily made to do whatever others wanted

**flank** (flangk), the side of an animal between ribs and hip; the side of anything

**flare** (flār), an open flame used for light; a sudden flash of bright light

**flaw** (flâ), a crack or break

**flecked with leafy light** (flekt), spotted with sunlight shining through the trees

**fleet** (flēt), swift; a group of wagons or ships or trucks traveling or working together

**flor in** (flor′in), an old coin worth about forty-eight cents at the time of the story

**folds,** sheep-pens

**fo li age** (fō′li-ạj), leaves

**fol ly** (fol′i), foolishness

**fore bears** (fōr′bārz), forefathers; ancestors

**fore man** (fōr′mạn), the man in charge of a group of workers

**for mer sub stance** (fôr′mèr sub′-stạns), the kind of material it was made of before

**fort night** (fôrt′nīt), two weeks

**forty winks,** short nap

**fowl ing piece** (fou′ling pēs), a light gun for shooting birds

**frame, in this frame of mind,** feeling this way

**franc** (frangk), a French coin

**Fran ces co** (frän-ches′kō)

**Fran cois** (frän-swo)

**fran tic** (fran′tik), greatly excited and upset

**Frau** (frou), a German word meaning wife or Mrs.

**fren zy** (fren′zi), wild excitement; **in a frenzy,** so excited as to be almost crazy

---

at, cāme, fär, âll, ȧsk, cāre, ạlone; end, bē, hèr, towẹl; it, līne; on, mōre, tö, ôff, actọr; oil, out; up, ūse, pùt, natụre; picture; th, thin; ᴛʜ, then. See full key on p. 435.

**fresh et** (fresh′et), the overflowing of a stream caused by heavy rains or melting snow

**fret-work** (fret′wèrk), ornamental openwork

**frol ic chase** (frol′ik chās), game of running after each other

**fu ri ous** (fū′ri-us), violent; wild with anger

**G**

**gal lant** (gal′ạnt), brave; polite and well-mannered

**game** (gām), birds and animals that are hunted for sport

**gauze** (gâz), thin, transparent material

**gen er a tion** (jen-ẹ-rā′shọn), the number of years a person usually lives; **three generations**, grandfather, father, son

**gen er a tor**, **e lec tric generator** (ẹ-lek′trik jen′ẹ-rā-tọr), machine for making electricity

**gen er os i ty** (jen-ẹ-ros′i-ti), willingness to share with others; unselfishness

**ge nie** (jē′ni), a powerful spirit

**Giot to's Tow er** (jot′tōz tou′èr). Giotto was a famous Italian artist. The tower he planned and built is one of the most beautiful in the world.

**Git che Gu mee** (gi′chẹ gö′mē), Lake Superior

**gladness breathes,** joy seems to come

**glad some** (glad′sum), joyful

**glory, heard the call to glory,** saw a chance to do something for their country

**glut ton** (glut′n), one who eats more food than he needs

**gnarled** (närld), twisted and knotty

**gold bright-wov en in the sun** (wō′vn), yellow flowers growing in the sun

**gra cious** (grā′shus), pleasant and kindly

**gran u lat ed** (gran′ụ-lā-ted), made up of small grains

**groomed** (grömd), combed, brushed, and fed

**grum py** (grum′pi), cross

**guard our honor** (gärd), protect our country's good name

**Gui llaume** (gē-yōm), French name for William

**gul ly** (gul′i), a small valley or hollow with steep sides

**gulp ing** (gul′ping), swallowing

**gur gling cry** (gèr′gling), a bubbling sound, like the noise water makes when it is poured out of a bottle

**guyed** (gīd), teased; made fun of

**H**

**Hal i fax** (hal′i-faks)

**Ham ma met** (hàm-mä′met)

**han gar** (hang′ạr), a shelter for airplanes

**hangbird,** Baltimore oriole, whose nest hangs from the limb of a tree

**hap pi ly** (hap′i-li), luckily

**haunch es** (hân′chez), hips

**haunt** (hânt), place often visited; to come back again and again

**hemp** (hemp), a plant whose fiber is used in making rope

**Hen ri co** (hen-rē′kọ)

**he ro ic** (hẹ-rō′ik), brave; fearless; daring

**Herr** (här), a German word meaning Mr. or sir

**hew ing** (hū′ing), cutting

**Hi a wa tha** (hī-ạ-wâ′thạ)

**hin der its prog ress** (hin′dèr; prog′res), delay it

**hin drance** (hin′drạns), any object standing in the way

**Hirsch vo gel** (hirsh′fō-gẹl)

**hoard** (hōrd), supply of money saved; anything saved up

**hob bled** (hob′ld), put a chain or rope upon their feet

**hogs head** (hogz′hed), a large cask or barrel

**hol ster** (hōl′stèr), leather case for pistol or gun

**home stead** (hōm′sted), the home place

**hoot ed** (hö′ted), made a sound like the cry of an owl

**hop per** (hop′ėr), a chute or box, open at the lower part, for feeding material into a machine

**ho ri zon** (hō-rī′zon), the place where earth and sky seem to meet

**horse-chest nut** (hôrs′ches′nut), a shade tree bearing a large, glossy brown nut

**hos tile** (hos′til), unfriendly

**Hous sam** (hö′säm)

**hue** (hū), color

**huff, in a huff,** angry

**hy e na** (hī-ē′nạ), a wild animal much like a large dog in shape and size

## I

**I a goo** (ē̱-ä′gö)

**im plor ing ly** (im-plōr′ing-li), in a begging manner; pleadingly

**im pulse** (im′puls), a sudden feeling or desire

**in cline** (in′klīn), slope

**in con ve nien ces** (in-kon-vē′nien-sez), troubles; discomforts

**in fir ma ry** (in-fėr′mạ-ri), a place where the sick are cared for; a hospital in a school or other institution

**in hal ing** (in-hā′ling), smelling

**in nu mer a ble** (i-nū′mẹ-rạ-bl), too many to count

**in quir ies** (in-kwīr′iz), questionings

**in spir ing** (in-spīr′ing), making one also want to do great deeds

**in tel li gent** (in-tel′i-jẹnt), understanding; wise; keen-minded

**ir ri ta ble** (ir′i-tạ-bl), easily angered

## J

**jaunt** (jânt), a journey

**jaun ti ly** (jân′ti-li), briskly; gayly

**ju ni per tree** (jö′ni-pėr), an evergreen tree with purple berries

**jus tice, bring them to justice** (jus′tis), have them arrested and brought to trial

## K

**Ka di jah** (kä-dē′jä)

**Kas son, Gun nar** (kas′son, gun′ạr)

**keel** (kēl), a heavy timber running along the center of the bottom of a ship

**kill er-whale** (kil′ėr-hwāl), a whale that kills large fish, seals, and even other whales

**kin dred** (kin′dred), those similar to him; relatives

## L

**lab o ra to ry** (lab′ọ-rạ-tọ-ri), workshop for doing certain careful work

**lair** (lâr), den of a wild beast

**lathe** (lāᴛʜ), a machine by which a piece of wood or metal is held and turned while being cut

**launch** (lânch), get it afloat

**league** (lēg), about three miles

**Le Bour get** (lê bör-zhā)

**lee of the land,** shelter of the shore

**lei sure** (lē′zhụr), time free from required work; spare time

**lin den** (lin′dẹn), made from the wood of the linden tree, which is a tree with heart-shaped leaves and small, sweet-smelling, greenish-yellow flowers

**loom** (lōm), machine for weaving cloth

**loomed up,** appeared

**lord ly** (lôrd′li), like a master over others; grand; magnificent

**lo tus** (lō′tus), a kind of large water lily

**M**

**mag ic arts** (maj′ik), power over spirits

**mag nif i cent** (mag-nif′i-sęnt), beautiful; splendid; grand

**Mahn go tay see** (män-gō̱-tā′sē̱), brave

**ma jes tic** (mạ-jes′tik), glorious; grand; splendid

**mal ice** (mal′is), ill-will; spite

**Mar ga ret ta** (mär-gạ-rä′tạ)

**mass,** large number

**mas ter work man** (màs′tẻr wẻrk′-mạn), a very skilful worker

**Mat te o** (mät-tā′ō̱)

**Maus sane** (mō-sàn)

**mead ow-floors** (med′ō-flōrz), level, grassy land

**mel low** (mel′ō), soft and rich

**me lo di ous** (me-lō′di-us), sweet-sounding; full of music

**mer chan dise** (mẻr′chạn-dĭz), goods to be sold or bought

**Mess Hall,** dining-hall

**Met e ghan** (met′ē̱-gạn)

**Mid sum mer Day** (mid′sum′ẻr), the twenty-fourth of June

**mi grat ing** (mĭ′grā-ting), passing from one region to another

**mil i ta ry** (mil′i-tạ-ri), belonging to the army

**Min ne wa wa** (min-ē̱-wâ′wâ)

**min now** (min′ō), any fish when it is very small

**mis judged a sharp curve** (mis-jujd′), failed to decide how sharp the curve was

**mis sion** (mish′ọn), errand

**mite** (mīt), a very small object

**M'na** (m'nä)

**molt en** (mōl′tn), melted

**mon o plane** (mon′ō̱-plān), an airplane with a single wing extending on each side

**Mon sieur le Cu re** (mè-syè̱ lè̱ kü-rä), a term of respect, meaning "your reverence," used by the French people toward the parish priest

**mop ing** (mō′ping), going about in a lifeless way

**Mor gi a na** (môr-gi-ä′nạ)

**mor sel** (môr′sl), a small piece or bite

**mor tar** (môr′tạr), a bowl of very hard material in which grain was crushed with a stone

**Mud way aush ka** (mud-wạ-oush′kạ)

**mum mies** (mum′iz), dead bodies which have dried or been preserved from decay

**mur mur** (mẻr′mẻr), low sound or noise

**Mus ta pha** (mös′tä-fạ)

**mute** (mūt), voiceless; quiet

**N**

**na tive lan guage** (nā′tiv lang′gwạj), language of one's own kind or people; **native soil,** land where person was born

**nat u ral death** (naṭ′ū̱-rạl), death from illness instead of from being killed

**Ne na na** (nạ-nä′nạ)

**New found land** (nū′fund-lạnd)

**niche** (nich), a narrow hollow or place set back in the wall for a vase or statue

**no els** (nō-elz′), Christmas carols; **Noel,** French word meaning Christmas

**No ko mis** (nō̱-kō′mis)

**Nome** (nōm)

**nook** (nůk), small, out-of-the-way place; a cozy little corner

**No va Sco tia** (nō′vạ skō′shiạ)

**numb** (num), unable to feel cold, heat, or pain

## O

**oc cu pied with her grief** (ok′ū-pĭd), filled with sadness

**on yx** (on′iks), a kind of stone, usually black

**O pe chee** (ō-pē′chē)

**op er at ed** (op′ė-rā-ted), sent out; had charge of

**o ver cast** (ō-vėr-kȧst′), darkened; clouded

**o ver lord** (ō′vėr-lôrd), one ruling over others

**O wais sa** (ō-wā′sạ̈)

## P

**pack et** (pak′et), bundle

**pal pi tat ed** (pal′pi-tā-ted), quivered; shook

**pan ic clutched at him** (pan′ik klucht). Suddenly he was seized with fear.

**par a dise, bird paradise** (par′ạ-dĭs), place where birds are free from enemies and well taken care of

**par al lel** (par′ạ-lel), side by side in straight lines

**par tic u lar ly** (pạr-tĭk′ū-lạr-li), very much

**Pat a go ni a** (pat-ạ-gō′ni-ạ), a country at the southern end of South America

**pen e trat ing** (pen′ė-trā-ting), going into

**pen guins** (pen′gwinz), sea birds that can dive and swim but cannot fly

**per se vered** (pėr-sẹ-vērd′), kept on trying

**pho tog ra pher** (fọ-tog′rạ-fėr), person taking pictures

**pho to workshop** (fō′tō), a place where camera plates or films are developed

**pi men to** (pi-men′tō), a kind of sweet pepper

**pin cers** (pin′sėrz), a tool used for holding objects

**pi o neers** (pĭ-ọ-nērz′), people seeking homes in a new country; people who go first and so prepare the way for others

**plains men** (plānz′men), men who lived on the plains

**plate,** the glass plate or film in the camera upon which the likeness of an object being photographed is made

**played out,** tired out; weary

**plead ed** (plē′ded), begged

**points,** spots or markings

**po lar** (pō′lạr), near either the North or the South Pole

**pom mel** (pum′ẹl), the knob on the front of a saddle, often called the "horn"

**Pon te Vec chi o** (pōn′tā vek′kē-ō), *ponte* = bridge; *vecchio* = old

**porce lain** (pôrs′lạn or pôr′sẹ-lạn), a kind of fine white china

**por trait** (pôr′trạt), a picture or likeness of a person

**Pos tal Ser vice** (pōs′tạl sėr′vis), the carrying of the mails

**potter,** one who makes articles from clay

**pounded into wakefulness,** shaken until he was awake

**prai rie** (prȧr′i), grassy plains

**pre dict ed** (prẹ-dik′ted), told beforehand; foretold

**pre serve** (prẹ-zėrv′), a place where wild fowl and animals are protected from hunters

**pres to** (pres′tō), quickly

**prim i tive** (prim′i-tiv), living in earliest times

**priv i lege** (priv′i-lej), favor; permission

**pro ceed ed** (prọ-sē′ded), went on, moved forward

---

at, cāme, fär, ȧll, ȧsk, cȧre, ạlone; end, bē, hėr, towẹl; it, līne; on, mōre, tö, ôff, actọr; oil, out; up, ūse, pút, natūre; picture; th, thin; ͡FH, then. See full key on p. 435.

**proof,** a trial photograph printed to see how good the film is

**pro posed** (prō-pōzd′), suggested

**pros pect** (pros′pekt), an expected happening or event

**Pro vence** (prо-vоns̀), a part of southeastern France

**pro vi sions** (prō-vizh′ọnz), supply of food

**pro voked** (prō-vōkt′), angered or vexed

**Pub lic Health Service** (pub′lik), those whose duty it is to care for the health of persons living in a community

**pulp** (pulp), a soft, wet mass

**pur suit** (pẻr-sūt′), chase

## Q

**quick-wit ted ness** (kwik′wit′ed-nes), quick thinking

**quiv er ing** (kwiv′ẻr-ing̀), trembling

## R

**rag a muf fin** (rag′ạ-muf-in), a ragged fellow

**ra ging** (rā′jing), blowing with great force

**raid ing** (rā′ding), robbing; plundering

**ram shack le** (ram′shak-l), tumbledown

**ra pid i ty** (rạ-pid′i-ti), speed

**rare** (rãr), not often found; unusual

**rare gift,** great talent or ability

**re ceipt** (rẽ-sēt′), a written record to show that you have given a thing to someone else

**rec ol lec tion** (rek-ọ-lek′shọn), memory

**re gret the pos ses sion of** (rẽ-gret′; pọ-zesh′ọn), be sorry to have it

**re joice** (rẽ-jois′), be glad

**re mote** (rẽ-mōt′), far away

**re mount cor ral** (rẽ-mount′ kọ-ral′), place where the rider changed to a fresh horse

**re pealed** (rẽ-pēld′), done away with

**re port** (rẽ-pōrt′), an explosive sound; sudden noise

**re port er** (rẽ-pōr′tẻr), a person employed to gather news for a newspaper

**rep re sent ing his fine pro por tions** (rep-rẽ-zen′ting; prō-pôr′shọnz), showing how well-built he was

**re quire ment** (rẽ-kwĭr′mẹnt), a rule

**re venge, for revenge** (rẽ-venj′), to get even with them

**re volv ing** (rẽ-vol′ving), turning over and over

**ridge** (rij), a raised narrow strip of ground

**ri val** (rĭ′vạl), one who tries to get ahead of another, or win his place from him

**rov ing** (rō′ving), wandering; roaming

**rud dy** (rud′i), having a healthy red color

**ruffed grouse** (ruft grous), a game bird about the size of a small chicken, with a tuft or "ruff" of feathers on each side of the neck. The ruffed grouse is sometimes called a partridge.

## S

**Sa doc** (sä′dok)

**Sa har a** (sạ-här′ạ)

**sau cy** (sâ′si), gay; pert

**sched ule** (sked′ūl), time required for a certain journey

**schoon er, prairie schooner** (skö′nẻr), covered wagon used by pioneers in crossing the plains

**score,** twenty

**scrub,** low thick bushes or shrubs

**scur ried** (skur′id), hurried

**scythe** (sīтн), a long, slightly curved blade on a long handle, for cutting grain

**se clud ed** (sē-klö′ded), out of sight; hidden

**se dan chair** (sē-dan′), a covered chair, usually carried on poles by two men

**sen sa tion** (sen-sā′shǫn), feeling

**sen ti nels** (sen′ti-nęlz), guards or watchmen

**Sep pa la** (sā-pä′lạ̈)

**served, has served his day,** can no longer be useful

**ses a me, open sesame** (ses′ạ-mē), a password which opens doors

**seven and one half degrees,** about five hundred miles

**shame faced ly** (shām′fāst-li), in an embarrassed manner; bashfully

**Shen an do ah** (shen-ạn-dō′ạ)

**shirk** (shėrk), to get out of work

**shoal** (shōl), a sand-bank or sand-bar which makes the water shallow

**shorn** (shôrn), clipped or shingled

**shrewd** (shröd), keen; wise

**shrub ber y** (shrub′ėr-i), bushes or shrubs

**shy** (shĭ), bashful

**sick le** (sik′l), a short, curved blade on a short handle for cutting grass or grain

**sin ews** (ǫin′ūz), tough, ǫtrong bands or cords that join muscle to bone. Sinews taken from animals were used for cord by the Indians.

**skill** (skil), ability to do something well

**skimp y** (skim′pi), barely enough; scanty

**skis** (skēz), a pair of long wooden strips fastened to the shoes and used for gliding over a snow-covered surface

**sleek** (slēk), smooth and shiny

**slick him down,** brush and comb his hair

**slo gan** (slō′gạn), saying or byword

**smart ly** (smärt′li), sharply

**smi lax** (smĭ′laks), vine used for decoration

**snarl** (snärl), to growl sharply and show the teeth; tangle

**Soan ge ta ha** (sōn′gē-tä-hä)

**sod,** upper layer of soil filled with grass and its roots

**sol emn ly** (sol′ęm-li), seriously

**sol i ta ry** (sol′i-tạ-ri), lonely

**source** (sōrs), place from which anything comes

**spare yards,** extra cross-poles used to support the sails

**spars** (spärz), long poles for carrying sails

**spec ta tor** (spek-tā′tǫr), one who watches a game or some other happening

**spikes** (spĭks), large, strong nails

**spi ral** (spĭ′rạl), winding

**spire** (spir), the top of a tower or steeple

**spir it, brave spirit** (spir′it), courage; bravery

**spyglass,** a small telescope, which is a strong glass for making distant objects seem nearer and larger

**stal wart** (stâl′wạrt), strong and bravc

**sta plers** (stā′plėrz), workmen for sorting wool

**stern,** the back end of a ship or boat

**Stone Age,** the time before men learned to use iron, copper, and other metals; when stone tools and weapons were used

**strand** (strand), a string or thread

**Strehl a** (strel′ạ̈)

**strong-box,** a chest or case for money and valuables

**Sul tan** (sul′tạn), ruler in some countries of the East

**sum mit** (sum′it), highest point; top

at, cāme, fär, âll, ȧsk, cāre, ạlone; end, bē, hėr, towęl; it, līne; on, mōre, tö, ôft, actǫr; oil, out; up, ūse, půt, natŭre; picṭure; th, thin; ŦH, then. See full key on p. 435.

**surged** (sėrjd), rushed; rose up
**surging up from the depths of his being** (depths), springing up in his heart
**sus pi cious** (sus-pish′us), not trusting
**sweetmeats,** candy; bonbons; candied fruits
**swoon** (swön), a faint
**sym bol** (sim′bọl), that which stands for something else, as our flag stands for our country

**T**

**ta bor** (tā′bọr), small drum
**tal low** (tal′ō), the melted fat of the cow and sheep
**tar ried** (tar′id), stayed on
**tat too, beating a tattoo** (ta-tö′), striking sharply against
**tem per** (tem′pėr), kind of humor they were in; disposition
**tem pest** (tem′pest), furious storm with much wind
**ter race** (ter′ạs), raised level platform of earth
**ter rif ic** (te-rif′ik), dreadful or terrible
**ter ror-strick en** (ter′ọr-strik′n), greatly frightened
**teth ered** (teͲн′ėrd), tied
**tex ture** (teks′t̗ur), material
**thongs** (thôngz), strips of leather
**thrash ing** (thrash′ing), striking or beating
**thrill** (thril), a shivering, exciting feeling
**throng** (thrông), a large crowd
**thrust, stop his thrust short** (thrust), keep him from stabbing deeper
**ti dings** (tī′dingz), news
**Tiet jens** (tēt′yẹns)
**ti mid i ty** (ti-mid′i-ti), shyness
**Ti no** (tē′nọ̄)
**tip up,** stick their bills under water for food, so that their tails are up in the air

**tor til la** (tôr-tēl′yä), thin, flat cake made from corn
**to to** (tō′tō), a young animal
**tour** (tör), trip
**Trach sel** (träk′sẹl)
**tract** (trakt), piece of land
**trance, in a trance** (trȧns), too surprised and frightened to move; in a daze
**trans at lan tic** (trans-at-lan′tik), across the Atlantic Ocean
**trans par ent** (trans-pȧr′ẹnt), able to be seen through
**trans port ed** (trans-pōr′ted), carried
**tri fle** (trī′fl), a very small amount; having little value
**trin kets** (tring′kets), ornaments; bits of jewelry
**tri pod** (trī′pod), a three-legged stand for a camera
**tri umph** (trī′umf), victory; success; joy because of victory or success
**trop ics** (trop′iks), lands lying close to the equator; hot regions
**trow el** (trou′ẹl), a small tool used by bricklayers and plasterers to spread or smooth plaster, etc.
**trudged** (trujd), walked heavily or wearily
**trum pet ing** (trum′pet-ing), the elephant's cry, which sounds like a trumpet
**trust wor thy** (trust′wėr′Ͳнi), faithful; to be depended on
**tu mult** (tū′mult), very loud noise; uproar
**tur quoise** (tėr′kwoiz), a precious blue stone
**ty rant** (tī′rȧnt), a cruel ruler

**U**

**U go** (ö′gō)
**un blem ished** (un-blem′isht), spotless; unstained
**un der went** (un-dėr-went′), became changed

**un eas i ness** (un-ē′zi-nes), an anx-ious or disturbed feeling

**u ni form** (ū′ni-fôrm), even; the same all through

**u nit** (ū′nit), a separate part or section

**un sul lied** (un-sul′id), free from dirt and stain

**un ti dy** (un-tī′di), not well trimmed

**un u su al being** (un-ū′zhū-ạl), a person not like other persons

**up land** (up′lạnd), on high land

**up roar** (up′rōr), great noise

**ur gent** (ėr′jẹnt), necessary; greatly needed

**V**

**vague** (vāg), not clear

**vale** (vāl), a little valley

**van ished** (van′isht), disappeared

**vast** (våst), very great in numbers or in size

**vat,** a large tank

**Vaughans** (vânz)

**ven tured** (ven′t̯ūrd), dared; did timidly

**ve ran da** (vẹ-ran′dạ), a porch, usu-ally roofed

**Ve su vi us** (vẹ-sū′vi-us), a volcano near Naples, Italy

**vil lain** (vil′ạn), wicked man

**vis i ble** (viz′i-bl), seen

**vi sions, rose visions of** (vizh′ọnz), he imagined he saw

**vi sor** (vī′zọr), the front part of a cap extending over the eyes

**vi zier** (vi-zēr′), a high state officer in countries of the East

**vol un teer** (vol-un-tēr′), coming up from seed dropped by other plants; one who offers his help without being asked

**W**

**Wah wah tay see** (wâ-wâ-tā′sẹ)

**wail ing** (wā′ling), a long-drawn-out, sad sound

**wain scot ing** (wān′skọt-ing), wood-en panels used to line the lower parts of walls

**war ble** (wâr′bl), a bird's song

**warehouse,** storehouse for goods

**war y** (wār′i), easily frightened; cautious

**wear i some** (wēr′i-sum), tiresome

**whirl pool of ac tiv i ty** (hwėrl′pöl; ak-tiv′i-ti), place where all began working suddenly

**wild ing** (wīl′ding), wild

**winced** (winst), shrank

**wist ful ly** (wist′fúl-i), longingly

**woe be gone** (wō′bẹ-gôn′), sorrow-ful; discouraged

**woe ful** (wō′fúl), sad

**Wol fer los** (vúl′fėr-lōs)

**wol ve rine** (wúl-vẹ-rēn′), an ani-mal about two and one-half feet long, of heavy build and with long, shaggy hair

**wood craft** (wúd′kråft), how to take care of one's self in the woods

**wor sted** (wús′ted), yarn or cloth made from long wool

**wren-talk,** the song of the wren

**Y**

**yards** (yärdz), poles fastened across a ship's masts to support the sails

**Yu kon** (yö′kon), a portion of Canada which borders Alaska; a river in Alaska

**Z**

**zoom ing** (zö′ming), moving sud-denly upward

at, cāme, fär, âll, ȧsk, cãre, ạlone; end, bē, hėr, towẹl; it, līne; on, mōre, tö, ôff, actọr; oil, out; up, ūse, půt, nat̯ūre; picture; th, thin; ŦH, then.　See full key on p. 435.